THE ENCYCLOPEDIA OF

MAMMALS

A Complete Visual Guide

THE ENCYCLOPEDIA OF

MAMMALS

CONSULTANT

Dr George McKay

Consultant in Conservation Biology

Sydney, Australia

FOG CITY PRESS

A Complete Visual Guide

Conceived and produced by Weldon Owen Pty Ltd
59 Victoria Street, McMahons Point
Sydney NSW 2060, Australia
Copyright © 2005 Weldon Owen Inc.

Chief Executive Officer John Owen
President Terry Newell
Publisher Sheena Coupe
Creative Director Sue Burk
Vice President International Sales Stuart Laurence
Administrator International Sales Kristine Ravn

Project Editors Stephanie Goodwin, Angela Handley, Jennifer Losco
Designers Clare Forte, Heather Menzies, Jacqueline Richards,
Karen Robertson
Picture Research Annette Crueger, Jennifer Losco, Heather Menzies
Text Jenni Bruce, Karen McGhee

Species Gallery Illustrations MagicGroup s.r.o. (Czech Republic) —
www.magicgroup.cz
Feature Illustrations Guy Troughton
Maps Andrew Davies Creative Communication, Map Illustrations
Information Graphics Andrew Davies Creative Communication
Index Sarah Plant/Puddingburn Publishing Services

Editorial Coordinators Helen Flint, Irene Mickaiel
Production Manager Louise Mitchell
Production Coordinator Monique Layt

This paperback edition first printed in 2007.
ISBN: 978-1-74089-668-9
1 2 3 4 5 6 7 8 9 10

Color reproduction by Chroma Graphics (Overseas) Pte Ltd
Printed by SNP Leefung Printers Ltd.
Printed in China

A Weldon Owen Production

CONTENTS

FOREWORD

Mammals are the most familiar group of animals, not only because they are our closest relatives but also because of their economic, esthetic, and—for many people—spiritual importance. Mammals play a vital role in maintaining life on Earth through their impact on our planet's ecosystems.

Although mammals were among the last major groups to evolve, rising to prominence only in the last 60 million years, they display a diversity in form, adaptation, and behavior that is the equal of any other group of animals. In this book we have selected nearly one-fifth of the total living species, including at least one representative from every family, to illustrate this extraordinary diversity.

Remarkably, new species continue to be discovered. Many of these are small and cryptic, but two spectacular recent discoveries of larger mammals are the saola (page 156) and the giant muntjac (page 165).

Despite these discoveries, a more disturbing trend is the rate at which one species, our own, is putting an unsustainable pressure on all others, with mammals bearing a disproportionately large share of this pressure. More than one in five mammal species are listed as seriously threatened by the World Conservation Union (IUCN) and an equal number are considered to be close to threatened. Many species have always been rare; some small rodents, especially, have only occasionally been seen as living animals. If their habitats are destroyed they will pass into oblivion unnoticed. Other species, however, are conspicuous when they are missed. A recent survey in the Congo failed to find any living wild members of our closest relative, the bonobo or "pygmy chimpanzee." Almost 80 mammal species are currently listed as extinct or extinct in the wild. This number will certainly increase in the near future.

Can we do anything to slow down, if not reverse, this trend? The best available evidence indicates that the only way to ensure the continued existence of viable mammal populations is by conserving broad landscapes and ecosystems. Only if we have the political will to insist that our governments adopt such conservation measures as a matter of urgency will we be able to keep more than a handful of common species for future generations. And only if we do that will this book be a guide to the variety and diversity of living mammals, rather than a catalog of what we have destroyed.

DR GEORGE MCKAY
Consultant in Conservation Biology, Sydney, Australia

HOW TO USE THIS BOOK

The first section of this book provides an introduction to mammals: their characteristics, evolution, classification, biology, behavior, habitats, adaptation, and conservation status. The second section surveys mammals according to their taxonomy. Larger groups, such as primates and carnivores, are further divided into subgroups such as monkeys and apes, or cats and the dog family. The book concludes with a comprehensive glossary and index.

Group global distribution
A map shows the worldwide distribution of the group being profiled, followed by text that discusses the distribution of particular groups in more detail.

HABITAT ICONS

The 18 habitat icons below indicate at a glance the various habitats in which a species or group can be found. It should be noted that the icons are used in the same order throughout the book, rather than in their order of significance. A more detailed profile of each habitat can be found on pages 26–31.

- Tropical rain forest
- Tropical monsoon forest
- Temperate forest
- Coniferous forest
- Moorlands and heath
- Open habitat, including savanna, grassland, fields, pampas, and steppes
- Desert and semidesert
- Mountains and highlands
- Tundra
- Polar regions
- Seas and oceans
- Coral reefs
- Mangrove swamps
- Coastal areas, including beaches, oceanic cliffs, sand dunes, intertidal rock pools, and/or coastal waters (as applicable to group)
- Rivers and streams, including river and stream banks
- Wetlands, including swamps, marshes, fens, floodplains, deltas, and bogs
- Lakes and ponds
- Urban areas

Section and chapter
This indicates the group of mammals under discussion.

Classification box
This shows the taxonomic groups to which mammals belong.

Lavish photographs
Taken by leading wildlife photographers, these portray the habits and habitats of different species.

Detailed diagram
Where appropriate, diagrams are included to illustrate points about anatomy or adaptation.

SEALS AND SEA LIONS

CLASS	Mammalia
ORDER	Carnivora
FAMILIES	3
GENERA	21
SPECIES	36

With flexible, torpedo-shaped bodies, limbs modified to become flippers, and insulating layers of blubber and hair, seals, sea lions, and walruses are superbly adapted to a life in water. They have not, however, completely severed their link with land and must return to shore to breed. Collectively known as pinnipeds, these marine mammals were once placed in their own order, but are now considered to be part of Carnivora. Most feed on fish, squid, and crustaceans, but some also eat penguins and carrion and may attack the pups of other seal species. They can dive to great depths in search of prey, with the elephant seal able to stay submerged for up to 2 hours at a time.

Cold-water creatures Although monk seals are found in warmer waters, most seals, sea lions, and walruses are restricted to the colder, highly productive seas of the world's polar and temperate regions. The fossil record shows that the three families all originated in the North Pacific. They are now most abundant in the North Pacific, North Atlantic, and Southern oceans.

Communal living Most pinnipeds are gregarious animals and tend to live in large colonies. Walrus herds can number in the hundreds or even thousands and may be single sex or mixed, with both body and tusk size determining rank.

THREE GROUPS

There are three pinniped families. The Phocidae are known as the true seals. They swim mainly with strokes of their hind flippers, which cannot bend forward to act as feet, making their movement on land particularly ungainly. Although their hearing, especially under water, is good, true seals lack external ears.

Sea lions and fur seals belong to the family Otariidae. These "eared seals" have small external ears. They rely mostly on their front flippers for swimming, and can bend their hind flippers forward when on land, allowing them to walk "four-footed" and sit in a semi-upright position.

The third family, Odobenidae, contains a single species, the walrus, instantly recognizable by the long canine teeth that form tusks on both sexes. Like true seals, walruses use their hind flippers for swimming and lack external ears. Like eared seals, however, walruses can bend their hind flippers forward.

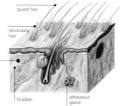

Insulating layers Pinnipeds have a thick layer of blubber that provides insulation, buoyancy, and a fat store. For further protection, all but the walrus have hairy bodies, and fur seals have dense secondary hairs that form a waterproof barrier.

BRINGING UP BABY
All pinnipeds return to land or ice to give birth and mate. Mating takes place just days after the usually single pup is born, but the fertilized egg does not become implanted in the uterus for months. This delayed implantation allows birthing, nursing, and mating to occur in one season so that the animals live on land, where they are most vulnerable, only once a year. Pups are dependent for varying lengths of time. Harp seals (right), for example, are nursed for only 12 days or so, while walruses stay with their mother for 2 years.

🐾 CONSERVATION WATCH

The commercial sealing operations that began in the 16th century had a devastating effect on pinniped populations. Of the 36 species of pinnipeds, 36% are listed on the IUCN Red List, as follows:

- 2 Extinct
- 1 Critically endangered
- 2 Endangered
- 7 Vulnerable
- 1 Near threatened

Feature box
This describes in detail a facet of the species' behavior or biology, and is accompanied by relevant photographs, illustrations, or diagrams.

Conservation watch box
This provides information about the status of a particular species, according to the IUCN Red List of Threatened Species. These boxes may also outline factors that threaten the mammal's survival.

CONSERVATION INFORMATION

Within the fact files, each profiled species is allocated a conservation status, using IUCN and other conservation categories, as follows:

† Indicates that a species is listed under the following categories:
Extinct (IUCN) It is beyond reasonable doubt that the last individual of a given species has died.
Extinct in the wild (IUCN) Only known to survive in captivity or as a naturalized population outside its former range.

⚡ Indicates that a species is listed under the following categories:
Critically endangered (IUCN) Facing a very high and immediate risk of extinction in the wild.
Endangered (IUCN) Facing a very high risk of extinction in the wild in the near future.

The following categories are also used:
Vulnerable (IUCN) Facing a high risk of extinction in the wild in the foreseeable future.
Near threatened (IUCN) Likely to qualify for one of the above categories in the near future.
Conservation dependent (IUCN) Dependent upon species- or habitat-specific conservation programs to keep it out of one of the above threatened categories.

Data deficient (IUCN) Inadequate information available to make an assessment of its risk.
Not known Not evaluated or little studied.
Common Widespread and abundant.
Locally common Widespread and abundant within its range.
Uncommon Occurs widely in low numbers in preferred habitat(s).
Rare Occurs in only some of preferred habitat or in small restricted areas.

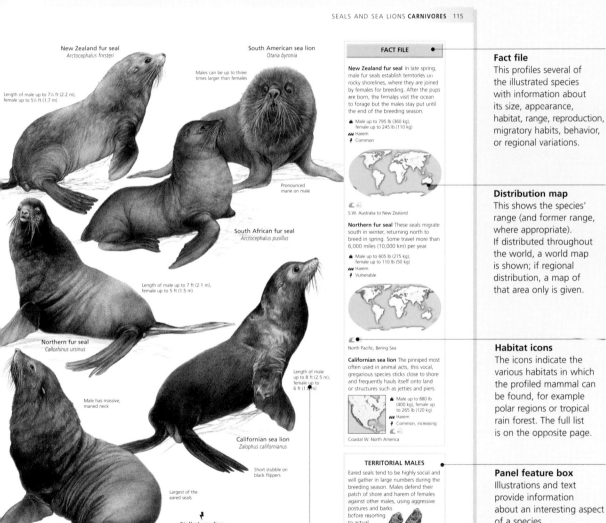

SEALS AND SEA LIONS **CARNIVORES** 115

New Zealand fur seal
Arctocephalus forsteri

Length of male up to 7¼ ft (2.2 m), female up to 5½ ft (1.7 m)

South American sea lion
Otaria byronia

Males can be up to three times larger than females

Pronounced mane on male

South African fur seal
Arctocephalus pusillus

Length of male up to 7 ft (2.1 m), female up to 5 ft (1.5 m)

Northern fur seal
Callorhinus ursinus

Male has massive, maned neck

Length of male up to 8 ft (2.5 m), female up to 6 ft (1.8 m)

Short stubble on black flippers

Californian sea lion
Zalophus californianus

Largest of the eared seals

Steller's sea lion
Eumetopias jubatus

FACT FILE

New Zealand fur seal In late spring, male fur seals establish territories on rocky shorelines, where they are joined by females for breeding. After the pups are born, the females visit the ocean to forage but the males stay put until the end of the breeding season.
🏋 Male up to 795 lb (360 kg), female up to 245 lb (110 kg)
🐾 Harem
⚡ Common

S.W. Australia to New Zealand

Northern fur seal These seals migrate south in winter, returning north to breed in spring. Some travel more than 6,000 miles (10,000 km) per year.
🏋 Male up to 605 lb (275 kg), female up to 110 lb (50 kg)
🐾 Harem
⚡ Vulnerable

North Pacific, Bering Sea

Californian sea lion The pinniped most often used in animal acts, this vocal, gregarious species sticks close to shore and frequently hauls itself onto land or structures such as jetties and piers.
🏋 Male up to 880 lb (400 kg), female up to 265 lb (120 kg)
🐾 Harem
⚡ Common, increasing

Coastal W. North America

TERRITORIAL MALES
Eared seals tend to be highly social and will gather in large numbers during the breeding season. Males defend their patch of shore and harem of females against other males, using aggressive postures and barks before resorting to actual fighting.

Fact file
This profiles several of the illustrated species with information about its size, appearance, habitat, range, reproduction, migratory habits, behavior, or regional variations.

Distribution map
This shows the species' range (and former range, where appropriate). If distributed throughout the world, a world map is shown; if regional distribution, a map of that area only is given.

Habitat icons
The icons indicate the various habitats in which the profiled mammal can be found, for example polar regions or tropical rain forest. The full list is on the opposite page.

Panel feature box
Illustrations and text provide information about an interesting aspect of a species.

FACT FILE STATISTICS
Important or interesting facts about profiled species use the following icons and information. All measurements are maximums.

Length
🏃 Head and body

Height
🏃 Shoulder height

Tail
🏃 Length of tail

Weight/Mass
⚖ Body weight

Social Unit
🐾 Solitary
🐾🐾 Pair
🐾🐾🐾 Small to large group
🐾🐾 Varies between the above

A YEAR AS A POLAR BEAR

THE POLAR BEAR **CARNIVORES**

Conservation symbols
A red cross above the species' name indicates that it is extinct or extinct in the wild; a red flash indicates that it is critically endangered or endangered according to the IUCN Red List.

Name labels
Labels provide the common and scientific name of the illustrated mammals.

Snippets
These highlight distinguishing aspects or characteristics of the species, such as color variations, behavior, habitat, size, and anatomical features.

Feature page
This explores topics of particular interest and provides insight into mammal behavior through text, illustrations, and photographs.

INTRODUCING MAMMALS

MAMMALS

CLASS	Mammalia
ORDERS	26
FAMILIES	137
GENERA	1,142
SPECIES	4,785

The diversity of mammals is astonishing. They range from field mice no bigger than a thimble to the massive blue whale—1,750 times heavier than a human. Adaptability and intelligence have helped modern mammals occupy all continents and most habitats. They exploit niches above and below ground, in fresh and salt water, in trees, and in the air. Mammals share many unique characteristics but, for scientists, one key defining feature is that the lower jaw bone, the dentary, attaches directly to the skull. More generally, however, mammals are endothermic ("warm-blooded") animals that suckle their young with milk produced by mammary glands.

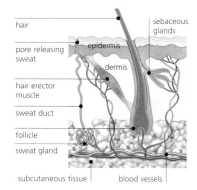

Skin deep Mammalian skin has two layers. The outer epidermis keeps body fluids in and disease-causing microbes out. Beneath it, the dermis contains blood vessels, nerve endings, and glands. Muscles can raise or lower hairs to trap or release an insulating layer of air.

COMMON FEATURES

Endothermy has been particularly significant to the spread of mammals. The ability to regulate the internal body temperature—through such methods as adjusting metabolic rate or blood flow and shivering, sweating, or panting—allows mammals to remain active in extreme external temperatures and has helped the group colonize a great range of habitats. Body hair or fur, which aids insulation, is another common attribute of mammals, even if, as in naked mole rats, it can appear so reduced it is barely visible. All mammals have three bones in the middle ear. Prominent external ears to collect sound are almost universal.

As well as milk-secreting mammary glands in females, mammalian skin contains several different types of glands. Sebaceous glands, for example, produce an oily lubricant to protect and waterproof fur. Sweat glands allow many mammals to release sweat and cool down through its evaporation. Scent glands produce complex odors that convey an individual's or group's status, sexual condition, and other information. Mammalian brains are large—relative to their body size—and complex. Smell is often important in communication. Color vision and binocular vision, which allows mammals to judge distance, have arisen independently in several groups.

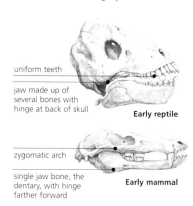

Early reptile

Early mammal

Modern mammal

Jaws and teeth Mammals, the only vertebrates that chew their food, differ from their reptilian ancestors by having a single jaw bone and powerful jaw muscles in a zygomatic arch. Teeth are more complex in both form and the way those of the upper and lower jaws lock together.

Fur and whiskers Insulation in most mammals, from Madagascar's ground-dwelling streaked tenrec (below) to sea otters (right), is provided by fur or hair. This can also form touch-sensitive whiskers, known as vibrissae, which gather information on surrounding environments.

MAMMALS THROUGH THE AGES

Mammals are considered to have arisen from the synapsids, or mammal-like reptiles, which dominated Earth's terrestrial habitats more than 300 million years ago. Although these creatures moved like reptiles and had a similar posture, key features of their skull, revealed in fossils, indicate they were the ancestors of the mammals. The first mammal probably appeared during the Triassic period—248-206 million years ago—around the same time as the first dinosaurs. The oldest known mammal fossils, which date back almost 200 million years, are of creatures that may have resembled today's shrews—small, nocturnal insectivores. They are indicative of most of the mammals that coexisted with dinosaurs, although there were some larger, carnivorous species, up to about 31 pounds (14 kg) in weight, that lived among and preyed on dinosaurs about 120 million years ago. Generally, however, mammals remained comparatively small and insignificant until the dinosaurs died out 65 million years ago, at the end of the Cretaceous period.

THE RISE OF MAMMALS

Many mammals also died out with the mass extinction that took the dinosaurs. But a few of those shrew-like forms survived. With no competition from or predation by dinosaurs, these tiny mammals spread, flourished, and diversified across the planet. Within about 5 million years of the Cretaceous extinction, several new kinds of mammals had evolved. They included the first large predatory mammals, known as creodonts; several groups of large grazing herbivores; and a small group of primitive primates—the plesiadapids —which were herbivorous and occupied niches that were later filled by rodents. Within about 15 million years of the Cretaceous extinction, the first true carnivores

had evolved. So too had the earliest member of the horse family, *Hyracotherium*. The first whales and other groups later to be highly successful, such as bats, rodents, elephants, and lemurs, had also appeared around this time.

About 40 million years ago, climate change caused the extinction of around one-third of the mammalian families existing at the time. This was followed by a long period of favorable climate during the Miocene—24–5 million years ago. It was the heyday of mammalian evolution, when more groups of mammals were present than ever before or ever since. One of the most significant developments at this time was the spread of grasses. They formed great plains on which herds of grazing animals could thrive.

Ancient ancestor *Cynognathus* was a cynodont—among the most advanced of the synapsids or mammal-like reptiles. A wolf-sized carnivore that lived about 240 million years ago, with powerful jaws and prominent canine teeth, it was probably endothermic ("warm-blooded").

Big and bizarre The herbivorous *Uintatherium* (above) was an extraordinary looking creature with a body like a rhinoceros, only larger, and a head from which three pairs of bony protuberances grew like stunted horns.

Largest mammal *Indricotherium* (below), probably the largest land mammal that has ever lived, grew to 18 feet (5.5 m) at the shoulder and may have weighed more than 40,000 pounds (20 tonnes), four times heavier than a modern elephant.

CLASSIFICATION

Many mammals have vernacular, or common, names but these often vary from language to language, country to country, and even within the same country. To avoid confusion, scientists use Latinized names to sort and classify mammals, just as they do for all organisms—plants, animals, fungi, and microbes. This provides universality and stability, and avoids the necessity of translating names into many different languages. In this way, no matter what one's native tongue, the Latinized scientific name is immediately associated with the same group of organisms. The basic category in classification is the species. These are individuals that share more key similarities with each other than they do with any other organisms. Almost 5,000 species of modern mammals are recognized. In turn, species with common features are grouped together in genera.

Close relations Scientists have documented behavioral and physiological similarities between humans and chimpanzees for centuries. Recently, they have been able to compare the DNA of the two species and found they share more than 98 percent of genes, reinforcing the view they should be classified within similar categories.

Linnaean classification Each grouping in this system of nested categories has progressively similar characteristics. The bobcat, for example, belongs to kingdom Animalia; phylum Chordata (animals with a centralized nerve chord); class Mammalia, and so on down to the species level.

KINGDOM
Animalia
bobcat, stick insect, sea urchin, parrot, crocodile

PHYLUM
Chordata
bobcat, shark, salamander, dinosaur, albatross

CLASS
Mammalia
bobcat, kangaroo, domestic cat, human, dolphin, woolly mammoth

ORDER
Carnivora
bobcat, seal, wolf, dog, bear

FAMILY
Felidae
bobcat, domestic cat ,lion, leopard, jaguar

GENUS
Lynx
bobcat, Eurasian lynx, Canadian lynx

SPECIES
Lynx rufous
bobcat

MAJOR GROUPINGS

Scientists recognize two major divisions of Class Mammalia. The Prototheria—unique among mammals because they reproduce by laying eggs—includes only the echidnas of Australia and New Guinea and Australia's platypus. All other mammals are within the Theria. This also has two major divisions. The Metatheria contains the order Marsupiala— the marsupials—whose young are born in an underdeveloped state and complete their development in an abdominal pouch or fold on the mother. Most modern mammals, however, belong to the second group, the Eutheria, whose young develop to a relatively advanced stage within the mother's body.

Modern mammals represent a fraction of the total kinds that have existed since the group first evolved. The fossil record indicates that many thousands of different mammal species have evolved, thrived, and gone extinct during the past 200 million years or so. Sometimes, fossils represent genera or even species known today, and many fossil mammals belong to the same orders and families as their modern counterparts.

Going solo Occasionally, a very strongly characterized species may be the sole member of its genus. The genus *Vulpes* includes a number of species of foxes, such as the red or common fox *Vulpes vulpes*, but the Arctic fox is considered sufficiently distinct from these other foxes to be placed by itself in a separate genus as *Alopex lagopus*.

MAMMALS

The 26 orders of mammals are divided into three major groups based on the structure of their reproductive tracts. The most primitive are the egg-laying mammals, with a single order, the monotremes. Marsupials, which give birth to young in a very early stage of development, are now considered to consist of seven orders. The other 18 orders are made up of placental mammals. The most recent evidence from DNA sequence analysis has revealed that whales and even-toed ungulates are more closely related to each other than to any other group. DNA also indicates that there have been three major radiations of placental mammals: in Africa, South America, and the Northern Hemisphere.

Class Mammalia

EGG-LAYING MAMMALS
Order Monotremata
Monotremes

MARSUPIALS
Order Didelphimorphia
American opossums

Order Paucituberculata
Shrew opossums

Order Monotremata, page 38

Order Microbiotheria
Monito del monte

Order Dasyuromorphia
Quolls, dunnarts, marsupial mice, numbat, and allies

Order Peramelemorphia
Bandicoots

Order Notoryctemorphia
Marsupial moles

Order Diprotodontia
Possums, kangaroos, koalas, wombats, and allies

PLACENTAL MAMMALS
Order Xenarthra
Sloths, anteaters, and armadillos

Order Pholidota
Pangolins

Order Insectivora
Insectivores

Order Dermoptera
Flying lemurs

Order Scandentia
Tree shrews

Order Chiroptera
Bats

Order Primates
Primates

Suborder Strepsirhini
Prosimians

Suborder Haplorhini
Monkeys and apes

Order Carnivora
Carnivores

Family Canidae
Dogs and foxes

Family Ursidae
Bear and pandas

Family Mustelidae
Mustelids

SEALS AND SEA LIONS
Family Phocidae
True seals

Family Otariidae
Sea lions and fur seals

Family Odobenidae
Walrus

Family Procyonidae
Raccoons

Family Hyaenidae
Hyenas and aardwolf

Family Ursidae, page 102

CIVETS AND MONGOOSES
Family Viverridae
Civets, genets, and linsangs

Family Herpestidae
Mongooses

Family Felidae
Cats

Order Proboscidea
Elephants

Order Sirenia
Dugong and manatees

Family Trichechidae
Manatees

Family Dugongidae
Dugong

Order Perissodactyla
Odd-toed ungulates

Family Equidae
Horses, zebras, and asses

Family Tapiridae
Tapirs

Family Rhinocerotidae
Rhinoceroses

Order Hyracoidea
Hyraxes

Order Tubulidentata
Aardvark

Order Artiodactyla
Even-toed ungulates

Family Bovidae
Cattle, antelopes, and sheep

DEER
Family Cervidae
Deer

Family Tragulidae
Chevrotains

Family Moschidae
Musk deer

Family Antilocapridae
Pronghorn

Family Giraffidae
Giraffe and okapi

Family Camelidae
Camels and llamas

Family Suidae
Pigs

Family Cervidae, page 162

Family Tayassuidae
Peccaries

Family Hippopotamidae
Hippopotamuses

Order Cetacea
Cetaceans

Suborder Odontoceti
Toothed whales

Suborder Mysticeti
Baleen whales

Order Rodentia
Rodents

Suborder Sciurognathi
Squirrel-like rodents, mouse-like rodents, and gundis

Suborder Hystricognathi
Cavy-like rodents

Order Lagomorpha
Hares, rabbits, and pikas

Order Macroscelidea
Elephant shrews

BIOLOGY AND BEHAVIOR

The biology and behavior of mammals have been shaped by the environments in which they live as well as physiological and evolutionary pressures to reproduce, eat, and avoid being eaten—all while maintaining a constant body temperature. To fuel the regulation of their temperature, mammals must consume either a rich or a plentiful diet. The eternal conflict between prey and predator has underpinned the evolution of many key adaptations. Jaw bone and muscle structure provide a powerful bite and the ability to cut and chew food. Teeth are highly specialized and reflect the diet of different species. The cheek teeth of carnivores, for example, are sharp for cutting flesh and bones; those of herbivores are broad for grinding plant matter; and omnivores have multicuspid teeth that enable them to chew both the animal and plant material on which they feed.

ADAPTABLE AND SOCIAL

The adaptability of mammals is reflected in the diversity of their social organization. Adult mammals may be solitary; live in pairs or small family groups; or form harems, herds, or colonies. These groupings may be flexible and temporary, or highly stable and permanent. In all mammals, the fact that young are nourished by their mothers' milk ensures the development of some kind of social bond. This bond may be rudimentary—the tree shrew, for example, visits its young only every couple of days for a brief nursing session, and many rodents are weaned after just a few weeks. Mammals can gain many advantages by living together with other members of the same species.

Quick learners Zebra foals can stand within 10 minutes of birth and walk shortly after—necessary when grazing on Africa's open grassy plains where keeping up with the herd is the best protection from predators. Zebra herds are territorial and each comprises a stallion and harem of females. Foals remain close to mothers until weaned at about 11 months.

Eternal battle Most carnivorous mammals, such as lions and the other big cats of the African savanna, have large, sharp teeth designed to rip and tear flesh; lightning-sharp reflexes; and the ability to run quickly. Large grazing mammals often form herds as a safety-in-numbers behavioral response to predators. Herds provide many eyes and ears to detect danger and lessen the chance that any one individual will be caught. Other tasks, such as finding, hunting for, or gathering food, can also be made considerably easier by working cooperatively in groups.

Nursing instinct Mammals are born with the instinct to suckle, and most could not survive without at least some early period of parental care. This, in at least 95 percent of mammal species, is done solely by the mother. The time spent by young with their mothers before weaning varies between species from a few days to several years. Mothers' milk is a complete food, providing all the nutrients young need until they are ready to eat by themselves.

Frenzied feeder To fuel a fast metabolism, the Eurasian common shrew must eat every few hours. It consumes up to 90 percent of its weight in invertebrates each day. It shelters in a burrow, often taking over one abandoned by another species.

SIZE MATTERS

Gravity helps define mammalian upper size limits, which is why the biggest—and largest mammal ever—the blue whale, lives in water that supports its huge bulk. Compared to large mammals, smaller species have higher surface-area-to-volume ratios so they lose heat faster. For this reason, mammals inhabiting colder climates tend to be larger than their relatives living closer to the tropics. For similar reasons, polar mammals, such as seals and the musk ox, usually have compact extremities to keep their surface-area-to-volume ratio as low as possible.

LEARNING POWER

All mammals are born with innate capabilities, responses, and adaptations, which are known collectively as instinct. Many, however, also have strong capabilities to learn. Those that live within well-defined social structures often learn by trial and error. Play is an important part of development for most mammals. While the young of primates and carnivores are particularly well known for indulging in play, it can be found in most mammals, from large herbivores such as elephants, to small marsupials such as antechinuses. The forms and intensity of this special social behavior vary between species.

Through imitation, some mammal populations transfer learned skills between individuals, and even generations, so that they develop a form of culture. Mammals in which this has been recognized include primates, cetaceans, and elephants. The ability to make and use tools is also seen as another yardstick of intelligence and it is displayed within several mammal groups. Tool-making ranges from the manipulation of sticks by chimpanzees to collect termites, to sea otters using stones to smash open the hard shells of mollusks.

SEX WARS

In many instances, male mammals prove their reproductive worth by battling one another. This is one key reason why they are frequently larger than the females of their species. The evolution of male combat equipment, such as horns in antelopes and antlers in deer, has also been driven by the need to secure reproductive rites. Behavioral displays are especially important to avoid or reduce the severity of aggressive encounters so that combatants are not left dead or disabled by battle. Conflict of a more physical nature occurs when a territory is seriously threatened.

Serious skirmishes Reproductive battles between male hippopotamus are occasionally fatal. However, one competitor usually concedes defeat before mortal wounds are inflicted and shuffles off to another part of the river.

Power playing Many young primates and carnivores learn survival skills through play. It gives them safe opportunity to make repeated mistakes until they learn the most advantageous way to perform particular behaviors.

Gain without pain In dominance encounters between male gray wolves, a resolution will be reached without serious injury when the vanquished signals submission by laying supine with his stomach exposed.

Sexual dimorphism Within mammal species, males and females often look different. Female blackbuck, for example, are hornless and colored white and brown. Dominant males are black and white with long, spiraling horns.

COURTSHIP AND MATING

Mammalian sexual behavior can vary from the short, rough, and frenetic couplings of the Australian bandicoot, to the Uganda kob antelope's highly stylized and ritualized courtship performances. Mating in both these examples is promiscuous, the male attending many females. Sometimes male and female mate for life, as in some of the small forest-dwelling antelopes. Usually, however, the mating system lies somewhere between the two extremes. Many non-promiscuous species show a degree of courtship,

during which male and female annex themselves from the group.

In some mammals, the close proximity of the male brings the female on heat, and only at this time will he attempt to mate with her. It is thought that pheromones (signaling odors) in the male's urine act to stimulate the female's reproductive system. Mating can involve rather fine judgment on the part of the male, since a female that is not on heat will reject his advances vigorously. In some species, the female may emit a special odor to lure males from afar.

Sole parents Adult male jaguars are solitary hunters that remain with females only briefly during the mating season. They participate in various mating rituals, as seen below. Mothers are left to raise the cubs—numbering up to four—on their own.

Casual flings Giraffes have a haphazard and promiscuous mating system in which adult males tend to wander, ever alert for a receptive female. When he finds one, he investigates her urine for her readiness. Adult males will mate with as many females as possible.

MAMMAL REPRODUCTION

In all mammals, the female's eggs are fertilized internally by the male's sperm. Monotremes lay the eggs after several days and incubate them externally until they hatch. Marsupials and placental mammals both give birth to live young. The young of marsupials have short gestations and are poorly developed at birth, but latch onto a teat and are nourished by the mother's milk. Placental mammals grow for longer inside the uterus, nourished by a placenta. At birth, they tend to be in a more advanced state of development.

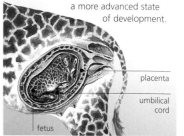

placenta

umbilical cord

fetus

Extreme polygamy Southern elephant seals are among the most sexually dimorphic of all mammals: full-grown males can attain weights of 8,800 pounds (4 tonnes) and lengths of 15 feet (4.5 m)—up to four times that of adult females. They have a polygamous mating system. One male controls a large harem of as many as 40 females, each of which he may impregnate in a season. Breeding season is from September to November. Large males arrive a month before females to fight for dominance and the right to a harem.

Group advantages Mandrills live in troops of between a few and several dozen individuals. Social bonds are reinforced by touch. The young learn about selecting and preparing food by observing their mothers and in this way, group traditions in food preference develop. Adults will also prevent juveniles from eating unfamiliar, and potentially poisonous, foods. Like other social primates, mandrills use various forms of touch, including grooming, to cement social bonds.

MAKING SENSE

Almost all mammals have, to some degree, capabilities to perceive the world around them using the same five basic senses as humans—sight, touch, taste, smell, and hearing. Most also have the same sorts of sense organs as humans—eyes, ears, tongue, nose, and touch receptors. The development and range of perception of sense organs, however, are often different from those of humans. Both elephants and cetaceans, for example, are able to perceive and communicate by deep, rumbling infrasound that is undetectable to the human ear.

Although many mammals rely on the basic senses to communicate with each other, some also rely on visual communication tools, such as posture and gesture, and use stylized movements and behaviors to send messages to other members of their species.

Echolocation is a notable mammalian sense for which humans have no equivalent. Bats, toothed whales, and porpoises use this elaborate form of sonar to navigate, locate and capture prey, and for social interactions. Some mammals, such as shrews and tenrecs, also use a basic form of echolocation to find their way in lightless conditions. An animal using echolocation will emit sounds, such as clicks in dolphins and clicks and squeaks in bats, that are beyond the range of human hearing. It then interprets the angle and quality of the echoes that bounce off solid objects nearby.

HABITATS AND ADAPTATIONS

As mammals diversified into different habitats, their anatomy, locomotion, diet, and social habits adapted to different niches. For example, the limbs and senses of permanent subterranean dwellers such as moles are well suited for burrowing in the dark. Likewise, aquatic mammals have developed streamlined bodies and limbs modified into flippers to allow efficient movement through water. Although most mammals occupy one habitat, some live in and move between two or more to exploit different conditions and resources at different times of the year.

Natural vegetation This map shows the vegetation that would occur naturally without human interference. Climate and soil determine the vegetation of an area, and the vegetation, in turn, determines the extent and diversity of animal life. Together, the plants and animals of each zone form an ecological community known as a biome. The rainfall and warmth of the tropics have given rise to the greatest biodiversity in the world.

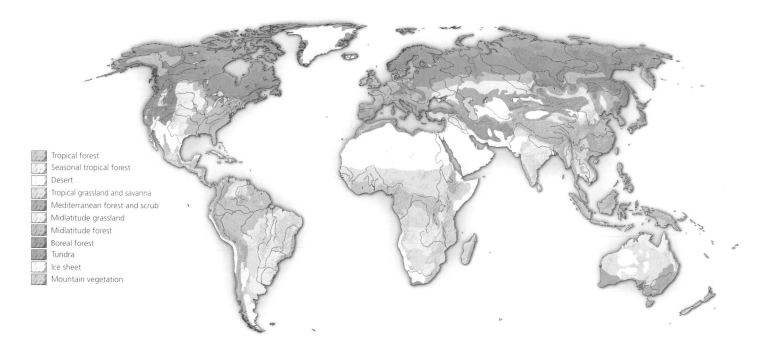

- Tropical forest
- Seasonal tropical forest
- Desert
- Tropical grassland and savanna
- Mediterranean forest and scrub
- Midlatitude grassland
- Midlatitude forest
- Boreal forest
- Tundra
- Ice sheet
- Mountain vegetation

FORESTS

There are four main types of forest: rain forest (including temperate and tropical), tropical monsoonal, coniferous, and temperate forests. Mammals occur in all but are best represented in the lush environments of tropical rain forests. These occur in more than 80 countries, located mainly between the tropics of Cancer and Capricorn, and are among the most biodiverse of all habitats. Low-light adapted shrubs and small trees frame an understory in which big cats, such as jaguar in South America and the clouded leopard in Southeast Asia, hunt. Some rodents and primates spend their entire lives in rain forest trees without ever descending to the forest floor. Mammals are also well represented in temperate forests, which occur around the world at latitudes between 25 and 50 degrees. These can be deciduous, in which mammals lead a distinctly seasonal life, often migrating or hibernating to avoid harsh winters. Seasons are not as well defined in evergreen temperate forests. Typical temperate forest mammals include raccoons, squirrels, and bears in the Northern Hemisphere, and possums and bats in the Southern Hemisphere.

Life in the forest Foxes rely on their excellent hearing, sight, and smell to locate and stalk prey. They are even able to hear small animals moving underground. Trees are critical to forest-dwelling mammals, particularly as sources of food, shelter, and routes of travel and escape.

High life As in other tropical rain forests, the highest vertical layers of this rain forest in French Guiana's Nouragues Reserve are noisy places. Dense foliage makes vision unreliable so mammals here communicate with loud howls, whistles, and screeches.

Mammalian aviators Bats are the only mammals to have evolved true flight, but some squirrel and possum species have developed a non-powered form known as volplaning. In this way, some flying squirrels can glide for 150 feet (46 m) or more between trees.

Tree dweller The maned three-toed sloth is both a slow eater and a slow digester of food. As much as a month may pass before foodstuffs finally pass from the multichambered stomach to the small intestine. Usually, sloths descend to the ground only to defecate.

GRASSLANDS

Sprawling, flat grasslands offer few hiding places. Nevertheless, this habitat is often dominated by large, herbivorous mammals that graze in huge herds to overwhelm and confuse potential predators such as big cats and wild dogs. Many smaller grassland mammals are adapted for burrowing while others must rely on speed, rather than concealment, as a method of escape. Large grassland habitats include the Ukrainian steppes, South American pampas, southern Africa's veldt, and North America's prairies. Australia's grasslands are grazed by its largest native mammal—kangaroos.

Cheetah chase Cheetahs choose a victim then pursue it to the exclusion of all others, even those nearer or more available. Chases seldom last more than 20 seconds. Such a burst of speed requires tremendous amounts of energy and builds up massive amounts of heat, so that the cat soon finds itself overheated and out of breath. Other predators may take advantage of the cheetah's vulnerability at this time, and steal its prey.

On the hop Powerful kangaroos gracefully move through the large open spaces of Australia's grasslands. Strong hindlimbs and long hindfeet enable them to hop fast, using their lengthy and rather inflexible tail for balance. This is an energy-efficient form of locomotion; a hopping kangaroo uses less energy than a four-legged animal of the same size moving at the same speed. When moving slowly, the tail acts like a fifth limb, to support the body.

TUNDRA

One of the harshest and least biologically diverse habitats, tundra is a vast, treeless world north of 55 degrees latitude, and covers one-fifth of Earth's land surface. Very little snow or rain falls and nutrients are scarce. Dark, bitter-cold winters, during which the ground is permanently frozen down to at least 10 inches (25 cm), endure most of the year. With winter's onset, the coats of Arctic hares, Arctic foxes, and collared lemmings turn white for camouflage and thicken to provide insulation. Arctic hares grow dense fur on the foot pads to increase surface area and aid movement across snow. Caribou—elk-like mammals that roam in large herds across tundra in North America and Greenland—survive the severe winter food shortage by eating lichen. Antlers are used to scrape away snow and ice and expose vegetation. Synchronized calving may be a response to constraints imposed by a short summer growing season. 80–90 percent of calves in a population are born within a 10-day period in late May or early June each year.

Short summer Caribou have unusually broad hooves that help them to walk across marshy ground in summer. The Sun shines 24 hours a day, the snow thaws briefly, and shallow, ephemeral lakes form in the wet ground.

Winter warmer The musk ox's shaggy coat has the longest guard hair of any mammal—24–36 inches (60–90 cm) long—which helps to insulate this species against the tundra's bitter cold. The dark color also helps the body retain heat.

DESERTS

Extreme temperatures and dryness are the major concerns of desert–dwelling mammals. Most avoid daytime temperatures and higher evaporation rates by being nocturnal. Underground burrows, with lower temperatures and higher relative humidity than aboveground, provide daytime shelter for species such as ground squirrels and kangaroo rats. Larger mammals, including camels and goats, reduce heat absorption with dense coats. They can tolerate unusually wide body temperature fluctuations and minimize water loss by using evaporate cooling only when their core temperature approaches lethal limits.

Hot strategies The gemsbok is superbly adapted to extreme heat. When it pants, air flowing rapidly in and out travels across a fine network of blood vessels that ensures blood is cooled before passing to the brain. The gemsbok feeds mostly at night when moisture in plant material is highest. To help it walk on shifting sands, it has splayed feet that provide grip and prevent sinking. The gemsbok's light-colored coat helps keep it cool by reflecting solar radiation. When deprived of water, the gemsbok can survive for weeks by ceasing to sweat.

Metabolic water The moisture needs of desert rodents, such as gerbils, are met almost entirely by water produced within their bodies as a by-product when they metabolize carbohydrates in seeds.

ADAPTATIONS

Success across a wide climate range is testament to mammalian adaptability. Precise tailoring to extreme conditions, however, increases vulnerability to climate change. Some specializations, such as insulating blubber in polar species, are physical. Others, including daytime burrowing by desert rodents, are behavioral. Evaporative cooling through sweating or panting helps endure hot conditions. Some mammals hibernate or become torpid whenever weather turns extreme. Others migrate.

Long or short Because mammals are endothermic ("warm-blooded"), body size and shape affect heat loss—it rises as surface area increases. This is why the extremities of hares differ with different habitats. Arctic and snowshoe hares have shorter ears and legs, minimizing body surface area and, consequently, heat loss. Longer limbs and ears in subtropical black-tailed and antelope jackrabbits aid heat loss.

Sublime adaptations Polar bears are so well suited to Arctic conditions they overheat with too much activity. A thick layer of blubber more than four inches (11 cm) thick provides perfect insulation from the cold. Polar bear fur, extending to the soles, appears white because individual coat hairs are completely lacking in pigment. The hollow hairs provide thermal insulation and excellent camouflage.

Arctic hare

Snowshoe hare

Black-tailed jackrabbit

Antelope jackrabbit

MAMMALS IN DANGER

Extinction is a natural part of evolution and most mammals that have ever evolved have gone extinct. Elevated extinction rates are not unprecedented and, in fact, they have risen to extraordinarily high levels on five previous occasions during the estimated 2 billion-year history of life on Earth. These peaks are known as mass extinctions and many scientists believe we presently face a sixth. This one, however, is different. While past mass extinctions have been caused by some sort of natural phenomenon, the current one is being blamed entirely on the impact of the human species and its rapid and uncontrollable population growth. The sixth extinction also differs from those of the past in the unparalleled rate at which it is progressing and its enormous scale. Mammals are rapidly losing their homes, food, water, and open space.

Rocky road The chamois—a goat-like, mountain-climbing member of the antelope family endemic to parts of Europe—is safe as a species, for now. However, excessive hunting and competition from livestock threaten the future of at least three subspecies, including one that is classified as critically endangered.

Making amends Hunting has been a major factor in worldwide whale declines. Many species were exploited sustainably for centuries by indigenous communities using traditional methods. However, 20th-century technological advances led to such dramatic and alarming declines that complete international bans have been in place for almost all whale species since the mid-1980s.

DISTURBING STATISTICS

The World Conservation Union included just over 1,100 mammals on the 2004 update of its Red List of Threatened Species. That figure has been hovering around the same level with little sign of improvement since the list was compiled in 1996. It represents a staggering one-quarter of all modern mammal species so far described by science. Most have natural distributions in Central and South America, sub-Saharan Africa, or tropical South and Southeast Asia. These areas contain significant rain forests and other highly biodiverse tropical ecosystems. Australia, however, is the continent with the highest rate of mammalian extinctions in recent times. Seventeen species of terrestrial mammals—all marsupials found nowhere else in the world—have gone extinct since European colonization of the continent began in the late 1700s. That represents half of the world's total mammal extinctions for the same period.

Overall, the Red List documents 73 modern mammal species as having gone extinct and four that exist only in captive populations. Another 162 have been assigned critically endangered status, facing an "extremely high risk of extinction in the wild in the immediate future." More than 350 are categorized as endangered, while almost 600 more are considered vulnerable.

Iconic decline China's giant panda has become a potent symbol for the demise of mammal species everywhere. Fewer than 1,000 individuals are now thought to survive in the wild, with about 100 more in zoos. The biggest threats have been habitat loss and hunting.

Non-renewable resource The Amazon rain forest—the world's largest—is often referred to as the planet's lungs. Much of its 1.5 million square miles (4 million sq km) faces threats from mining, agriculture, and logging, with 15 percent already cleared. Hunting is another threat to its mammals.

Red for danger The bald uakari, a South American primate, is listed as near threatened by the World Conservation Union, due to mining and logging. These activities have also provided easier access to poachers of the species, servicing the food and pet trades.

THE HUMAN FACTOR

People are the major threat to most other life-forms and the leading cause of biotic impoverishment. We are now more destructive as a species than we have ever been, although the fossil record shows our impact on other mammals stretches back farther than most people realize. Archaeologists sleuthing through ancient "boneyards" of the late Pleistocene (100,000–10,000 years ago), for example, have found that prehistoric people, despite their small size and puny weapons, grouped together to kill huge mammals, known as megafauna, in large numbers. Each time humans arrived on a new land mass, a wave of extinction followed. For instance, shortly after humans crossed the Bering Strait to North America (15,000–10,000 years ago), there was a rapid disappearance of giant beavers, elephants, mastodons, camels, woolly mammoths, saber-toothed tigers, and giant bison.

Similar extinctions have coincided with the arrival or spread of humans in parts of Europe, Africa, Latin America, and Australasia.

Historically, the biggest cause of human-induced mammal extinctions has been hunting. Technologies designed to locate and kill have become increasingly efficient. Another significant threat to modern mammals comes from habitat clearing and fragmentation, both of which are proceeding worldwide at an unprecedented rate. Many other environmental abuses also affect mammals, including pollution such as acid rain and soil degradation. There is no way of knowing exactly how many mammals take sick or die from drinking contaminated water, eating poisoned plants, or living in water polluted with toxic waste. But research has documented phenomena such as physiological deformities and declining birth rates directly linked to environmental degradation.

Raging inferno In the natural world, almost all fires are caused by lightning strikes. Today, however, the majority of blazes are deliberately lit. Other human activity, including deliberate burnoffs that get out of control, unextinguished campfires, and discarded cigarette butts, has increased the frequency of wildfires.

Mixed blessing More and more food is needed to sustain the planet's ever-growing human population. An outstanding example of how the world's burgeoning need for food is increasing pressure on global climate change is the clearing of heavily forested mountain slopes for the planting of methane-producing rice fields.

Creature of myth and mystery Snow leopards are elusive, endangered inhabitants of high mountain areas in central Asia. Radio tracking has increased our knowledge of these animals and helps with conservation efforts to save the species. Farmers are also being taught ways to protect livestock without resorting to killing these big cats.

REVERSING FORTUNES

Although the outlook remains grim for many species, conservation efforts are underway in almost every country to help reduce alarming mammal losses besetting many nations. Hundreds of organizations now exist worldwide with the aim of reducing and ultimately reversing biodiversity losses. And legislation is increasingly being enacted to protect the future of threatened mammals and other organisms.

Conservation laws can be difficult to enforce, and international effort is required to ensure the survival of some species. For example, the world's African elephant population has been halved to some 600,000 due largely to ivory hunting last century. The species is now legally protected across its range, but poachers and rebels still shoot elephants and sell the ivory to feed their families and finance civil wars. Ivory, however, has been placed on the prohibited products list of the Convention on International Trade in Endangered Species (CITES), the rules of which are observed by more than 75 nations. This action reduces global demand for ivory and therefore incentives for poachers. Captive breeding has also helped several mammal species. There have been successes, for example, with the golden lion tamarin, Arabian oryx, and red panda. While conservation efforts continue to focus on the more spectacular species, there is concern it is the less obvious mammals—such as small, nocturnal bats, shrews, and rodents—that are most in peril.

Safe havens Some 50–60 million bison once roamed the American prairies. Following the arrival of Europeans, professional hide and meat hunters slaughtered them in their millions. By 1884, the species had almost disappeared from the United States. It was rescued from the brink of extinction by the establishment of reserves to protect the few remaining animals. Limited genetic exchange between these isolated populations, however, means the species will inevitably be harmed by inbreeding and gene losses.

KINDS OF MAMMALS

MONOTREMES

CLASS Mammalia	
ORDER Monotremata	
FAMILIES 2	
GENERA 3	
SPECIES 3	

Like other mammals, monotremes are covered in fur, lactate to feed their young, and have a four-chambered heart, a single bone in the lower jaw, and three bones in the middle ear. They are unusual, however, because they lay eggs rather than give birth to live young, and also have some anatomical similarities to reptiles, such as extra bones in their shoulders. The two families in this order are Tachyglossidae, which includes two species of echidna, and Ornithorhynchidae, which contains just the platypus. With its duck-like bill, webbed feet, furred body, and beaver-like tail, the platypus has fascinated scientists since the first specimen was sent to Britain in 1799.

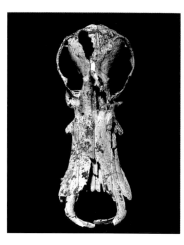

Fossil platypus This 15-million-year-old platypus skull is among the handful of monotreme fossils so far discovered. The fossil record suggests that monotremes originated at least 110 million years ago, when Australia was still part of Gondwana.

Underwater forager When diving underwater, the platypus closes the groove that contains both its eyes and ears. It relies instead on its soft bill, which not only has sensitive touch but can also detect electrical signals coming from its prey of bottom-dwelling invertebrates.

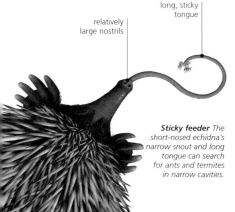

relatively large nostrils

long, sticky tongue

Sticky feeder The short-nosed echidna's narrow snout and long tongue can search for ants and termites in narrow cavities.

Spiny defense To protect itself from predators such as dingoes, the short-nosed echidna can speedily burrow vertically down into the earth until only the tips of its spines are visible. If threatened on hard ground, the echidna curls into a spiky ball.

EGG-LAYING MAMMALS

Monotreme eggs are soft-shelled and hatch after about 10 days. Once hatched, the young rely on their mother's milk for several months, a dependence typical of mammals.

After mating in spring, female platypuses lay up to three eggs in a bankside nesting burrow, and curl up to incubate them between the tail and body. The hatched young stay in the burrow for 3–4 months, feeding on milk that oozes from two nipple-like patches onto the mother's fur. After they emerge from the burrow, the young are gradually weaned and eventually disperse to a largely solitary life. Wild platypuses have been known to live for at least 15 years.

During their winter mating season, several male short-nosed echidnas may follow a female for up to 14 days, conducting digging and pushing contests until one wins the right to mate. The female then lays a single egg into her pouch. After hatching, the young stays in the pouch until it develops spines and moves to a burrow. The mother lacks teats but her mammary glands open into patches of skin in her pouch. She may continue to feed the young for up to 7 months. A short-nosed echidna has survived for 49 years in captivity, but 16 years is the oldest recorded age in the wild.

Although little is known of the long-nosed echidna's breeding cycle, it is thought to resemble that of the short-nosed echidna.

Fat stored in
broad tail

Partially webbed
hindfeet used
as rudders

Platypus
Ornithorhynchus anatinus

Webs of forefeet can be
folded back to free claws
for walking or digging

Each spine is an
individual hair
anchored in muscle

Pliable, sensitive bill
helps platypus find
food and navigate

Long snout can
be used as a snorkel
when crossing water

Short-nosed echidna
Tachyglossus aculeatus

Long-nosed echidna
Zaglossus bruijni

Mouth at end of snout

Walks with
a rolling gait

FACT FILE

Platypus Perhaps one of the most
unusual of all animals, this amphibious
mammal has a pliable duck-like bill,
thick fur, and webbed feet. It lives in
riverbank burrows and feeds on insect
larvae and other invertebrates.

Up to 16 in (40 cm)
Up to 6 in (15 cm)
Up to 5½ lb (2.4 kg)
Solitary
Locally common

E. Australia, Tasmania, Kangaroo I., King I.

Short-nosed echidna Its stout body
covered in long spines and shorter fur,
this echidna walks with a rolling gait.
It survives in a wide range of habitats,
from semiarid to alpine, and feeds
mainly on ants and termites.

Up to 14 in (35 cm)
Up to 4 in (10 cm)
Up to 15½ lb (7 kg)
Solitary
Locally common

Australia, Tasmania, New Guinea

Long-nosed echidna This echidna has
more hair and fewer spines than the
short-nosed species. Tiny spines on its
tongue help capture the earthworms
that make up the bulk of its diet.

Up to 31½ in (80 cm)
None
Up to 22 lb (10 kg)
Solitary
Endangered

New Guinea

POISONOUS SPUR

The male platypus can use the spur
on its rear ankle to inflict a paralyzing
sting, making it one of the world's few
venomous mammals. This feature may
help it fight other males for territory
and mates during the breeding season.

venom gland

venom duct

spur

CONSERVATION WATCH

Long-nosed echidna Found only in
the alpine forests and meadows of
New Guinea, the current population
of approximately 300,000 long-nosed
echidnas is hunted by humans for
food. It is also threatened by habitat
loss, as more and more farms are
created through land-clearing.

MARSUPIALS

CLASS	Mammalia
ORDERS	7
FAMILIES	19
GENERA	83
SPECIES	295

Commonly known as the pouched mammals, marsupials are virtually embryonic when born and must immediately drag themselves to their mother's teats, which are usually enclosed in a pouch of some kind. They latch firmly onto a teat for some weeks or months and come off only after reaching a level of development comparable to that of newborn mammals that have been nourished by a placenta in the womb. Most marsupials differ from placental mammals in other ways as well, with more incisors in each jaw, an opposable toe on the hindfoot, a relatively smaller brain, and a slightly lower body temperature and metabolism.

Marsupial success While some have flourished in the Americas, marsupials are most diverse in Australia and New Guinea, where there were no placental mammals. They have been introduced in New Zealand, Hawaii, and Britain.

Sibling rivalry The common opossum may give birth to more than 50 young at a time, but only those that attach to one of her 13 nipples will survive. Once the young have developed further, but are still quite helpless, the mother will leave them in the nest while she forages for food.

FINDING A NICHE

Once considered a single order, marsupials are much more diverse than any order of placental mammals and are now classified into seven orders. Of these, Didelphimorphia (containing American opossums), Paucituberculata (shrew opossums), and Microbiotheria (monito del monte) are found in the Americas, while the Australia–New Guinea region hosts Dasyuromorphia (quolls, dunnarts, marsupial mice, numbat), Peramelemorphia (bandicoots), Notoryctemorphia (marsupial moles), and Diprodontia (possums, kangaroos, koala, and wombats).

The fossil record suggests that marsupials and placental mammals diverged more than 100 million years ago. In North America and Europe, marsupials died out as placental mammals diversified. South America, on the other hand, was isolated from North America for about 60 million years, and marsupials evolved to fill a variety of ecological niches. When the Americas joined up, 2–5 million years ago, northern carnivores such as the jaguar soon displaced South America's large carnivorous marsupials, but small omnivorous marsupials persisted, with some, including the common opossum, recolonizing North America. It was in the region of Australia and New Guinea, however, that marsupials remained free of competition for the longest period and attained their greatest diversity.

Life in the pouch Wallabies, kangaroos, and other large marsupials give birth to a single young and carry it in a capacious, forward-opening pouch. Even once fully weaned, the young continues to use the pouch for transport and sleeping.

SIMILAR SOLUTIONS

Isolated for millions of years from the rest of the world, the marsupials of Australia and New Guinea occupy the same ecological niches as placental mammals fill elsewhere, and often display similar adaptations, a phenomenon known as convergent evolution. The striped possum, a marsupial of Australia and New Guinea, and the aye-aye, a placental mammal of Madagascar, are both tree-dwelling insectivores. Each species has one especially long finger that allows it to dig out wood-burrowing grubs.

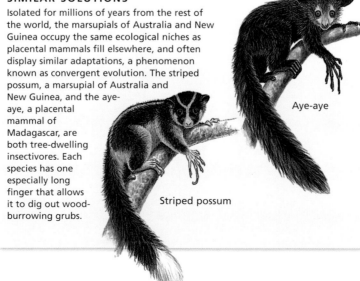

Aye-aye

Striped possum

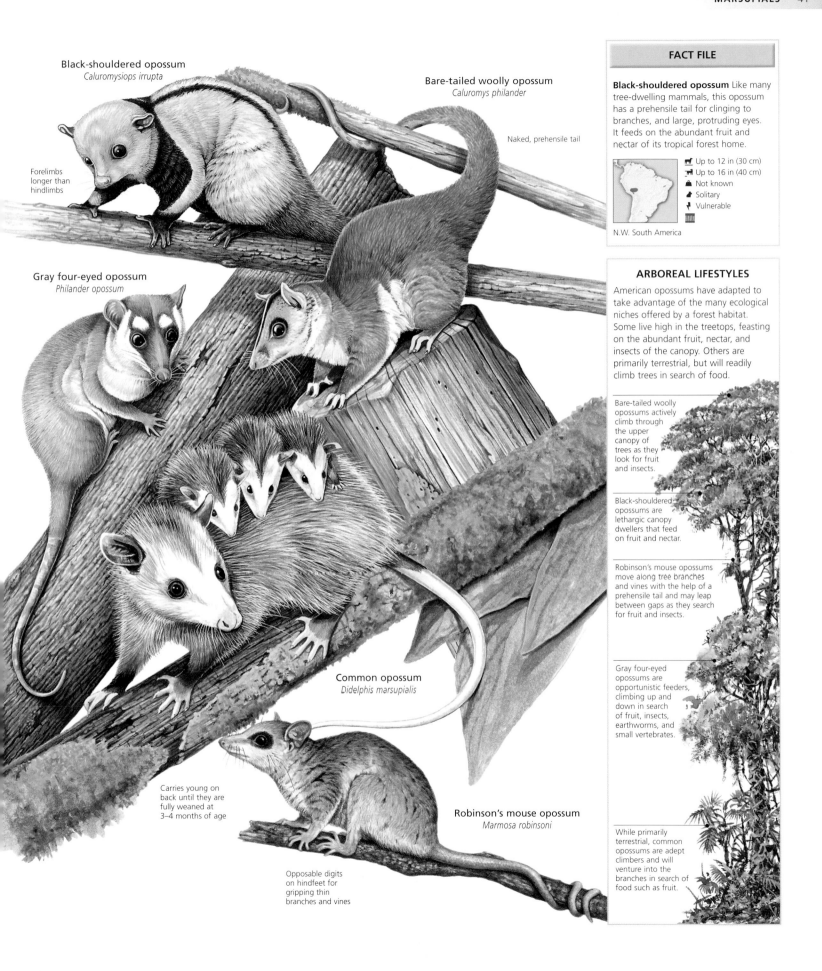

Black-shouldered opossum
Caluromysiops irrupta

Forelimbs longer than hindlimbs

Bare-tailed woolly opossum
Caluromys philander

Naked, prehensile tail

Gray four-eyed opossum
Philander opossum

Common opossum
Didelphis marsupialis

Carries young on back until they are fully weaned at 3–4 months of age

Opposable digits on hindfeet for gripping thin branches and vines

Robinson's mouse opossum
Marmosa robinsoni

FACT FILE

Black-shouldered opossum Like many tree-dwelling mammals, this opossum has a prehensile tail for clinging to branches, and large, protruding eyes. It feeds on the abundant fruit and nectar of its tropical forest home.

- Up to 12 in (30 cm)
- Up to 16 in (40 cm)
- Not known
- Solitary
- Vulnerable

N.W. South America

ARBOREAL LIFESTYLES

American opossums have adapted to take advantage of the many ecological niches offered by a forest habitat. Some live high in the treetops, feasting on the abundant fruit, nectar, and insects of the canopy. Others are primarily terrestrial, but will readily climb trees in search of food.

Bare-tailed woolly opossums actively climb through the upper canopy of trees as they look for fruit and insects.

Black-shouldered opossums are lethargic canopy dwellers that feed on fruit and nectar.

Robinson's mouse opossums move along tree branches and vines with the help of a prehensile tail and may leap between gaps as they search for fruit and insects.

Gray four-eyed opossums are opportunistic feeders, climbing up and down in search of fruit, insects, earthworms, and small vertebrates.

While primarily terrestrial, common opossums are adept climbers and will venture into the branches in search of food such as fruit.

IN THE SWIM

The only truly aquatic marsupial, the yapok of Central and South America is superbly adapted to a life in water. It has long webbed toes on its hindfeet, water-repellent fur, and a pouch that closes during dives. It hunts its aquatic prey of fish, frogs, crustaceans, and insects mostly at night, and rests in a riverbank den by day.

Strong stroke
The yapok uses its webbed hindfeet to move through the water, leaving its forefeet free to sift through the stream bottom for food.

MARSUPIAL ORIGINS

DNA studies have confirmed that the monito del monte of Argentina and Chile is the only living member of the Microbiotheriidae, a family of South American marsupials more closely related to Australian marsupials than to the other marsupials of South America. Together with fossil marsupials found in the Antarctic Peninsula, the monito del monte studies support the theory that marsupials spread from South America to Australia via Antarctica between 100 and 65 million years ago, when these continents formed a single landmass known as Gondwana.

North America

South America   Antarctica   Australia

Separate populations
Marsupials radiated from South America to Antarctica and Australia. They flourished in Australia, where there was little competition, but vanished from Antarctica, which split away and moved south. When North and South America joined up again, northern carnivores displaced South America's large marsupials.

Little monkey
The monito del monte ("little monkey of the mountain") lives in the dense, humid forests of highland Chile and Argentina.

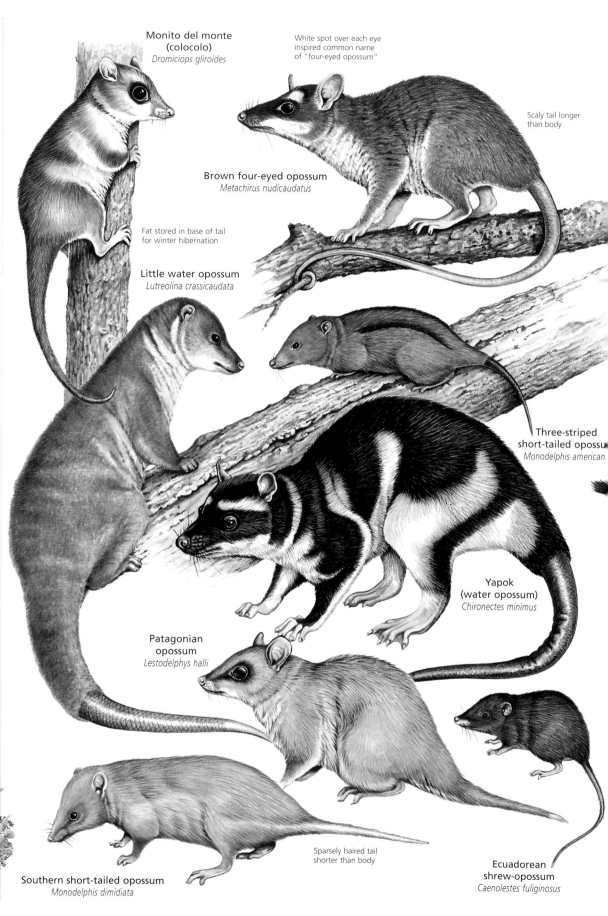

Monito del monte
(colocolo)
Dromiciops gliroides

White spot over each eye inspired common name of "four-eyed opossum"

Brown four-eyed opossum
Metachirus nudicaudatus

Scaly tail longer than body

Fat stored in base of tail for winter hibernation

Little water opossum
Lutreolina crassicaudata

Three-striped
short-tailed opossu[m]
Monodelphis american[a]

Yapok
(water opossum)
Chironectes minimus

Patagonian
opossum
Lestodelphys halli

Southern short-tailed opossum
Monodelphis dimidiata

Sparsely haired tail shorter than body

Ecuadorean
shrew-opossum
Caenolestes fuliginosus

✝
Thylacine (Tasmanian tiger)
Thylacinus cynocephalus

13–19 dark vertical stripes along back

Stiff tail thick at base but tapers to a point

Padded, five-toed paws

Massive head with strong jaw and heavy, bone-crushing molar teeth

Tasmanian devil
Sarcophilus harrisii

Numbat
Myrmecobius fasciatus

Sticky cylindrical tongue can extend up to 4 inches (10 cm) from small mouth

Vertical white bands along back

Long, bushy tail

Lacks external ears; tiny, non-functional eyes are hidden in fur; horny shield on nose

Southern marsupial mole
Notoryctes typhlops

Spade-like claws for digging through sandy soil

Silky, iridescent fur stained pinkish or reddish by iron-rich soil

---

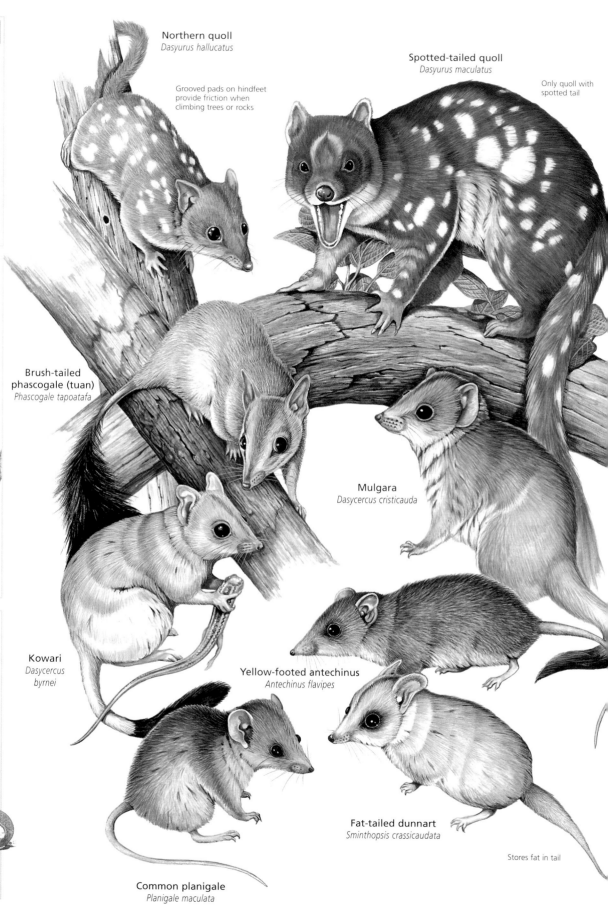

FACT FILE

Kowari In Central Australia's stony deserts and dry grasslands, this little marsupial carnivore preys on insects and small birds, reptiles, and mammals. To survive in the arid climate, the kowari shelters in burrows and obtains all its moisture from its food, eliminating the need to drink water.

↤ Up to 7 in (18 cm)
↦ Up to 5½ in (14 cm)
⬛ Up to 5 oz (140 g)
♟ Solitary
⚑ Vulnerable

C. Australia

ANNUAL DIE-OFF

One of the most unusual life-cycles occurs in all *Antechinus* and two *Phascogale* species, which breed just once annually. At the same time every year, following an exceptionally intense 2-week mating season, all the males within a population die off. Their vigorous mating efforts induce very high stress levels, which allow them to forgo food in favor of reproduction but also make them vulnerable to diseases such as stomach and intestinal ulcers. Females may live for a second year, but usually produce only one or two litters in their lifetime.

Sole parent *The female dusky antechinus (*Antechinus swainsonii*) raises her litter after all the males in her population have died off.*

SLOWING DOWN

Dunnarts and other small insectivorous marsupials sometimes enter periods of torpor, during which the metabolism decreases and the heart and respiratory system slows down. By conserving energy, this state reduces the need to eat, a great advantage during winter months when food can be scarce. A torpid period may last from a few hours up to several days.

A winter's tail *In winter, the fat-tailed dunnart may enter a torpid state and live off the fat that has been stored in its tail during more plentiful times.*

Northern quoll
Dasyurus hallucatus

Spotted-tailed quoll
Dasyurus maculatus

Only quoll with spotted tail

Grooved pads on hindfeet provide friction when climbing trees or rocks

Brush-tailed phascogale (tuan)
Phascogale tapoatafa

Mulgara
Dasycercus cristicauda

Kowari
Dasycercus byrnei

Yellow-footed antechinus
Antechinus flavipes

Fat-tailed dunnart
Sminthopsis crassicaudata

Stores fat in tail

Common planigale
Planigale maculata

Bilby
Macrotis lagotis

Long ears

Long, pointed snout

Bicolored tail

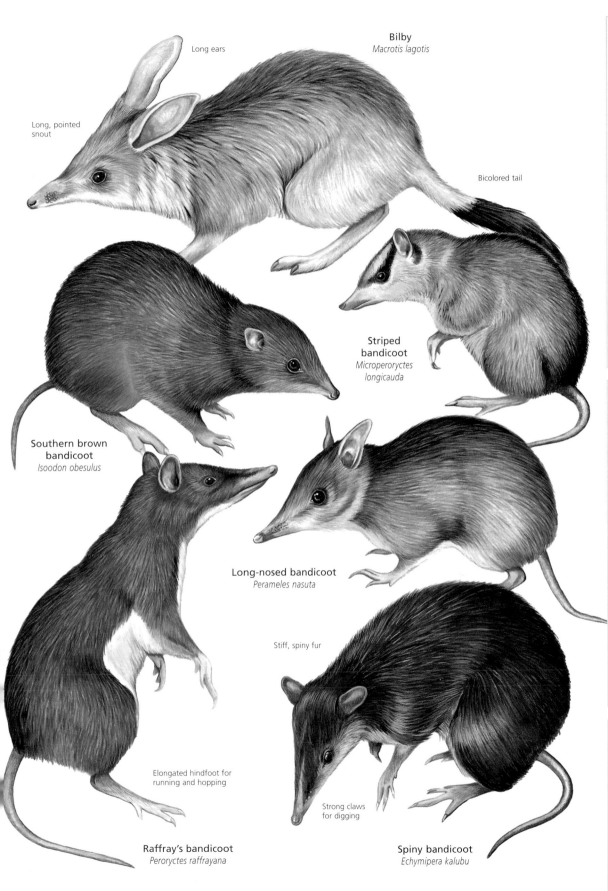

Striped bandicoot
Microperoryctes longicauda

Southern brown bandicoot
Isoodon obesulus

Long-nosed bandicoot
Perameles nasuta

Stiff, spiny fur

Elongated hindfoot for running and hopping

Strong claws for digging

Raffray's bandicoot
Peroryctes raffrayana

Spiny bandicoot
Echymipera kalubu

FACT FILE

Bilby The bilby is a powerful digger and may build up to 12 burrows on its home range. It can be distinguished from other bandicoots by its long ears.

	Up to 22 in (55 cm)
	Up to 11½ in (29 cm)
	Up to 5½ lb (2.5 kg)
	Solitary
	Vulnerable

C. Australia
● Former range

Southern brown bandicoot This omnivore digs for insects and worms with its sharp front claws, killing the prey by stamping on it repeatedly. It also eats fruit, seeds, and fungi.

	Up to 14 in (36 cm)
	Up to 5½ in (14 cm)
	Up to 3½ lb (1.6 kg)
	Solitary
	Uncommon

Coastal S. and E. Australia, Tasmania

BANDICOOTS

The relationship of the omnivorous bandicoots to other marsupials is unclear. They have an arrangement of teeth similar to that of carnivorous marsupials, but they also have fused toes on the hindfoot, a feature known as syndactyly that is shared with herbivores such as kangaroos and wombats. Bandicoots are divided into two families: the mainly Australian Peramelidae (comprising the *Perameles* and *Isoodon* species) and the mainly New Guinean Peroryctidae (including the spiny bandicoot).

Rapid reproduction
After a short gestation period lasting 12 days or so, bandicoot young develop quickly and may reach sexual maturity in about 90 days.

⚑ CONSERVATION WATCH

Saving the bilby During the past 100 years, the number and range of bilbies have been dramatically reduced, with much bilby habitat lost to farming. Introduced species have also taken their toll, with foxes and feral cats preying upon bilbies, and cattle, sheep, and rabbits competing for food. Now protected, the species is being bred in captivity and then released into the wild in an attempt to rebuild populations.

FACT FILE

Spotted cuscus This rain-forest marsupial spends most of its time in trees, sleeping by day in a small bed of leaves and feeding at night on a diet of fruit, flowers, and leaves. While males are white with gray spots, females tend to be uniformly gray and unspotted. Intensively hunted in New Guinea, the spotted cuscus is also threatened by habitat loss from logging and farming.

- 📏 Up to 23 in (58 cm)
- 📏 Up to 17½ in (45 cm)
- ⚖ Up to 11 lb (4.9 kg)
- 🐾 Solitary
- ⚡ Vulnerable
- ▦

N. Australia, New Guinea, some islands

MOUNTAIN MEALS

The only Australian marsupial to live above the snowline, the mountain pygmy-possum makes the most of its habitat's resources by eating a wide range of food types, but specializing according to the season. During the warmer months, it feeds mostly on Bogong moths, which migrate annually to the Australian Alps, and also eats small amounts of other insects. As the moths become less abundant around January, it switches to seeds and berries, storing caches of these for the cold winter months ahead.

- 📏 Up to 4½ in (12 cm)
- 📏 Up to 6 in (15 cm)
- ⚖ Up to 3 oz (80 g)
- 🐾 Solitary
- ⚡ Endangered

Australian Alps

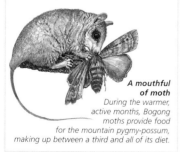

A mouthful of moth
During the warmer, active months, Bogong moths provide food for the mountain pygmy-possum, making up between a third and all of its diet.

⚡ CONSERVATION WATCH

Mountain pygmy-possum With a total population of fewer than 2,000 adults, this marsupial species is classified as endangered. Once believed to be extinct, the mountain pygmy-possum has a very restricted range in the mountains of eastern Australia. Much of its habitat has been destroyed or fragmented by the building of roads, dams, and ski resorts, and by recent wildfires.

Bobuk
(mountain brushtail possum)
Trichosurus caninus

Gray cuscus
Phalanger orientalis

Spotted cuscus
Spilocuscus maculatus

Brushtail possum
Trichosurus vulpecula

Feathertail glider
Acrobates pygmaeus

Gliding membrane extends from wrist to knee

Feather-like arrangement of fur on tail unique among mammals

Prehensile tail covered in thick scales

Mountain pygmy-possum
Burramys parvus

Scaly-tailed possum
Wyulda squamicaudata

Rock ringtail possum
Petropseudes dahli

Green ringtail possum
Pseudochirops archeri

Lemuroid
ringtail possum
*Hemibelideus
lemuroides*

Common
ringtail possum
*Pseudocheirus
peregrinus*

Two opposable
digits on each
front paw

Highly arboreal, rarely
descends to ground

Herbert River ringtail possum
Pseudochirulus herbertensis

Tail tightly curled
when not in use

FACT FILE

Rock ringtail possum By day, this possum stays cool and safe in rock crevices, emerging at night to feed in trees. Males and females share care of the young equally, a level of male participation that is rare in mammals and unknown in other marsupials.

🐾 Up to 15½ in (39 cm)
🐾 Up to 10½ in (27 cm)
⚖ Up to 4½ lb (2 kg)
♣ Pair
↟ Locally common
✳

N. Australia

Green ringtail possum Bands of black, yellow, and white on its hairs combine to give this possum a distinctive lime-green appearance, helping it to remain hidden from predators in the trees of its rain-forest home. It feeds primarily on leaves.

🐾 Up to 15 in (38 cm)
🐾 Up to 15 in (38 cm)
⚖ Up to 3 lb (1.3 kg)
♣ Solitary
↟ Near threatened
▦

N.E. Australia

Common ringtail possum Most of this nocturnal animal's diet is made up of eucalyptus leaves, but it also feeds on fruit, flowers, and nectar, even eating rosebuds in urban areas. Small family groups live in dreys—nests of bark, twigs, and ferns built in the fork of a tree or in dense shrubs.

🐾 Up to 15 in (38 cm)
🐾 Up to 15 in (38 cm)
⚖ Up to 2 lb (1 kg)
♣ Solitary
↟ Locally common
▦ ✳ ♣ ♣

E. Australia

A POISONOUS DIET

The common ringtail primarily eats eucalyptus leaves, which are usually toxic and lacking in nutritional value. A specialized digestive system featuring an enlarged cecum (a pouch in the large intestine) detoxifies the leaves and then releases soft fecal pellets that the possum can eat. Any undigested material is then expelled as hard pellets. To cope with this low-energy diet, the ringtail has a slow metabolism.

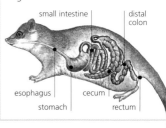

small intestine | distal colon

esophagus | cecum

stomach | rectum

FACT FILE

Leadbeater's possum This possum has exploited a niche created by the wildfire ecology of its highland forest home. When fires sweep through an area, they may kill some old trees and clear the way for new growth of wattle trees. Family groups may share nests of shredded bark in the hollow center of large trees, feeding on the insects that breed in the bark.

🐃 Up to 6½ in (17 cm)
🐃 Up to 7 in (18 cm)
⬛ Up to 5½ oz (160 g)
🐾 Pair, family group
🌿 Endangered

S.E. Australia

Possum pickings
Leadbeater's possums feed not only on the insects that breed in the bark of wattle trees but also on the sap of the surrounding wattles.

SAP SUCKERS

A membrane extending from the wrists to the ankles allows gliders to travel substantial distances through the air from one feeding tree to another. Once landed, they cut notches in the bark with their teeth and lap up the sap and gum. The yellow-bellied glider targets a number of eucalypt species, while the sugar glider prefers wattles and *Eucalyptus resinifera* trees.

Sticky feeders
Yellow-bellied gliders will vigorously defend their sap-feeding sites.

⚡ CONSERVATION WATCH

Specialized nests The Leadbeater's possum relies on a very specialized habitat, nesting in hollow old-growth trees that can take up to 150 years to become suitable. Presumed extinct after a wildfire in 1939 that burned nearly 70 percent of its range, Leadbeater's possums now number about 5,000, but are endangered by timber logging. Even with conservation measures, there may not be enough remaining nesting sites to sustain this species.

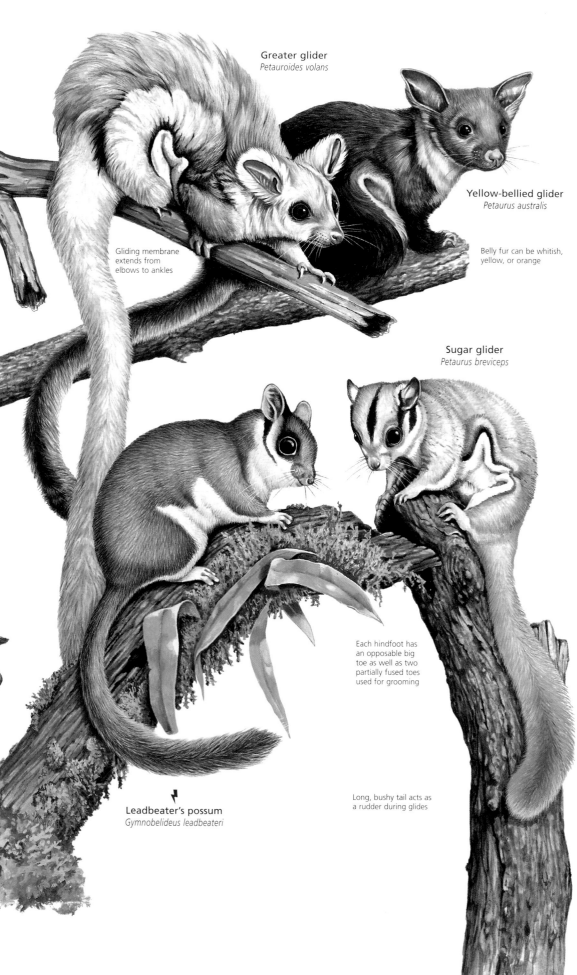

Greater glider
Petauroides volans

Yellow-bellied glider
Petaurus australis

Gliding membrane extends from elbows to ankles

Belly fur can be whitish, yellow, or orange

Sugar glider
Petaurus breviceps

Each hindfoot has an opposable big toe as well as two partially fused toes used for grooming

⚡ Leadbeater's possum
Gymnobelideus leadbeateri

Long, bushy tail acts as a rudder during glides

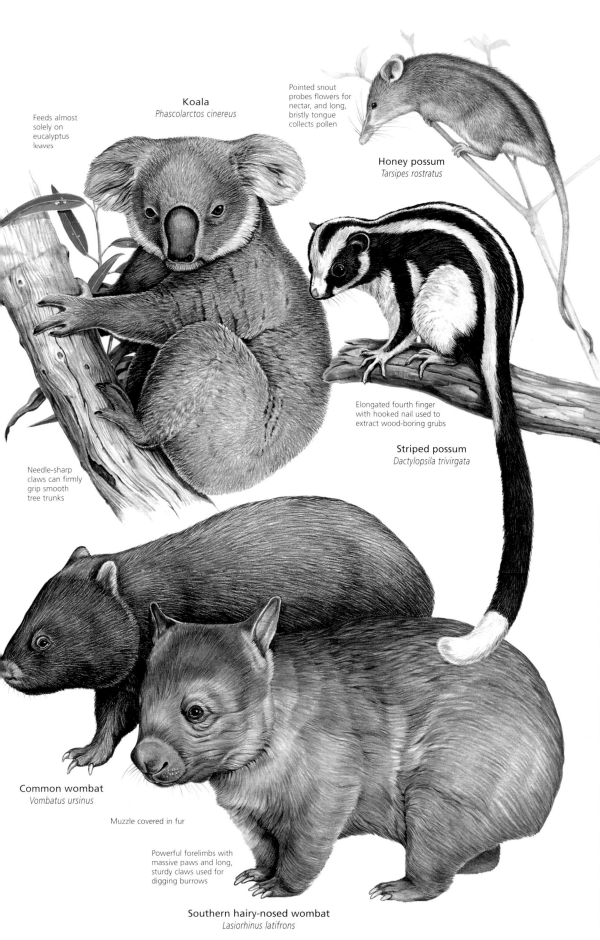

Koala
Phascolarctos cinereus

Feeds almost solely on eucalyptus leaves

Pointed snout probes flowers for nectar, and long, bristly tongue collects pollen

Honey possum
Tarsipes rostratus

Elongated fourth finger with hooked nail used to extract wood-boring grubs

Striped possum
Dactylopsila trivirgata

Needle-sharp claws can firmly grip smooth tree trunks

Common wombat
Vombatus ursinus

Muzzle covered in fur

Powerful forelimbs with massive paws and long, sturdy claws used for digging burrows

Southern hairy-nosed wombat
Lasiorhinus latifrons

FACT FILE

Goodfellow's tree kangaroo Limbs of equal length and sharp claws help this marsupial climb through rain-forest trees, where it shelters in small groups and feeds on leaves and fruit.

🦘	Up to 25 in (63 cm)
🦘	Up to 30 in (76 cm)
⚖️	Up to 18½ lb (8.5 kg)
♟	Solitary
⚡	Endangered

New Guinea

Northern nail-tailed wallaby Named after the horny spur on its tail, this animal spends the day in a shallow nest beneath a bush. At night, it feeds on the roots of the grasses that grow in its savanna or open woodland home.

🦘	Up to 27½ in (70 cm)
🦘	Up to 29 in (74 cm)
⚖️	Up to 20 lb (9 kg)
♟	Solitary
⚡	Locally common

N. Australia

Brush-tailed bettong Adapted to a range of habitats, from temperate forests to arid grasslands, the brush-tailed bettong does not consume green plants or water. Its main food is fungi, which it digs from the ground.

🦘	Up to 15 in (38 cm)
🦘	Up to 14 in (35 cm)
⚖️	Up to 3½ lb (1.6 kg)
♟	Solitary
⚡	Conserv. dependent

S.W. Australia
● Former range

Red-legged pademelon The only ground-dwelling wallaby to live in wet tropical forests, this nocturnal creature searches the dense understory for food such as leaves, fruit, bark, and cicadas.

🦘	Up to 21 in (54 cm)
🦘	Up to 18½ in (47 cm)
⚖️	Up to 14 lb (6.5 kg)
♟	Solitary
⚡	Locally common

E. Australia, New Guinea

⚡ CONSERVATION WATCH

Brush-tailed bettong Although it once ranged over 60 percent of Australia, the brush-tailed bettong is now restricted to a handful of small areas, a victim of predation and competition from introduced species, and habitat loss from farming. In recent years, captive-breeding programs and fox controls have enabled the reintroduction of this marsupial in South Australia.

Joey carried in pouch until it is a subadult

Bennett's tree kangaroo
Dendrolagus bennettianus

Goodfellow's tree kangaroo
Dendrolagus goodfellowi

Four limbs of roughly equal length

Long-nosed potoroo
Potorous tridactylus

Northern nail-tailed wallaby
Onychogalea unguifera

Brush-tailed bettong
Bettongia penicillata

Red-legged pademelon
Thylogale stigmatica

Musky rat-kangaroo
Hypsiprymnodon moschatus

Rufous bettong
Aepyprymnus rufescens

MAKING MARSUPIALS

The unique nature of marsupial reproduction begins with the anatomy of the parents. On the outside, the female system seems simpler than in placental mammals, with a single opening, called a cloaca, for the digestive and reproductive tracts. Inside, however, there is a double reproductive tract involving two uteri, each with its own vagina. Many male marsupials have a forked penis, which directs semen into both vaginas. A pregnant female develops a third vagina as a birth canal. After a short gestation, ranging from 12 days in some bandicoot species to 38 days in the eastern gray kangaroo, almost embryonic young are born that crawl to a teat, which is usually protected by a pouch. Once the young are fully formed, they leave the teat, but are weaned gradually, usually taking several months to become fully independent.

Doubling up Featuring two uteri and two vaginas, the internal anatomy of female marsupials differs markedly from that of placental mammals. Once a female marsupial becomes pregnant, she develops a third canal for the birth of her young.

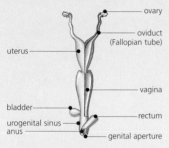

Female placental mammal
This system has a single uterus and a single vagina, and separate openings for the reproductive and digestive tracts.

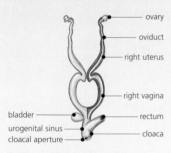

Non-pregnant female marsupial
Two uteruses lead to two vaginas. Both vaginas and the rectum lead to a single opening, which is known as the cloaca.

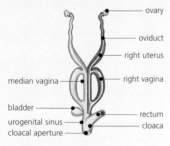

Pregnant female marsupial
A median birth canal develops during pregnancy. In most marsupial species, this disappears after the birth, but it remains as a permanent structure in kangaroos and the honey possum.

Pouch time A marsupial is tiny when born—a red kangaroo's newborn is 0.003 percent of the mother's weight, while a human baby is about 5 percent of its mother's weight. By the end of weaning, however, the ratio of a marsupial offspring's weight to the mother's is comparable to that of placental mammals.

Raising a family Most kangaroos and wallabies give birth to a single young, but mate within a day or two of its birth. When a female is suckling a joey that can move in and out of the pouch, she usually also has a pouch embryo—a younger offspring attached to a teat inside the pouch. In addition, she is likely to be carrying a blastocyst, a fertilized egg that stays quiescent until the pouch embryo is ready to detach from the teat.

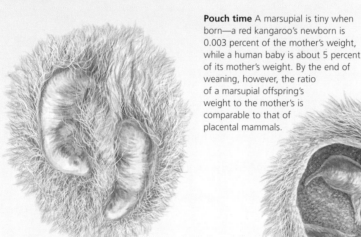

1. On their way
Newborn eastern quolls (Dasyurus viverrinus) *crawl through their mother's belly hairs to find the teats in her pouch. At this stage, their eyes, ears, and hindlimbs are embryonic, but their nostrils, mouth, and forelimbs are all large and functioning. While as many as 30 quolls may be born, only the 6 or so that attach to the mother's teats will survive.*

2. Latched on
The young quolls remain firmly attached to their mother's teats during 8 weeks of passive development, when they are known as pouch embryos. To avoid the danger of choking, a large glottis shuts off a baby's mouth from its air passage.

3. Into the world
Once fully formed, the young quolls detach from the teats and leave the pouch, but remain with the mother for some months, clinging to her back while she is foraging, sharing a den for sleeping, and feeding on her milk.

FACT FILE

Parma wallaby The smallest wallaby, this animal was believed to be extinct for decades until its rediscovery in 1965 on New Zealand's Kawau Island, where it had been introduced long before. Other surviving populations were later found in Eastern Australia.

Up to 21 in (53 cm)
Up to 21¼ in (54 cm)
Up to 13 lb (6 kg)
Solitary
Near threatened

E. Australia

Red kangaroo The largest of the marsupials, the red kangaroo usually hops slowly, but can reach speeds of 35–45 miles per hour (55–70 km/h). Males of this species have a reddish coat, but females are bluish gray.

Up to 55 in (140 cm)
Up to 39 in (99 cm)
Up to 187 lb (85 kg)
Herd
Common

Australia

MOB MEMBERSHIP

Large kangaroos often congregate in groups, or mobs, of 50 or more, a strategy that helps deter predators such as dingoes. While males are not territorial, their access to mates depends on their position in the mob's hierarchy, which tends to be based on size. A dominant male Eastern gray kangaroo may father up to 30 young in a season, but most males never get the chance to mate.

Kickboxing
Male kangaroos sometimes fight to establish dominance, delivering kicks with their powerful back legs.

⚡ CONSERVATION WATCH

Of the 295 species of marsupials, 56% are listed on the IUCN Red List, as follows:

10	Extinct
5	Critically endangered
27	Endangered
47	Vulnerable
45	Near threatened
32	Data deficient

Yellow-footed rock wallaby
Petrogale xanthopus

Nabarlek
Petrogale concinna

Striking coat pattern distinguished by rich red to yellow limbs and striped tail

Brush-tailed rock wallaby
Petrogale penicillata

Hindfeet have rough soles for gripping rocks

Parma wallaby
Macropus parma

Spectacled hare-wallaby
Lagorchestes conspicillatus

Red kangaroo
Macropus rufus

Eastern gray kangaroo
Macropus giganteus

Quokka
Setonix brachyurus

Hops on fourth and fifth toes of hindfeet

XENARTHRANS

CLASS	Mammalia
ORDER	Xenarthra
FAMILIES	4
GENERA	13
SPECIES	29

Some of the world's most bizarre animals—anteaters, sloths, and armadillos—make up Xenarthra, an ancient order that was once much more diverse and included ground sloths larger than elephants, and armored mammals bigger than polar bears. Originating in and confined to the Americas, xenarthrans all have extra joints, known as xenarthrales, in the lower spine, which limit twisting and turning but strengthen the lower back and hips, a particular advantage for the burrowing armadillos. The brains of xenarthrans are small and their teeth are rudimentary or, in the case of anteaters, absent. A slow metabolism has allowed these species to take advantage of narrow niches.

Clingy child Following a gestation period of a year, female sloths give birth to a single young and nurse it for roughly a month. The young then stays with the mother for several months, clinging to her thick fur with its curved claws.

Toilet stop About once a week, a sloth leaves the trees to defecate on the ground. Unable to support its body weight, the animal use its long forelimbs to drag itself along. The toilet site is carefully selected, suggesting that the sloth may be fertilizing favorite feeding trees.

BUILT-IN BLANKET
The giant anteater spends up to 15 hours a day resting. It digs a shallow depression in the ground and lies down, curling its bushy, fan-like tail around itself. As well as providing warmth, this arrangement helps to disguise the anteater when it is at its most vulnerable.

Digging deep An anteater's sharp front talons can rip into concrete-like termite mounds, allowing its long, sticky tongue to collect the insects. An attack causes little permanent damage to a nest, however, because it lasts just a few minutes and only a small number of termites are eaten. The mound is repaired by the surviving termites.

SLOW AND STEADY

The low metabolic rate and body temperature of anteaters and sloths have enabled them to become highly specialized feeders, exploiting food sources that are abundant but low in energy content. Armadillos, on the other hand, have a varied diet, but live in deep underground tunnels, where their slow metabolism helps them to avoid overheating.

Ranging from the terrestrial giant anteater to the tree-dwelling silky anteater and tamanduas, anteaters use their keen sense of smell to detect ants and termites. From an especially long, tubular snout, an even longer tongue darts out, covered in tiny spines and sticky saliva to capture the prey.

Remarkably sluggish, sloths spend almost all their waking hours feeding on forest leaves, consuming such quantities that a full stomach can account for nearly a third of their body weight. Inside a sloth's multichambered stomach, toxins in the leaves are neutralized and the leaves slowly break down, taking a month or more to be fully digested.

With a carapace of bony horn-covered plates, armadillos are not only shielded from predators but are also at ease foraging in dry, thorny vegetation. While much of their diet is made up of invertebrates, they may also consume fruit and small reptiles. They use their powerful limbs and sharp claws to excavate up to 20 burrows in their home range and to dig for prey.

Maned three-toed sloth Apart from a black mane on the shoulders, this animal's coarse, shaggy fur is grizzled tan, often tinged green by algae. The green helps to camouflage the slow-moving sloth in its treetop home.

- Up to 19½ in (50 cm)
- Up to 2 in (5 cm)
- Up to 9½ lb (4.2 kg)
- Solitary
- Endangered

N.E. South America

Silky anteater This little tree-dwelling anteater clings to the branches with its long claws and prehensile tail, feasting on arboreal ants and termites. A single young is raised by both parents.

- Up to 8½ in (21 cm)
- Up to 9 in (23 cm)
- Up to 9½ oz (275 g)
- Solitary
- Uncommon

Central America and N. South America

IDENTICAL QUADRUPLETS

The only xenarthran in the United States, the nine-banded armadillo has rapidly expanded its range in the past 150 years. Along with the other species in the genus *Dasypus,* it is unique among vertebrates because the female produces a single fertilized egg that divides into a number of genetically identical embryos.

Family likeness
The nine-banded armadillo usually gives birth to four identical pups.

- Up to 22½ in (57 cm)
- Up to 17½ in (45 cm)
- Up to 13 lb (6 kg)
- Solitary
- Common

North America & South America

Vulnerable sloths So specialized that they have few natural competitors or predators, sloths have been remarkably successful in Central and South America. Their future, however, depends on the survival of their rain-forest habitat, which has been disappearing at an alarming rate. Already, the maned three-toed sloth is endangered, restricted to small areas of Brazil's coastal forest.

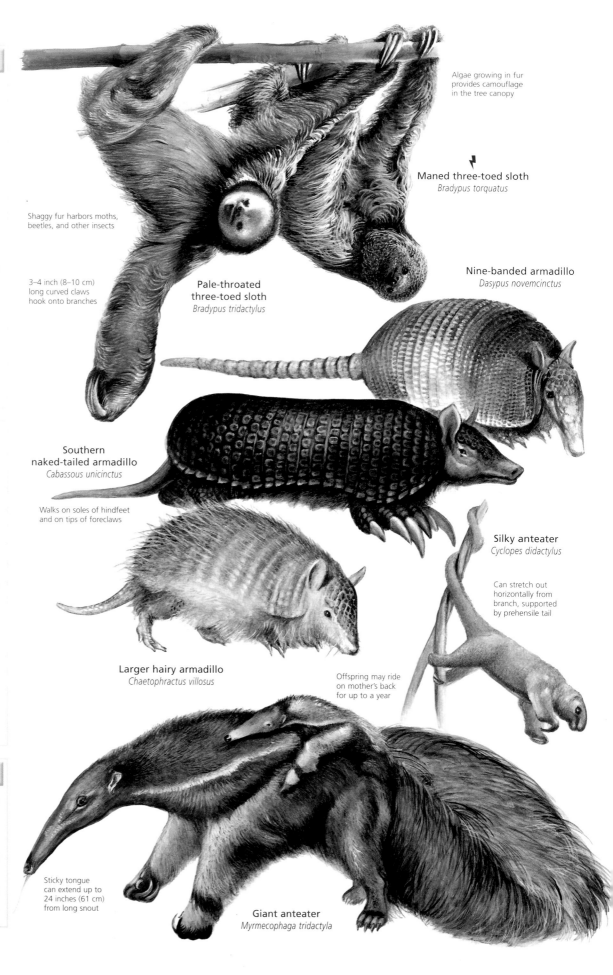

Algae growing in fur provides camouflage in the tree canopy

Maned three-toed sloth
Bradypus torquatus

Shaggy fur harbors moths, beetles, and other insects

3–4 inch (8–10 cm) long curved claws hook onto branches

Pale-throated three-toed sloth
Bradypus tridactylus

Nine-banded armadillo
Dasypus novemcinctus

Southern naked-tailed armadillo
Cabassous unicinctus

Walks on soles of hindfeet and on tips of foreclaws

Silky anteater
Cyclopes didactylus

Can stretch out horizontally from branch, supported by prehensile tail

Larger hairy armadillo
Chaetophractus villosus

Offspring may ride on mother's back for up to a year

Sticky tongue can extend up to 24 inches (61 cm) from long snout

Giant anteater
Myrmecophaga tridactyla

Giant armadillo
Priodontes maximus

Protected from
predators and thorny
plants by shield of
bony plates covered
by horny skin

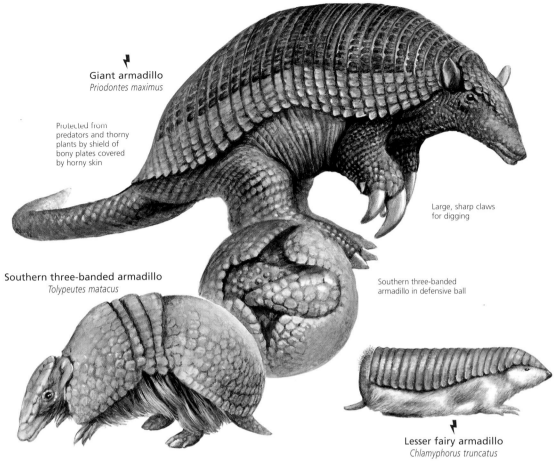

Large, sharp claws
for digging

Southern three-banded armadillo
Tolypeutes matacus

Southern three-banded
armadillo in defensive ball

Lesser fairy armadillo
Chlamyphorus truncatus

PANGOLINS

CLASS Mammalia
ORDER Pholidota
FAMILY Manidae
GENUS *Manis*
SPECIES 7

A covering of horny body scales growing from a thick underlying skin distinguishes pangolins from all other mammals. An extraordinary tongue, longer than the animal's head and body, is coiled in the animal's mouth when at rest, but can be extended and flicked into ant nests and termite mounds. Pangolins lack teeth, relying instead on powerful muscles and small pebbles in their stomachs to grind up their food. Terrestrial species, such as the giant ground pangolin, dig out underground burrows for shelter during the day. The long-tailed pangolin and other tree–dwelling species have a prehensile tail for help with climbing, and curl up into balls in tree hollows when resting.

Overlapping scales cover
entire body except for
belly, inner limbs, and
underside of tail

Scales are shed and
replaced throughout life

Giant ground pangolin
Manis gigantea

FACT FILE

Giant armadillo About the size of a German shepherd dog, the giant armadillo has huge front claws that it uses for building its own burrows and for digging into termite mounds. While it prefers termites, it will also eat other insects and worms, snakes, and carrion.

Up to 39½ in (100 cm)
Up to 21½ in (55 cm)
Up to 66 lb (30 kg)
Solitary
Endangered

N. South America

Southern three-banded armadillo Unlike other armadillos, which will speedily burrow if threatened, this species can roll itself into a tight ball, so that it is entirely protected by armor. It may leave a slight opening that can snap shut on the probing paw of a predator. This defense strategy is ineffective against humans, however, who hunt this armadillo for food.

Up to 10½ in (27 cm)
Up to 3 in (8 cm)
Up to 2½ lb (1.2 kg)
Solitary
Near threatened

C. South America

Asia and Africa Pangolins are found in much of Southeast Asia and subtropical Africa. While the Asian species have external ears and grow hair at the base of their scales, the African species lack external ears and have no scales on the tail's underside. Like anteaters in the Americas and echidnas in Australia and New Guinea, pangolins are specialized to feed on ants and termites.

CONSERVATION WATCH

Hunted scales Pangolins have been relentlessly hunted, prized as meat in Africa and for the medicinal value of their scales in Asia. Destruction of their rain-forest habitat threatens these specialized creatures. The Cape pangolin (*Manis temminckii*) of Africa, as well as all of the three Asian species—the Indian pangolin (*M. crassicaudata*), Malayan pangolin (*M. javanica*), and Chinese pangolin (*M. pentadactyla*)—are listed on the IUCN Red List as near threatened.

INSECTIVORES

CLASS	Mammalia
ORDER	Insectivora
FAMILIES	7
GENERA	68
SPECIES	428

Small, quick creatures with long, narrow snouts, shrews, moles, hedgehogs, and other insectivores make up a diverse order whose classification is much debated. While they share primitive features such as a small, smooth brain, simple bones in the ear, and rudimentary teeth, many also display specializations such as burrowing adaptations, defensive spines, or poisonous saliva. Insectivores were named after their tendency to eat insects, but many will take advantage of any available food source and readily consume plants and other animals. Usually shy and nocturnal, they rely on acute senses of smell and touch rather than vision and have very small or even minute eyes.

Worldwide spread While three insectivore families—hedgehogs and moonrats; moles and desmans; and shrews—are found in much of the world, solenodons, tenrecs, and otter shrews are highly localized.

All in a row To avoid getting lost, young of the white-toothed shrew (*Crocidura russula*) "caravan," forming a chain behind the mother by tenaciously gripping the rear end of the animal in front.

Fast food Because of their extremely fast metabolisms, shrews must eat vast amounts for their size and usually live where food is abundant. The diet of the Eurasian water shrew (*Neomys fodiens*) features aquatic invertebrates, fish, and frogs.

CONVERGING SPECIES

The order Insectivora contains numerous examples of convergent evolution, with animals in similar habitats displaying similar behaviors or physical adaptations, even though they are not closely related.

Some insectivores have exploited an aquatic niche. The desmans of Europe and the web-footed tenrec (*Limnogale mergulus*) of Madagascar evolved in total isolation from each other, but they share a dense, waterproof coat, a streamlined body, partially webbed feet, a long tail that acts as a rudder, and specialized mechanisms for breathing and detecting underwater prey.

European moles and African golden moles are very distantly related, with true moles evolving from a shrew-like animal, and golden moles more closely related to tenrecs. Nevertheless, they look very much alike and both display adaptations to a burrowing lifestyle. Their bodies are compact and cylindrical, their limbs are short and powerful, with large digging claws on the forefeet, and their eyes are minute and hidden by fur or skin.

The hedgehogs of Europe and the tenrecs of Africa employ similar means of self-defense. Both have a thick coat of spines and will curl up when threatened, becoming a spiky ball to discourage predators.

The solenodons of Cuba and Hispaniola and the tenrecs of Africa appear to have developed echolocation, a method of locating prey by bouncing sounds off the surrounding environment.

Opportunity knocks Insectivores are often opportunistic feeders, prepared to eat a wide variety of prey and plants. The Western European hedgehog mostly eats invertebrates such as earthworms, slugs, beetles, and grasshoppers, but will also devour vertebrate carrion and young birds.

Flat-footed walkers
Almost all insectivores have a plantigrade gait, keeping heels, soles, and toes on the ground when walking.

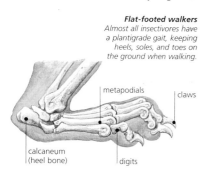

metapodials

claws

calcaneum
(heel bone)

digits

Raises stiff hairs along neck into a crest when threatened

Covered in coarse hair and sharp spines

Tail-less tenrec (common tenrec)
Tenrec ecaudatus

Large-eared tenrec
Geogale aurita

Thick, scaly tail

Strong claws for digging insects, worms, and small lizards out of leaf litter

Cuban solenodon
Solenodon cubanus

Flattened head allows nostrils, eyes, and ears to stay above water's surface while body is submerged

Dense fur traps insulating layer of air when swimming

Fused toes on hindfoot used for grooming

Locates prey using sensitive whiskers

Giant otter shrew
Potamogale velox

Tail used for propulsion and steering in water

Ruwenzori otter shrew
Micropotamogale ruwenzorii

Webbed feet

FACT FILE

Moonrat The smell of rotting onions, stale sweat, or ammonia may indicate the presence of a moonrat, which produces a strong scent from two glands near the anus. The animal uses this powerful odor to mark its territory. A solitary creature, the moonrat will emit threatening hiss-puffs and low roars if it encounters another member of its species. It rests by day in hollow logs or crevices, and hunts its prey of insects, earthworms, crustaceans, mollusks, frogs, and fish at night.

Up to 18 in (46 cm)
Up to 12 in (30 cm)
Up to 4½ lb (2 kg)
Solitary
Locally common

Malay Peninsula, Sumatra, Borneo

Lesser moonrat Spending most of its time on the floor of humid mountain forests, this animal moves in short leaps and sometimes climbs through bushes. It often nests under rocks.

Up to 5½ in (14 cm)
Up to 1 in (3 cm)
Up to 3 oz (80 g)
Solitary
Locally common

Indochina, Malaysia, Indonesia

Hottentot golden mole A horny pad on the nose and four clawed toes on each forepaw help this golden mole build extensive tunnel networks beneath the surface. Like the unrelated Australian marsupial mole, it is sightless, with fur covering its residual eyes.

Up to 5½ in (14 cm)
None
Up to 3½ oz (100 g)
Solitary
Locally common

S. South Africa

⚡ CONSERVATION WATCH

Population pressure Among the 1,000 rarest animals in the world, the giant golden mole *Chrysospalax trevelyani* survives in just a few small areas in South Africa's East Cape region. Already endangered, the species is under ever greater pressure as the human population increases. It has been wrongly blamed for crop damage that was actually caused by mole-rats and other rodents. Predation by domestic dogs has had a serious impact, as has the fragmentation of the mole's forest habitat, with people collecting firewood, cutting down trees for building, and introducing livestock.

Moonrat
Echinosorex gymnura

Coarse, spiky hair

Long canine teeth

Shrew-hedgehog
Neotetracus sinensis

Lesser moonrat
(lesser gymnure)
Hylomys suillus

Eats invertebrates such
as worms and insects

Mindanao moonrat
Podogymnura truei

Sharp spines erected
when threatened

Horny pad on nose

Hottentot golden mole
Amblysomus hottentotus

Western European hedgehog
Erinaceus europaeus

Belly covered
in soft fur

Four-toed hedgehog
Atelerix albiventris

Powerful forelimbs and claws
used for digging burrows
and unearthing prey

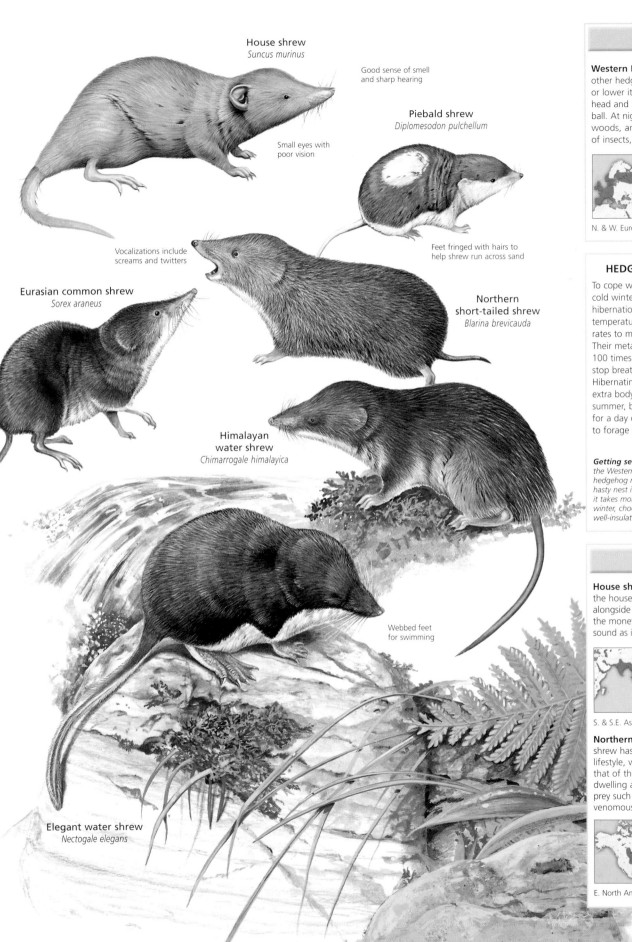

House shrew
Suncus murinus

Good sense of smell
and sharp hearing

Small eyes with
poor vision

Piebald shrew
Diplomesodon pulchellum

Feet fringed with hairs to
help shrew run across sand

Vocalizations include
screams and twitters

Eurasian common shrew
Sorex araneus

Northern
short-tailed shrew
Blarina brevicauda

Himalayan
water shrew
Chimarrogale himalayica

Webbed feet
for swimming

Elegant water shrew
Nectogale elegans

FACT FILE

Western European hedgehog Like other hedgehogs, this species can raise or lower its spines and will protect its head and belly by rolling into a spiky ball. At night, it snuffles through fields, woods, and urban gardens in search of insects, worms, eggs, and carrion.

🐾 Up to 10 in (26 cm)
Up to 1 in (3 cm)
⚖ Up to 3½ lb (1.6 kg)
Solitary
Common

N. & W. Europe

HEDGEHOG HIBERNATION

To cope with the lack of food during cold winters, hedgehogs will go into hibernation, lowering their body temperature and heart and respiration rates to minimize their energy needs. Their metabolic rate can become 100 times slower and they may even stop breathing for up to 2 hours. Hibernating hedgehogs live off the extra body fat accumulated in late summer, but also rouse themselves for a day or so every couple of weeks to forage and defecate.

Getting settled While the Western European hedgehog makes a hasty nest in summer, it takes more care in winter, choosing a well-insulated site.

FACT FILE

House shrew Like the house mouse, the house shrew has flourished living alongside humans. Also known as the money shrew, it makes a jangling sound as it forages for insects in houses.

🐾 Up to 6½ in (16 cm)
Up to 3½ in (9 cm)
⚖ Up to 3 oz (90 g)
Solitary, commensal
Common

S. & S.E. Asia

Northern short-tailed shrew This shrew has adapted to a burrowing lifestyle, with a body shape similar to that of the true moles. It hunts soil-dwelling animals, immobilizing larger prey such as voles and mice by injecting venomous saliva when it bites.

🐾 Up to 3 in (8 cm)
Up to 1 in (3 cm)
⚖ Up to 1 oz (30 g)
Solitary
Common

E. North America

FACT FILE

Russian desman Once found across Europe, this gregarious species is now restricted to a handful of river basins in Russia. Its soft coat made it a target of trappers, but it is now legally protected.

🐾 Up to 8½ in (22 cm)
🐾 Up to 8½ in (22 cm)
⚖ Up to 8 oz (220 g)
🐾 Solitary
⚡ Vulnerable

E. Europe

American shrew mole About the size of a shrew and without the large forelimbs of other moles, this animal is North America's smallest mole. It is also the only mole able to climb bushes.

🐾 Up to 3 in (8 cm)
🐾 Up to 1½ in (4 cm)
⚖ Up to ⅓ oz (11 g)
🐾 Solitary
⚡ Locally common

W. North America

SENSITIVE STARS

An arrangement of fleshy tentacles around its nose helps the star-nosed mole sense small fishes, leeches, snails, and other aquatic prey. When this agile swimmer leaves the water, it usually retreats to its network of tunnels.

🐾 Up to 5 in (13 cm)
🐾 Up to 3 in (8 cm)
⚖ Up to 3 oz (85 g)
🐾 Solitary
⚡ Locally common

E. North America

Perceptive rays Each of the star-nosed mole's 22 rays bears thousands of sensory organs.

⚡ CONSERVATION WATCH

Of the 428 species of insectivores, 40% are listed on the IUCN Red List, as follows:

   5 Extinct
 36 Critically endangered
 45 Endangered
 69 Vulnerable
   5 Near threatened
   9 Data deficient

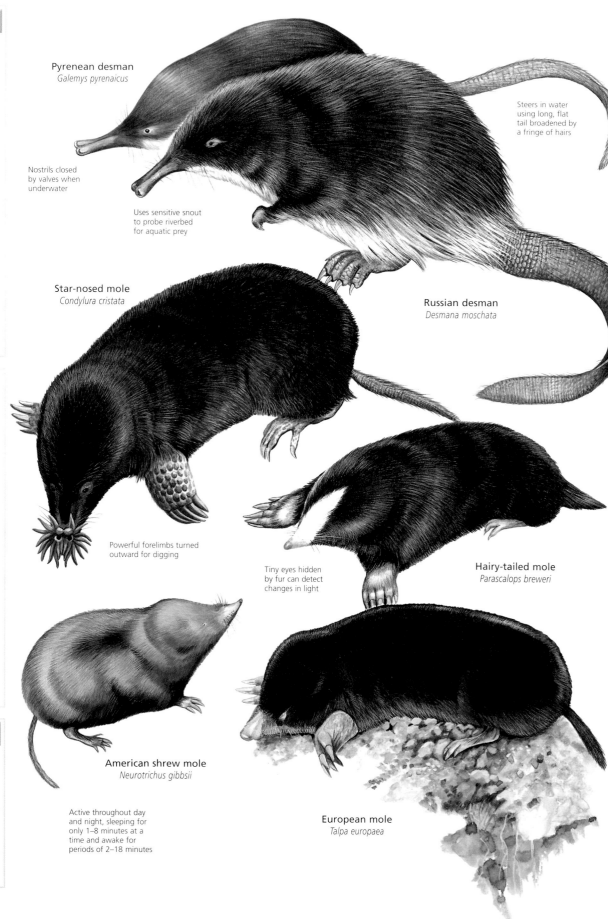

Pyrenean desman
Galemys pyrenaicus

Nostrils closed by valves when underwater

Uses sensitive snout to probe riverbed for aquatic prey

Steers in water using long, flat tail broadened by a fringe of hairs

Russian desman
Desmana moschata

Star-nosed mole
Condylura cristata

Powerful forelimbs turned outward for digging

Tiny eyes hidden by fur can detect changes in light

Hairy-tailed mole
Parascalops breweri

American shrew mole
Neurotrichus gibbsii

Active throughout day and night, sleeping for only 1–8 minutes at a time and awake for periods of 2–18 minutes

European mole
Talpa europaea

LIFE BELOW THE SURFACE

Often the only sign of moles in an area is the presence of molehills, small mounds of dirt created when a mole digs a vertical shaft to the surface. Spending almost their entire lives underground, moles dwell in a network of tunnels, sleeping and raising young in a subterranean nest and foraging in the tunnels for earthworms, insect larvae, slugs, and other soil invertebrates. A mole can create up to 65 feet (20 m) of tunnels per day. It usually comes to the surface only to collect grasses and leaf litter to line a nest, or if a stronger animal has evicted it from its home and it needs to find a new territory.

Raised in the dark Moles mate in the female's burrow during a frantic breeding season of just 24–48 hours. An average of three young are born a month later, and will be nursed in the nest for a further month. After initially exploring the tunnel system with the mother, young moles must soon leave and build their own tunnels elsewhere.

Designed to dig Most moles have enormous, powerful forelimbs with outward-facing hands and spade-like claws. To dig a tunnel, a mole scoops soil sideways and backward, using the smaller hindlimbs to brace itself.

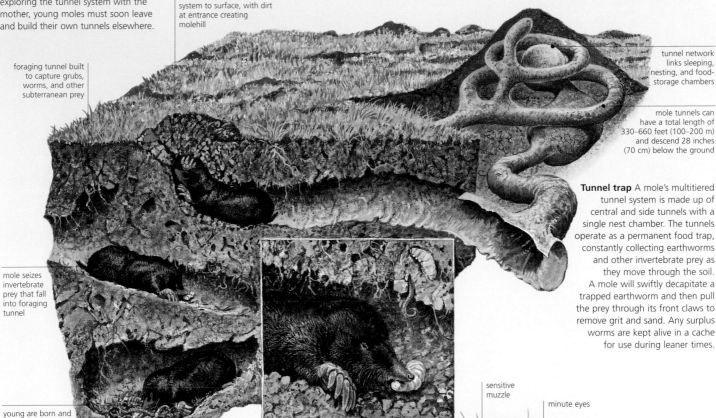

vertical shaft links tunnel system to surface, with dirt at entrance creating molehill

foraging tunnel built to capture grubs, worms, and other subterranean prey

tunnel network links sleeping, nesting, and food-storage chambers

mole tunnels can have a total length of 330–660 feet (100–200 m) and descend 28 inches (70 cm) below the ground

Tunnel trap A mole's multitiered tunnel system is made up of central and side tunnels with a single nest chamber. The tunnels operate as a permanent food trap, constantly collecting earthworms and other invertebrate prey as they move through the soil. A mole will swiftly decapitate a trapped earthworm and then pull the prey through its front claws to remove grit and sand. Any surplus worms are kept alive in a cache for use during leaner times.

mole seizes invertebrate prey that fall into foraging tunnel

young are born and raised in leaf-lined nesting burrow

sensitive muzzle

minute eyes

reversible fur

spade-like claws

huge forelimbs

Subterranean special A mole's anatomy is highly specialized for an underground life. Muscular shoulders and enlarged forelimbs make it a powerful digger. The dense fur can lie in any direction, allowing the mole to move forward or backward with ease. Virtually hidden by the fur, the tiny eyes do sense changes in light, but can barely see. Instead, the mole relies on touch, with a sensitive, mobile muzzle to seek out food.

FLYING LEMURS

A lso known as colugos, flying lemurs do not really fly and are not true lemurs. Instead, they glide through the air, and are placed in their own small order, Dermoptera ("skin wing"). These cat-sized animals are helpless on the ground and climb awkwardly in a lurching fashion, but travel easily between the tall trees of their rain-forest home. To minimize the risk of being picked off by a swift bird of prey during a glide, flying lemurs are nocturnal. They spend the day resting, either nestled in tree hollows or clinging to a trunk with their needle-sharp claws. A female flying lemur usually gives birth to a single, rather undeveloped young and then carries it on her belly until it is weaned. Her gliding membrane can be folded to create a snug pouch for the young, and becomes a hammock when she hangs upside down from a branch.

CLASS Mammalia
ORDER Dermoptera
FAMILY Cynocephalidae
GENUS Cynocephalus
SPECIES 2

Narrow distribution The Malayan flying lemur is found in Malaysia, Thailand, and Indonesia, while the Philippine flying lemur lives only in the Philippines. Both species are hunted by local people for their fur and meat and are threatened by the destruction of their rain-forest habitat.

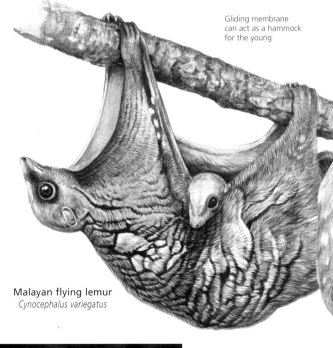

Gliding membrane can act as a hammock for the young

Malayan flying lemur
Cynocephalus variegatus

LEAF-EATER

A specialized stomach allows flying lemurs to digest the large amounts of leafy vegetation that make up the bulk of their diet. Other foods include buds, flowers, fruit, and possibly tree sap.

Ascends tree trunk in a series of hops, clinging to bark with sharp claws

Like a kite Stretching from the neck to the fingers, toes, and tail, the flying lemur's gliding membrane is the most extensive of any glider. A flying lemur can travel through the air for up to 450 feet (135 m), making an accurate landing with the help of its stereoscopic vision. Four other groups of forest mammals—flying squirrels (*Sciuridae*), scaly-tails (*Anomaluridae*), sugar gliders (*Petauridae*), and the greater glider (*Pseudocheiridae*)—independently evolved with the ability to glide.

Philippine flying lemur
Cynocephalus volans

TREE SHREWS

CLASS	Mammalia
ORDER	Scandentia
FAMILY	Tupaiidae
GENERA	5
SPECIES	19

In some Asian tropical forests, small, squirrel-like mammals known as tree shrews scurry along the ground and up trees, foraging for insects, worms, small vertebrates, and fruit. Their sharp claws and splayed toes keep a firm grip on bark and rock alike, while a long tail helps with balance. When eating, they hold food in their hands and may sit on their haunches, alert for predators such as birds of prey, snakes, and mongooses. An average of three young are born in a nest of leaves, which is often made by the father in a tree hollow. Maternal care tends to be limited, with some females visiting only once every 2 days. Considered a primitive form of placental mammal, tree shrews have no direct relationship to true shrews. While a few tree-shrew species spend almost all their time in trees, most are semi-terrestrial and some rarely venture into trees at all.

Divided family Tree shrews live in the tropical rain forests of south and Southeast Asia. Initially considered to be insectivores and then grouped with primates, they are now classified in their own order (Scandentia) in a single family (Tupaiidae), which is divided into two subfamilies. The subfamily Ptilocercinae contains just one species, the pen-tailed tree shrew, which is found on Borneo and the Malay Peninsula. The subfamily Tupaiinae contains the other 18 species of tree shrew. The majority of these make their home on the island of Borneo, while the remainder are distributed throughout eastern India and Southeast Asia.

Philippine tree shrew
Urogale everetti

Pen-tailed tree shrew
Ptilocercus lowii

Only fully nocturnal tree shrew

Scaly tail twitches continuously

Common tree shrew
Tupaia glis

Uses long snout to root through leaf litter on forest floor for insects and seeds

Large tree shrew
Tupaia tana

High fidelity During their 2- to 3-year life, common tree shrews form a permanent pair and display a high degree of fidelity to their mate. While each partner forages alone by day, the pair shares a territory and will defend it against other members of the species. To advertise ownership, they mark strategic sites and new objects with urine or feces or with a scent produced by glands on the chest and abdomen, rubbing their bodies along branches and other surfaces to deposit the scent. Tree shrews also scentmark their partners and young. If the scent is rubbed off, a female shrew will fail to recognize her offspring and may eat them.

⚡ CONSERVATION WATCH

Of the 19 species of tree shrews, 32% are listed on the IUCN Red List, as follows:

    2   Endangered
    4   Vulnerable

BATS

CLASS	Mammalia
ORDER	Chiroptera
FAMILY	18
GENERA	177
SPECIES	993

The only mammals with flapping wings and therefore the only ones capable of true flight, bats can travel through the air at speeds of up to 30 miles per hour (50 km/h). This ability has enabled them to cover great distances, exploiting food sources over a wide range and colonizing most parts of the globe, including far-flung islands such as New Zealand and Hawaii, where they are the only native land mammals. Almost 1,000 species of bat form the order Chiroptera, which is the second-largest mammal order. Chiroptera is split into two suborders: the Old World fruit bats, known as Megachiroptera, and the mostly insect-eating New World bats, known as Microchiroptera.

All over the world Bats make up nearly one-quarter of all mammal species. While most numerous in warmer regions, bat species are found worldwide except for the polar zones and a few isolated islands. Forest bats usually have relatively large, wide wings that offer maneuverability, while bats in open habitats tend to have small, narrow wings, which provide speed.

Mothers' group As in many bat species, female little bent-winged bats (*Miniopterus australis*) raise young together in nursery colonies. After returning from foraging, the mothers are able to recognize their own offspring among the thousands of young by their cries and odor.

On the wing A bat has very long arms and highly modified hands, with all digits except the thumb greatly elongated to support the wing membrane, which is called the patagium. A double layer of skin, the patagium is both flexible and tough.

FLYING FEEDERS

Bats are popularly portrayed as blood-sucking fiends, but only three species of bat drink blood and even these vampire bats display genuine altruism, sharing their food with hungry companions. Most bats are gregarious creatures, with some living in colonies of thousands or even millions of individuals.

More than 70 percent of bats consume insects that fly at night, a source of food exploited by few other animals. In addition to their flying ability, these hunters rely on echolocation, a means of locating both obstacles and prey by emitting high-pitched sounds and detecting the echoes. In many ecosystems, bats play a crucial role in keeping insect populations under control.

Most other bats are herbivores, using a keen sense of smell and effective night vision to locate fruit, flowers, nectar, and pollen. Such bats can be vital for pollination and seed dispersal, and some plants have adapted specifically to attract them, producing large fruits and strongly scented night-blooming flowers.

To minimize their consumption of energy, many bats regulate their body temperature, lowering it when roosting during the day. To cope with the scarcity of food in winter, some temperate species enter longer periods of hibernation, living off body fat deposited in autumn. Others migrate to warmer climes, with one species, the European noctule, flying up to 1,200 miles (2,000 km).

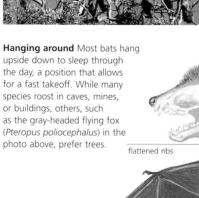

Hanging around Most bats hang upside down to sleep through the day, a position that allows for a fast takeoff. While many species roost in caves, mines, or buildings, others, such as the gray-headed flying fox (*Pteropus poliocephalus*) in the photo above, prefer trees.

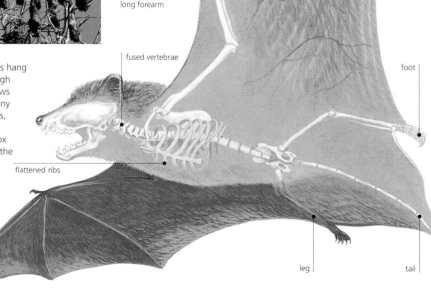

third finger

fourth finger

second finger

thumb

fifth finger

long forearm

fused vertebrae

foot

flattened ribs

leg

tail

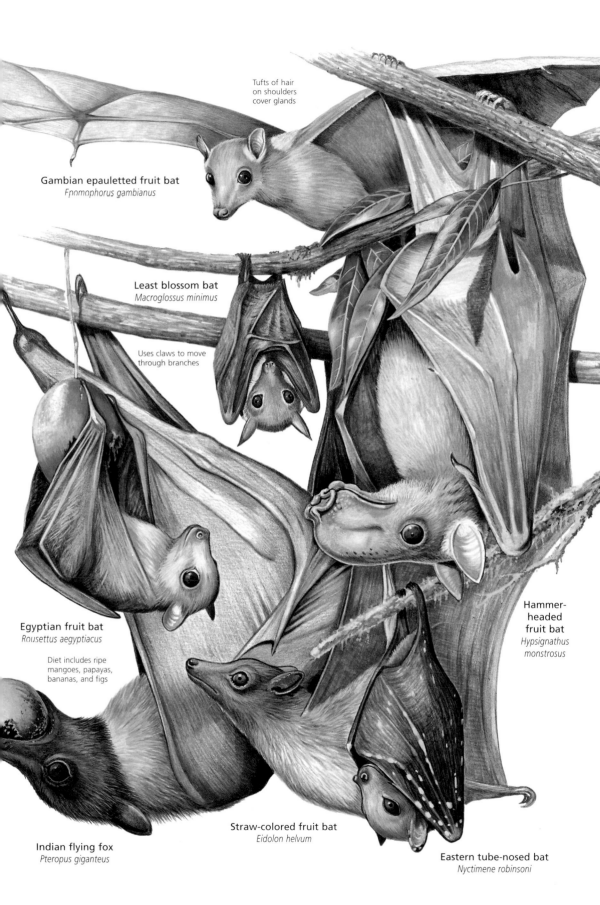

Gambian epauletted fruit bat
Epomophorus gambianus

Tufts of hair on shoulders cover glands

Least blossom bat
Macroglossus minimus

Uses claws to move through branches

Egyptian fruit bat
Rousettus aegyptiacus

Diet includes ripe mangoes, papayas, bananas, and figs

Indian flying fox
Pteropus giganteus

Straw-colored fruit bat
Eidolon helvum

Hammer-headed fruit bat
Hypsignathus monstrosus

Eastern tube-nosed bat
Nyctimene robinsoni

FACT FILE

Least blossom bat This small bat uses a very long tongue to extract nectar and pollen from the blooms of banana, coconut, and mangrove trees. As the bat travels from feeding site to feeding site, it helps to pollinate the plants.

🦇	Up to 3 in (7 cm)
🦇	Up to ½ in (1 cm)
🦇	Up to ½ oz (18 g)
🦇	Solitary, pairs
↯	Locally common

N. Australia, New Guinea, some islands

Egyptian fruit bat While this species relies mostly on vision, it is one of the few Old World fruit bats with a crude echolocation mechanism, which comes in handy in its dim roosting caves.

🦇	Up to 5½ in (14 cm)
🦇	Up to 1 in (2 cm)
🦇	Up to 5½ oz (160 g)
🦇	Colonial
↯	Common

Africa & Middle East

Hammer-headed fruit bat Males of this large, canopy-roosting species have an enlarged snout and larynx, enabling them to produce loud calls.

🦇	Up to 12 in (30 cm)
🦇	None
🦇	Up to 15 oz (420 g)
🦇	Colonial, lekking
↯	Locally common

W. & C. Africa

ALL WRAPPED UP

A roosting Old World fruit bat wraps its wings around its body and holds its head at a right angle to its chest. New World bats tend to fold the wings at the side of the body and hang the head down or at a right angle to the back.

⚡ CONSERVATION WATCH

Bat vulnerability Because most bats raise just one young per year—a very low reproductive rate for their size—they are especially vulnerable and populations can easily plummet. Fruit bats are traditionally hunted for food in many parts of Africa, Asia, and the Pacific. More recent threats include habitat destruction and pesticide poisoning.

FACT FILE

Yellow-winged bat Umbrella thorn trees are among this species' favorite roosting sites. When the trees flower, they attract swarms of insects, which are kept in check by the bats.

🐾 Up to 3 in (8 cm)
🦴 None
⚖ Up to 1¼ oz (36 g)
🐾 Pair, colonial
🦴 Locally common
☀

Sub-Saharan Africa

Greater bulldog bat This species zig-zags over ponds, rivers, and coastal waters, using echolocation and large, taloned feet to find and capture fish.

🐾 Up to 5 in (13 cm)
🦴 Up to 1½ in (4 cm)
⚖ Up to 3 oz (90 g)
🐾 Colonial
🦴 Locally common
🏛 ☀

Central & South America, Caribbean

MAKING A TENT

Rather than hang in a cave or from a branch, the little Honduran tent bat is one of several fruit bats that create their own shelter. It curls a palm frond by chewing through the connection between the leaf's midrib and edges.

Egyptian slit-faced bat
Nycteris thebaica

Long tail separate from flying membrane

Yellow-winged bat
Lavia frons

Greater mouse-tailed bat
Rhinopoma microphyllum

Muzzle divided by furrow

Noseleaf focuses ultrasonic squeaks produced in larynx for echolocation

Roosts in tombs, abandoned buildings, rock crevices, caves, and trees

Mauritian tomb bat
Taphozous mauritianus

Cheek pouches store chewed fish so bat can continue fishing

Long hindlimbs with huge feet and strong claws for snatching fish from water

Greater bulldog bat
Noctilio leporinus

⚡ CONSERVATION WATCH

Of the 993 species of bats, 52% are listed on the IUCN Red List, as follows:

12	Extinct
29	Critically endangered
37	Endangered
173	Vulnerable
209	Near threatened
61	Data deficient

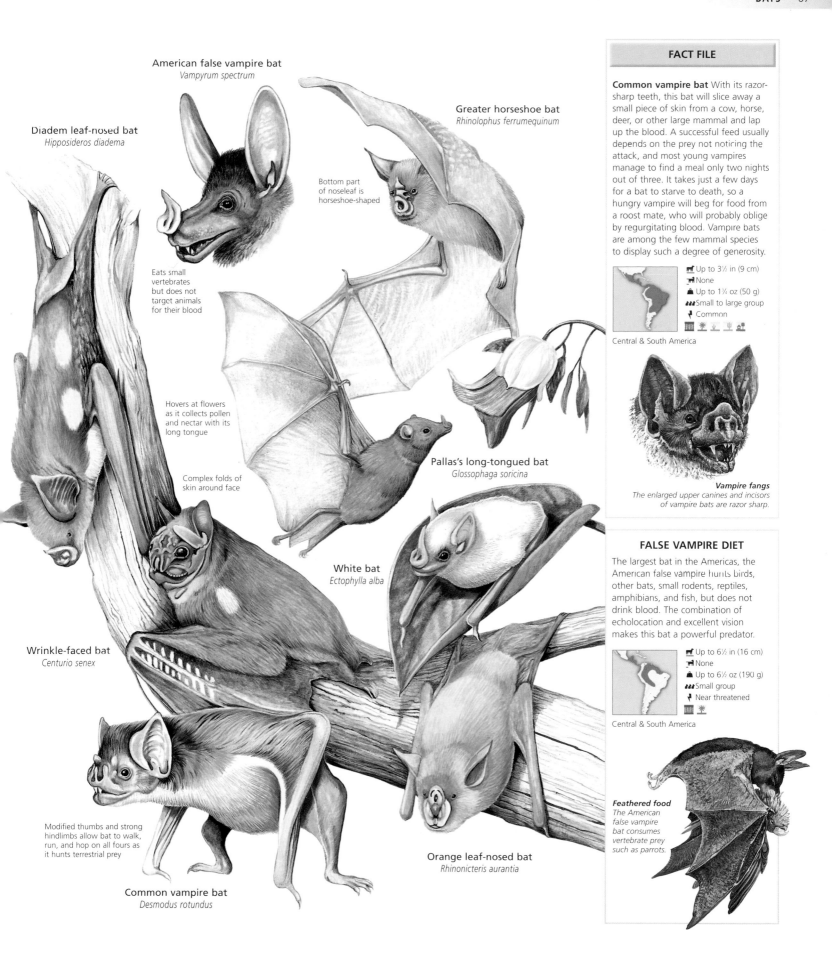

Diadem leaf-nosed bat
Hipposideros diadema

American false vampire bat
Vampyrum spectrum

Greater horseshoe bat
Rhinolophus ferrumequinum

Bottom part
of noseleaf is
horseshoe-shaped

Eats small
vertebrates
but does not
target animals
for their blood

Hovers at flowers
as it collects pollen
and nectar with its
long tongue

Complex folds of
skin around face

Pallas's long-tongued bat
Glossophaga soricina

White bat
Ectophylla alba

Wrinkle-faced bat
Centurio senex

Modified thumbs and strong
hindlimbs allow bat to walk,
run, and hop on all fours as
it hunts terrestrial prey

Common vampire bat
Desmodus rotundus

Orange leaf-nosed bat
Rhinonicteris aurantia

FACT FILE

Common vampire bat With its razor-sharp teeth, this bat will slice away a small piece of skin from a cow, horse, deer, or other large mammal and lap up the blood. A successful feed usually depends on the prey not noticing the attack, and most young vampires manage to find a meal only two nights out of three. It takes just a few days for a bat to starve to death, so a hungry vampire will beg for food from a roost mate, who will probably oblige by regurgitating blood. Vampire bats are among the few mammal species to display such a degree of generosity.

Up to 3½ in (9 cm)
None
Up to 1¾ oz (50 g)
Small to large group
Common

Central & South America

Vampire fangs
The enlarged upper canines and incisors of vampire bats are razor sharp.

FALSE VAMPIRE DIET

The largest bat in the Americas, the American false vampire hunts birds, other bats, small rodents, reptiles, amphibians, and fish, but does not drink blood. The combination of echolocation and excellent vision makes this bat a powerful predator.

Up to 6½ in (16 cm)
None
Up to 6½ oz (190 g)
Small group
Near threatened

Central & South America

Feathered food
The American false vampire bat consumes vertebrate prey such as parrots.

FACT FILE

Western barbastelle This medium-sized bat roosts in caves, mines, cellars, hollow trees, or under loose bark. It emerges at dusk to search for moths. Although widespread, it appears to be rare almost everywhere in its range.

🐁 Up to 2½ in (6 cm)
🐀 Up to 1½ in (4 cm)
⚖ Up to ¼ oz (10 g)
🐾 Small group
⚑ Vulnerable

W. Europe, Morocco, Canary Islands

Schreiber's bent-winged bat In some regions, this species migrates to warmer locations in winter. It roosts by day in caves or buildings, with the young placed in a communal group separate from the adults.

🐁 Up to 2½ in (6 cm)
🐀 Up to 2½ in (6 cm)
⚖ Up to ½ oz (20 g)
🐾 Large group
⚑ Near threatened

Europe, Africa, S. Asia, Australasia

Large mouse-eared bat Consuming up to half its body weight each night, this bat preys on beetles and moths. Groups of 10–100 individuals share roosts in caves and attics. Young are born in April to June and must build up fat to survive the winter hibernation.

🐁 Up to 3 in (8 cm)
🐀 Up to 2½ in (6 cm)
⚖ Up to 1½ oz (45 g)
🐾 Small to large group
⚑ Near threatened

Europe & Israel

⚑ CONSERVATION WATCH

Vespertilionid bats This page shows just a few of the bats in the family Vespertilionidae, the largest, most widely distributed bat family, which includes a species that lives along the arctic treeline. Its members use almost every kind of roosting site, including buildings. Despite this resourcefulness, 2 species are extinct and many depend on conservation efforts, with 7 critically endangered, 20 endangered, and 52 vulnerable species. Even Britain's most abundant bats, the pipistrelles, have declined by more than 60 percent since 1986.

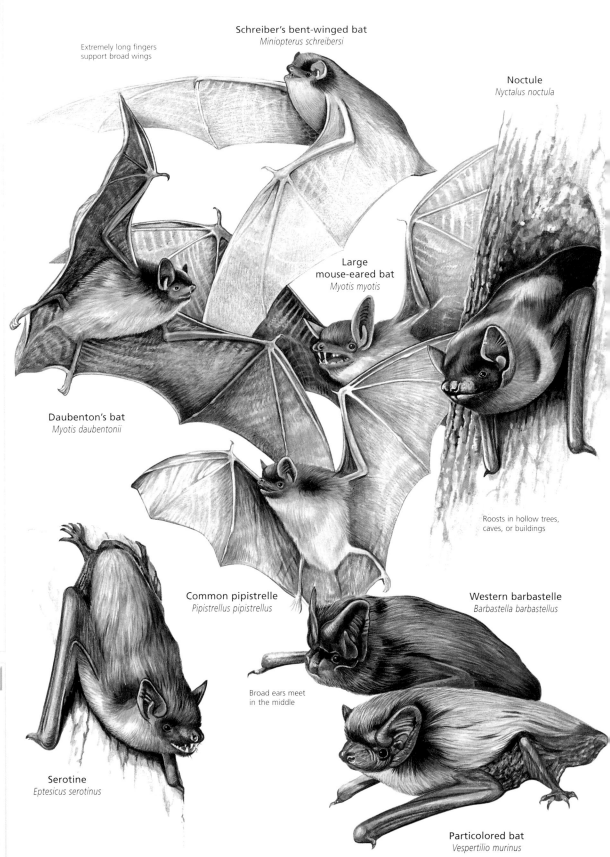

Extremely long fingers support broad wings

Schreiber's bent-winged bat
Miniopterus schreibersi

Noctule
Nyctalus noctula

Large mouse-eared bat
Myotis myotis

Daubenton's bat
Myotis daubentonii

Roosts in hollow trees, caves, or buildings

Common pipistrelle
Pipistrellus pipistrellus

Western barbastelle
Barbastella barbastellus

Broad ears meet in the middle

Serotine
Eptesicus serotinus

Particolored bat
Vespertilio murinus

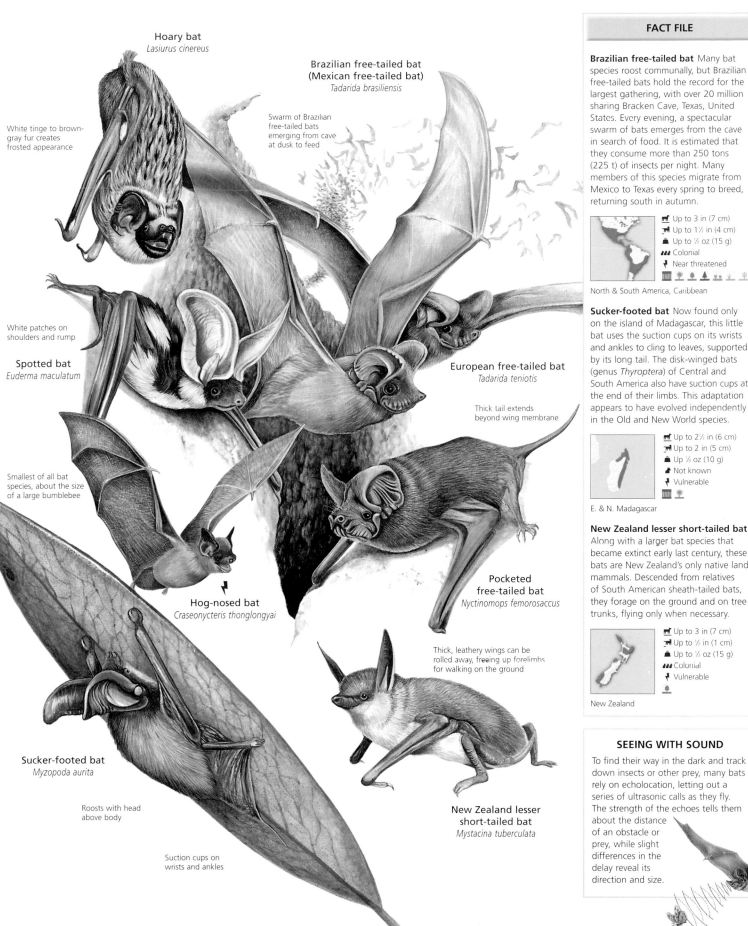

Hoary bat
Lasiurus cinereus

White tinge to brown-gray fur creates frosted appearance

Brazilian free-tailed bat
(Mexican free-tailed bat)
Tadarida brasiliensis

Swarm of Brazilian free-tailed bats emerging from cave at dusk to feed

White patches on shoulders and rump

Spotted bat
Euderma maculatum

Smallest of all bat species, about the size of a large bumblebee

European free-tailed bat
Tadarida teniotis

Thick tail extends beyond wing membrane

Hog-nosed bat
Craseonycteris thonglongyai

Pocketed free-tailed bat
Nyctinomops femorosaccus

Thick, leathery wings can be rolled away, freeing up forelimbs for walking on the ground

Sucker-footed bat
Myzopoda aurita

Roosts with head above body

Suction cups on wrists and ankles

New Zealand lesser short-tailed bat
Mystacina tuberculata

FACT FILE

Brazilian free-tailed bat Many bat species roost communally, but Brazilian free-tailed bats hold the record for the largest gathering, with over 20 million sharing Bracken Cave, Texas, United States. Every evening, a spectacular swarm of bats emerges from the cave in search of food. It is estimated that they consume more than 250 tons (225 t) of insects per night. Many members of this species migrate from Mexico to Texas every spring to breed, returning south in autumn.

- Up to 3 in (7 cm)
- Up to 1½ in (4 cm)
- Up to ½ oz (15 g)
- Colonial
- Near threatened

North & South America, Caribbean

Sucker-footed bat Now found only on the island of Madagascar, this little bat uses the suction cups on its wrists and ankles to cling to leaves, supported by its long tail. The disk-winged bats (genus *Thyroptera*) of Central and South America also have suction cups at the end of their limbs. This adaptation appears to have evolved independently in the Old and New World species.

- Up to 2½ in (6 cm)
- Up to 2 in (5 cm)
- Up ¼ oz (10 g)
- Not known
- Vulnerable

E. & N. Madagascar

New Zealand lesser short-tailed bat Along with a larger bat species that became extinct early last century, these bats are New Zealand's only native land mammals. Descended from relatives of South American sheath-tailed bats, they forage on the ground and on tree trunks, flying only when necessary.

- Up to 3 in (7 cm)
- Up to ½ in (1 cm)
- Up to ½ oz (15 g)
- Colonial
- Vulnerable

New Zealand

SEEING WITH SOUND

To find their way in the dark and track down insects or other prey, many bats rely on echolocation, letting out a series of ultrasonic calls as they fly. The strength of the echoes tells them about the distance of an obstacle or prey, while slight differences in the delay reveal its direction and size.

PRIMATES

CLASS	Mammalia
ORDER	Primates
FAMILIES	13
GENERA	60
SPECIES	295

Charismatic and intelligent, lemurs, monkeys, apes, and their close relatives make up the order known as Primates. Early primates were tree-dwellers and developed adaptations for an arboreal lifestyle: forward-facing eyes with stereoscopic vision to help judge distances when traveling through the trees; dextrous hands and feet to firmly grasp branches; and long, flexible limbs to enhance agility when foraging. Most primates are still largely arboreal, but even those that have opted for life on the ground retain at least some of these adaptations. Perhaps the most fascinating aspect of this order is the complex social behavior displayed by many species.

Tropical distribution Although most primates live in the tropical rain forests between 25°N and 30°S, a handful of species are found farther afield, in North Africa, China, and Japan.

EVOLUTION OF PRIMATES

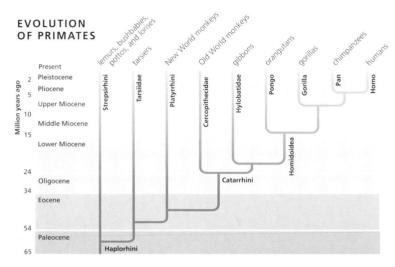

Strepsirhine primate Like other members of the suborder Strepsirhini, the Coquerel's dwarf lemur is distinguished by a moist, pointed snout and a keen sense of smell. Nocturnal and solitary, this small primate forages for flowers, fruit, and insects.

Meat eater For most primates, leaves, fruit, and insects make up the bulk of the diet, but baboons, chimpanzees, and humans also hunt large vertebrates. Here, an olive baboon (*Papio hamadryas anubis*) returns with its kill of a young gazelle.

Haplorhine primate Along with monkeys and humans, the gorillas and other apes make up the suborder Haplorhini. Gorillas are social animals, living in troops of one or two silverback males, a few younger males, and several females and young.

PRIMATE DIVERSITY

While some small primates are solitary foragers, relying on hiding and nocturnal habits to escape predators, many larger primates are active by day and form groups as protection. A group offers many pairs of eyes to watch for predators. Even when a predator does attack, there is a good chance that it will take another member of the group. Some primates will fight off an attack together—baboons have been known to kill an attacking leopard.

The size and organization of primate groups vary enormously. Some species live in monogamous pairs, while others form troops of several females and one or more males. Stable troops of 150 geladas sometimes combine into herds of 600 individuals. The most common structure is based on related females

and their offspring, often headed by a single male. Group living leads to greater competition for food and mates, which is negotiated through complex hierarchies and alliances. These elaborate social networks rely on precise communication, with many species employing a range of nuanced visual and vocal signals. Relative to body size, primates have much larger brains than most other mammals, a feature that may be linked to their complex social lives.

The life of a primate moves slowly. Gestation periods are long; birth rates are low, with just one or two young in a litter; growth rates are slow, with long periods of dependency as infants and juveniles; and lifespans are long. This may be the cost of the large primate brain, which uses energy that would otherwise be available for growth and reproduction.

Primates range from the pygmy mouse lemur (*Microcebus myoxinus*), at 4 inches (10 cm) long and 1 ounce (30 g) in weight, to the gorilla, standing more than 5 feet (1.5 m) high and weighing 400 pounds

Temperate life Japanese macaques are among the few primates to live outside the tropics and subtropics. During the cold, snowy winters, their furry coats thicken. They feed on bark, buds, and stored food reserves, and warm up in thermal pools.

Vertical posture Chimpanzees and other apes sit and sometimes walk upright, supported by a shorter back, broader rib-cage, and stronger pelvis than those of monkeys and lemurs. The arms, often used in locomotion, are longer than the legs, and the wrists are highly flexible.

Swinging through the trees Gibbons use their extremely long arms to swing from tree to tree, a form of movement known as brachiation. They rely on stereoscopic vision to accurately judge the distance of their next handhold.

Busy social lives The large brains of primates such as baboons may be needed to manage the complex social relationships associated with living in a hierarchical group. While group living leads to greater competition for food, it reduces the risk of being attacked by predators.

Primate survival About a third of all primate species are at risk of extinction, victims of habitat loss and hunting. Large species such as the orangutan are especially vulnerable as they are easy for hunters to find.

(180 kg). Many small primates feed primarily on insects, a quickly processed food source to fuel their fast metabolisms. Larger species need greater volumes of food and often concentrate on leaves, shoots, and fruit, which are slow to digest but are in abundant supply. The general reliance on fruit, shoots, leaves, and insects has probably helped restrict primates largely to the tropics, where these foods are available year round.

The order Primates is split into two suborders: Strepsirhini, made up of lemurs and their relatives, and Haplorhini, comprised of tarsiers, monkeys, apes, and humans. Tarsiers and strepsirhines share a number of primitive features and have been collectively referred to as prosimians.

PROSIMIANS

CLASS	Mammalia
ORDER	Primates
FAMILIES	8
GENERA	22
SPECIES	63

The name *prosimians* means "before monkeys," a reference to the fact that these creatures retain many features of the early primates. Absent from the Americas, prosimians include the lemurs of Madagascar, the bushbabies and pottos of Africa, and the lorises of Asia—all members of the suborder Strepsirhini. These species all possess a moist, pointed snout and most have a light-reflecting disk in the eye, a long toilet claw, and compressed lower teeth forming a dental comb. Tarsiers, now classified in the suborder Haplorhini, are also often referred to as prosimians because their appearance and solitary, nocturnal behavior is like that of many strepsirhines.

Getting grubby The only strepsirhine to lack the dental comb and toilet claw, the aye-aye has huge, continually growing incisors for gnawing through bark, and a spindly middle finger for extracting grubs.

SPECIALIZED SENSES

Prosimians tend to be relatively small, nocturnal tree-dwellers who forage alone but may occasionally form limited groups. Most are largely insectivorous but will also consume fruit, leaves, flowers, nectar, and gum. They display two specializations for grooming: a long claw on the second toe of the foot, known as the toilet claw; and the dental comb, a compressed row of protruding lower teeth. The dental comb also seems to be used for scraping resin off trees.

The moist, dog-like snout shared by lemurs, lorises, and the other strepsirhines supplies them with a wealth of information through smell. Sight is also important, but they do not have the full color vision of monkeys and apes. Sophisticated color vision would be of limited use

Arboreal attitude Like other prosimians, the slender loris is superbly adapted for a life in trees. Its large, forward-facing eyes provide stereoscopic vision to accurately judge distances, while its dextrous hands and feet keep a firm grip on the branches.

to creatures that forage in the low-light conditions of night. Instead, most prosimians have a tapetum lucidum, a crystalline layer behind the retina that reflects light and produces the characteristic eyeshine of many nocturnal mammals.

While sound is important in prosimian communication, with many species employing alarm and territorial calls, scent plays a major role. Territories are often marked with urine, feces, or secretions from special scent glands, which can convey an individual's sex, identity, and breeding status.

Terrestrial troops Unusually among prosimians, ring-tailed lemurs are active during the day and spend most of their time on the ground. Their troops of between 3 and 20 animals are dominated by female lemurs, a matriarchal structure found in few other primates. Females give birth to one or two young, whose care is shared by the troop.

Broad-nosed gentle lemur
Hapalemur simus

Mongoose lemur
Eulemur mongoz

Ring-tailed lemur
Lemur catta

Large forward-facing eyes

Black lemur
Eulemur macaco

Brown lemur
Eulemur fulvus

Coquerel's dwarf lemur
Microcebus coquereli

Long tail can store fat reserves

Characteristic forked stripe on head

Fork-marked lemur
Phaner furcifer

FACT FILE

Broad-nosed gentle lemur More than 95 percent of this lemur's diet is made up of bamboo shoots, leaves, and stalks. One of the world's rarest mammals, it was not seen for a century and was considered extinct until its rediscovery in 1972.

🐾 Up to 17½ in (45 cm)
🐾 Up to 22 in (56 cm)
⚖ Up to 5½ lb (2.5 kg)
🐾 Family band
✳ Critically endangered

S.E. Madagascar

Mongoose lemur Usually nocturnal during the dry season, mongoose lemurs switch to daytime activity for the colder wet season. They live in small groups made up of a male and female pair and their offspring.

🐾 Up to 17½ in (45 cm)
🐾 Up to 25 in (64 cm)
⚖ Up to 6½ lb (3 kg)
🐾 Family band
✳ Vulnerable

N.W. Madagascar (S. of Narinda Bay), Comoro I.

Black lemur For years, male and female black lemurs were considered different species because they look so unalike. Males are black, but females are chestnut-brown with white bellies and ear tufts. This tree-dwelling species feeds on fruit, flowers, and nectar.

🐾 Up to 17½ in (45 cm)
🐾 Up to 25 in (64 cm)
⚖ Up to 6½ lb (3 kg)
🐾 Family band
✳ Vulnerable

N.W. Madagascar (N. of Narinda Bay)

LEMURS OF MADAGASCAR

For millions of years, lemurs have been isolated on the island of Madagascar, where they have adapted to a variety of forest niches and developed the remarkable diversity evident today. They now range from the size of a mouse to that of a medium domestic dog, but the recently extinct giant sloth lemur (*Archaeoindris fontoynontii*) was bigger than a male gorilla. Most lemurs are arboreal and nocturnal, but some live on the ground and are active by day. They can be solitary, live in pairs, or form larger permanent troops.

Habitat loss *Like all Madagascar's lemurs, the red-bellied lemur* (Eulemur rubriventer) *is declining as its rain-forest habitat is destroyed.*

HANDS AND FEET

The contrasting lifestyles of primates are evident in the shape of their hands and feet. The indri and the tarsiers cling vertically and leap from tree to tree, while the aye-aye climbs through the branches. The gorilla can climb but spends most of its time on the ground.

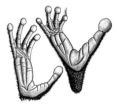

Clinging indri
The indri's stout thumb and big toe help it to cling firmly to tree trunks.

Digging aye-aye
Rather than cling, the aye-aye climbs by digging its long claws into the bark.

Tarsier friction
A tarsier's grip is strengthened by the friction of the disk-like pads on its fingers and toes.

Broad-handed gorilla
Largely terrestrial, a gorilla has broad hands and feet to help support its great weight.

⚡ CONSERVATION WATCH

Of the 63 species of prosimians, 76% are listed on the IUCN Red List, as follows:

- 3 Critically endangered
- 8 Endangered
- 12 Vulnerable
- 17 Near threatened
- 8 Data deficient

Weasel sportive lemur
Lepilemur mustelinus

Red-tailed sportive lemur
Lepilemur ruficaudatus

Rests in vertical position and moves between trees in short leaps

Aye-aye
Daubentonia madagascariensis

Long, powerful hindlimbs power great leaps

Long middle finger for extracting grubs

Coat of a ruffed lemur can be black and red, or black and white

Black face, hands, feet, and tail regardless of coat color

Ruffed lemur
Varecia variegata

Woolly lemur
Avahi laniger

Thick, woolly coat

Large, black,
tufted ears

Indri
Indri indri

Furless black face

Only lemur with
a very short tail

Verreaux's sifaka
Propithecus verreauxi

Diadem sifaka
Propithecus diadema

Almost
completely
arboreal

LEAVING A TRACE

Lemurs scentmark their territories with secretions from glands on the head, hands, or rear. The indri's scent glands are in its cheeks, while the woolly lemur has them in its neck.

CLING AND LEAP

The indri, sifakas, and woolly lemurs are all vertical clingers and leapers. They remain upright as they travel from tree to tree, propelled for up to 30 feet (10 m) by their long, powerful legs. On the rare occasions that these lemurs descend to the ground, they jump about on their legs, holding their arms above the head for balance.

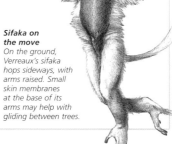

Sifaka on the move
On the ground, Verreaux's sifaka hops sideways, with arms raised. Small skin membranes at the base of its arms may help with gliding between trees.

FACT FILE

Lesser bushbaby This nocturnal animal prefers to feed on grasshoppers and other insect prey. When insects become rare during times of drought, it will feed solely on acacia gum, allowing it to survive in drier habitats.

- Up to 8 in (20 cm)
- Up to 12 in (30 cm)
- Up to 10½ oz (300 g)
- Family band
- Common

C. & S. Africa

Demidoff's galago By day, Demidoff's galago sleeps in an elaborate spherical nest of leaves. One of the smalllest primates, it has a fast metabolism and requires an energy-rich diet, 70 percent of which is made up of insects.

- Up to 6 in (15 cm)
- Up to 8½ in (21 cm)
- Up to 4 oz (120 g)
- Family band
- Locally common

C. Africa

CONTRASTING FAMILIES

Bushbabies or galagos belong to the family Galagonidae. Using their long hindlimbs for propulsion and long, bushy tails for balance, they leap from tree to tree with great agility (below). In contrast, the lorises, pottos, and angwantibos of the family Loridae creep slowly through the branches. As with other primates that move on all fours, their limbs are of roughly equal length and their tails are short.

⚡ CONSERVATION WATCH

Bushbaby threats While only one bushbaby species, the Rondo dwarf galago (*Galago rondoensis*), is listed as endangered, six others are near threatened. Of the remainder, many have not been studied enough for an accurate assessment of their status to be made. Several species were identified only in recent years and it is likely that more remain to be discovered. Meanwhile, their tropical forest habitat is being rapidly degraded and fragmented by logging and farming.

Lesser bushbaby
Galago senegalensis

Large, bat-like ears help to detect insects at night

Eastern needle-clawed bushbaby
Euoticus inustus

Large hands and feet with nails forming claws

Demidoff's galago
Galagoides demidoff

Needle-like claws on digits to grip branches

Western needle-clawed bushbaby
Euoticus elegantulus

Allen's bushbaby
Galago alleni

Bushy tail longer than body acts as stabilizer during leaps

Eyes cannot move but head can rotate almost a full circle

Naked tail tipped with tuft of hair

Slender loris
Loris tardigradus

Climbs on all fours with slender limbs of equal length

Western tarsier
Tarsius bancanus

Angwantibo (golden potto)
Arctocebus calabarensis

Potto
Perodicticus potto

Moves slowly through branches on all fours

Spectral tarsier
Tarsius spectrum

Very long, skinny digits for grasping branches

Slow loris
Nycticebus coucang

MONKEYS

CLASS	Mammalia
ORDER	Primates
FAMILIES	3
GENERA	33
SPECIES	214

Geography has determined two separate lineages of monkeys: the New World monkeys of the Americas, classified within the suborder Haplorhini as platyrrhines; and the Old World monkeys of Africa and Asia, grouped with apes and humans as catarrhines. New and Old World monkeys are most easily distinguished by the shape of their noses and by the arrangement of their teeth. All New World monkeys live in trees and many have strong prehensile tails to grip branches. While most Old World monkeys are also arboreal, none has a prehensile tail and some species are semi-terrestrial. Some Old World monkeys have callous pads on their rumps, a feature found on no New World species.

Old and new
Old World monkeys (above) have prominent noses with narrow, forward-facing nostrils. The noses of New World monkeys (right) are flattened with nostrils facing sideways.

Treetop life South America's gray woolly monkey (*Lagothrix cana*) is superbly adapted for an arboreal lifestyle. It swings through the trees, aided by muscular shoulders and hips, long, strong limbs, and grasping hands and feet. The prehensile tail acts as a fifth limb and features a bare gripping pad on the underside near the tip.

Pulling rank Many baboons live in large multi-male troops, and males will fight furiously to establish their dominance and gain access to the females. A troop's rank order, decided by both fighting and alliances, is not permanent, changing as the dominant male grows older or as males join or leave the troop.

SOCIAL SIMIANS

Monkeys tend to be medium-sized, ranging from the pygmy marmoset, with a length of 6 inches (15 cm) and a weight of 5 ounces (140 g), to the mandrill, measuring 30 inches (76 cm) long and weighing in at 55 pounds (25 kg). Most live in social groups, are active by day, and eat mainly fruit and leaves. All Old World monkeys and many New World monkeys have developed full color vision, which allows them to easily spot fruit among the foliage.

Like apes, monkeys differ from lemurs and other strepsirhines by having a dry, slightly hairy muzzle, a greater dependence on sight over smell, and a larger brain relative to body size. Not only are the brains of monkeys and apes larger, but the neocortex, the brain's outer sheath, is especially well developed. The neocortex is associated with creative thinking, an advantage when dealing with the machinations of group life. Monkeys are known to deliberately deceive other members of their group, raising false alarm calls, for example, in order to distract them from a source of food.

The social arrangements of monkeys display great variety: small family groups may contain just one monogamous breeding pair and their offspring; harems of several females may be dominated by a single adult male; and large troops may include several adult males and many females. While large groups often involve fierce competition to establish rank, they also feature extensive cooperation. Relationships among monkeys tend to be close and enduring, cemented by regular episodes of mutual grooming.

Golden lion tamarin
Leontopithecus rosalia

Striking reddish-gold
coat with long mane
framing black face

**Golden-headed
lion tamarin**
Leontopithecus chrysomelas

Pygmy marmoset
Callithrix pygmaea

Claws on all
digits except
big toe, which
has a flat nail

White ear tufts on
adults and juveniles,
absent from infants

**Cotton-top
tamarin**
Saguinus oedipus

Geoffroy's tamarin
Saguinus geoffroyi

Common marmoset
Callithrix jacchus

FACT FILE

Golden lion tamarin There are only
about 800 golden lion tamarins left
in the wild. Their striking appearance
made them popular pets and zoo
exhibits, with many falling victim to the
live-animal trade until it became illegal
in the 1970s. Deforestation continues
to have a serious impact.

🐾 Up to 11 in (28 cm)
🐒 Up to 16 in (40 cm)
⚖ Up to 1½ lb (650 g)
👥 Family band
⚡ Endangered
🏛

Coastal forest in Brazil

Pygmy marmoset The smallest of the
world's monkeys, this species gouges
out holes in trees to release its favorite
food of sap and gum. It runs on all
fours along branches, leaping from
tree to tree. Group members use high-
pitched trillings to communicate.

🐾 Up to 6 in (15 cm)
🐒 Up to 8½ in (22 cm)
⚖ Up to 5 oz (140 g)
👥 Family band
⚡ Locally common
🏛

W. Amazon basin

Cotton-top tamarin After spending
the night resting in the forks of their
sleeping tree, a group of 3–9 cotton-
top tamarins will move through
the trees of the canopy searching for
insects, fruit, and gum.

🐾 Up to 10 in (25 cm)
🐒 Up to 16 in (40 cm)
⚖ Up to 1 lb (500 g)
👥 Family band
⚡ Endangered
🏛

N. Colombia

COOPERATIVE BREEDING

Marmosets and tamarins usually live in
small groups of several unrelated adult
males and females. There tends to be
only one breeding female, who often
mates with more than one male and
gives birth to twins. Uniquely among
primates, the young are then cared
for by all members of
the group, including
the unrelated males.

Babysitting duties
*A male Geoffroy's
tamarin will carry
the young of a
female in his
group even
though they
may not be
his own.*

Northern night monkey The world's only nocturnal monkeys, night monkeys use their acute sense of smell and large eyes to find insects, fruit, nectar, and leaves in low light. They live in monogamous pairs, with the male responsible for the bulk of infant care.

Up to 18½ in (47 cm)
Up to 16 in (41 cm)
Up to 2½ lb (1.2 kg)
Pair
Common

S.W. Venezuela, N.W. Brazil

Dusky titi Titi monkeys live in closely bonded family groups, and a pair will often sit side by side with their tails entwined. They are active by day, when they consume large amounts of fruit.

Up to 14 in (36 cm)
Up to 18 in (46 cm)
Up to 3 lb (1.4 kg)
Family band
Locally common

C. Amazon basin

White-faced saki The long hindlimbs of these active tree-dwellers enable them to leap up to 30 feet (10 m) between trees. At night, they sleep curled up on branches like cats.

Up to 19 in (48 cm)
Up to 17½ in (45 cm)
Up to 5½ lb (2.4 kg)
Family band
Uncommon

Guianas, Venezuela, N. Brazil

Black-headed uakari This species lives in groups of up to 50 individuals, which include more than one adult male. Adult females and young engage in social grooming. For a tree-dweller, the uakari has an unusually short tail.

Up to 19½ in (50 cm)
Up to 8½ in (21 cm)
Up to 9 lb (4 kg)
Large troop
Rare

Upper Amazon basin

Northern night monkey
Aotus trivirgatus

Large eyes for better night vision

Dusky titi
Callicebus moloch

White-faced saki
Pithecia pithecia

White-nosed saki
Chiropotes albinasus

Bald uakari (red uakari)
Cacajao calvus

Black-headed uakari
Cacajao melanocephalus

Black howler
Alouatta caraya

Males are black, females are brown or olive, and infants are golden

Prehensile tail grips branches

Common squirrel monkey
Saimiri sciureus

Mantled howler
Alouatta palliata

Red howler
Alouatta seniculus

White-fronted capuchin
Cebus albifrons

Weeping capuchin
Cebus olivaceus

Brown capuchin
Cebus apella

White-throated capuchin
Cebus capucinus

HOWLING

One of the loudest calls in the animal world is made by howler monkeys. At dawn, howler troops announce their presence with a deafening conversation of howls that resonate through the forest, traveling up to 3 miles (5 km) away. By helping troops avoid one another, the howls prevent territorial skirmishes that would waste time and energy that could be better spent eating or resting.

Common woolly monkey This heavy monkey spends most of its time in trees, but often descends to the forest floor, where it can walk upright on its back legs. Large, multi-male groups of up to 70 individuals sleep together at night, but may split into smaller family groups to look for fruit and other food by day.

🐒 Up to 23 in (58 cm)
🐒 Up to 31½ in (80 cm)
⚖ Up to 22 lb (10 kg)
🔀 Variable
❗ Uncommon
🏛

Upper Amazon basin

Woolly spider monkey Also known as muriquis, woolly spider monkeys are found only in undisturbed high forest, 95 percent of which has been destroyed. Fewer than 500 individuals remain in the wild. Unusually for primates, males stay with their birth troop all their lives, while females must leave and join another troop when they reach adulthood.

🐒 Up to 25 in (63 cm)
🐒 Up to 31½ in (80 cm)
⚖ Up to 33 lb (15 kg)
🔀 Variable
❗ Endangered
🏛

S.E. Brazil

Black spider monkey Groups of about 20 black spider monkeys will cooperatively defend their territory or mob a predator, but they will split into subgroups of up to six for foraging.

🐒 Up to 24½ in (62 cm)
🐒 Up to 35½ in (90 cm)
⚖ Up to 28½ lb (13 kg)
🔀 Variable
❗ Locally common
🏛

N. of Amazon & E. of Rio Negro

TREETOP ANATOMY

Extremely agile climbers, spider monkeys have a slender body, long limbs, thumbless hands that act as simple hooks, and a flexible prehensile tail that functions as a fifth limb. They often scurry along branches on all fours, but will also swing swiftly through the trees, holding on with their hands and tail. A troop tends to travel in line, with the first member testing branches for the followers.

Very long prehensile tail strong enough to support monkey's weight

Thumbless hand acts as hook when swinging

Common woolly monkey
Lagothrix lagotricha

Woolly spider monkey
Brachyteles arachnoides

Coat can be reddish, dark to light brown, or dark to light gray

Long-haired spider monkey
Ateles belzebuth

Face color ranges from pink to black

Black-handed spider monkey
Ateles geoffroyi

Black spider monkey
Ateles paniscus

Capped leaf monkey
Trachypithecus pileatus

Hanuman langur
Semnopithecus entellus

Coat can be
dark brown,
fawn, or gray

Douc langur
Pygathrix nemaeus

Female has
brown face, male
has blue face

Male's pendulous
nose adds
resonance to calls

Chinese snub-nosed monkey
Rhinopithecus roxellana

Slight webbing between
digits helps to make
proboscis monkey an
excellent swimmer

Proboscis monkey
Nasalis larvatus

FACT FILE

Proboscis monkey This monkey is
named after the pendulous nose of the
male. It lives in stable harems of one
adult male and several females. Sexual
contact is initiated by the female, who
indicates her interest in a male by
pursing her lips. If the male returns her
gaze, she shakes her head. The male
then mirrors her pouting expression
and she presents her hindquarters to
him. During copulation, both male and
female proboscis monkeys maintain a
pouting expression and the female
keeps rapidly shaking her head.

Up to 30 in (76 cm)
Up to 30 in (76 cm)
Up to 51 lb (23 kg)
Harem
Endangered

Lowland Borneo

INFANTICIDE

Although most thoroughly studied
among Hanuman langurs, infanticide is
practiced by many primates. It occurs
when a new male becomes dominant
in a troop, often after a bachelor band
has invaded. The new male kills all the
troop's unweaned infants, presumably
because lactation prevents the mothers
from conceiving. Although the mothers
often try to defend their young, they
are usually unsuccessful. With their
infants dead, the females stop lactating
and are able to conceive the offspring
of the newly dominant male.

Competition and cooperation *The
intense rivalry that leads to infanticide
among Hanuman langurs is in stark
contrast to the high level of care and
cooperation within an established troop.*

Rival males *When young male Hanuman
langurs are expelled from their birth troop,
they form bachelor bands, which may
invade a breeding troop, usurp the resident
male's position, and kill the nursing infants.*

COLOBUS MONKEYS

Like the langurs of Asia, the colobus monkeys of Africa have a specialized stomach that has allowed them to exploit the most reliable food source in their forest habitat. Divided into a very large, chambered upper region and a lower acid region, the stomach can hold up to a quarter of the animal's weight in leaves, and contains a special bacteria to break down the vegetation and neutralize any toxins. Colobus monkeys demonstrate great agility as they gallop along branches and take flying leaps to neighboring trees, using their thumbless hands as hooks to secure themselves. Most colobus monkeys live in groups of 10 or so individuals, with a fixed core of related females. Females often "babysit" young that are not their own and may even suckle them.

Lift off Colobus monkeys can leap spectacularly from one tree to another, either to reach a new source of food or to escape a pursuing predator.

Mixed alliances
Colobus monkeys often form temporary or even stable associations with other monkey species. Red colobus monkeys and vervets, for example, may cooperate during the dangerous activity of drinking from a water hole, taking turns to keep an eye out for predators.

Olive colobus
Procolobus verus

Often forms permanent associations with Diana monkeys, which act as sentinels

Pied colobus
Colobus guereza

U-shaped white mantle on sides and back

Hook-like, thumbless hand allows quick movement through trees

Red colobus
Procolobus badius

Characteristic solemn expression

Black colobus
Colobus satanas

White tuft on end of tail

King colobus
Colobus polykomos

⚡ CONSERVATION WATCH

Disappearing red colobus All eight subspecies of red colobus are classified as endangered or critically endangered. Another subspecies, Miss Waldron's red colobus monkey (*Procolobus badius waldroni*), was declared extinct in 2000, the first documented extinction of a primate since 1900. Hunted for meat, red colobus monkeys make easy targets because they are brightly colored and vocal. They are also rapidly losing much of their forest habitat to logging, road building, and farming.

Rhesus macaque
Macaca mulatta

Cheek pouches
store food

Barbary ape
Macaca sylvanus

Mane of gray hair

Pig-tailed
macaque
Macaca nemestrina

Lion-tailed
macaque
Macaca silenus

Coat thickens
in winter

Short tail is
almost hairless

Bear macaque
(stump-tailed macaque)
Macaca arctoides

Japanese macaque
Macaca fuscata

FACT FILE

Rhesus macaque Up to 200 of these gregarious monkeys live together in a group. Adapted to a wide range of habitats, they vary their diet according to season and location, with some in urban areas raiding gardens and trash cans. The species has been extensively used in medical research.

🐒 Up to 25½ in (65 cm)
🐒 Up to 12 in (30 cm)
🏋 Up to 22 lb (10 kg)
👪 Large band
⚡ Near threatened

Afghanistan & India to China

Barbary ape This species lives in multi-male troops of up to 40 animals who maintain a home range. Females mate with all males in the troop. Each male chooses a single infant to help raise, but this may not be his own offspring.

🐒 Up to 27½ in (70 cm)
🐒 None
🏋 Up to 22 lb (10 kg)
👪 Variable
⚡ Vulnerable

N. Morocco, N. Algeria; introd. Gibraltar

SNOW MONKEYS

Japanese macaques live farther north than any other primate (apart from humans). During the cold, snowy winters, they live off tree buds and bark, as well as stores of fat. Troops of 20–30 Japanese macaques are headed by a dominant male. Their social lives tend to be harmonious, with much time spent grooming each other and sharing the care of the young.

🐒 Up to 23½ in (60 cm)
🐒 Up to 6 in (15 cm)
🏋 Up to 22 lb (10 kg)
👪 Variable
⚡ Data deficient

Japan

Making snowballs
Entire troops of Japanese macaques make snowballs, fashioning a small ball in their hands then rolling it along the ground so it grows in size.

FACT FILE

Hamadryas baboon At night, troops of up to 750 of these baboons sleep together on rocky outcrops, splitting into bands of 20–70 animals at dawn to forage for grass, fruit, leaves, flowers, and small vertebrates. These bands are made up of harem families—a single dominant male, with several females, and their juvenile offspring.

- 🐒 Up to 35½ in (90 cm)
- 🐒 Up to 27½ in (70 cm)
- 🏋 Up to 44 lb (20 kg)
- 🐾 Family band, troop
- ⚑ Near threatened
- ☀ 👥 ⬇ ⬇ 🌵 ▬

Ethiopia, Somalia, Eritrea, Sudan, Arabian P.

Chacma baboon This species lives in a variety of habitats, including the most arid environments inhabited by any primate other than humans. One troop of chacma baboons in the Namib Desert was observed to survive without water for 116 days, obtaining all their moisture from figs. A more typical diet includes fruit, leaves, roots, and insects.

- 🐒 Up to 35½ in (90 cm)
- 🐒 Up to 29½ in (75 cm)
- 🏋 Up to 88 lb (40 kg)
- 🐾 Herd, large troop
- ⚑ Least common
- ☀ ⬇ 🌵

S. Africa

Male is grayish brown with shaggy mantle of silver hair on head

Hamadryas baboon (savanna baboon)
Papio hamadryas

Female is olive-brown

Bright red callous pads on rump

Mane of hair on head of male

Gelada
Theropithecus gelada

Heart-shaped patch of hairless skin on chest

Highly opposable thumbs provide dexterity to select the best grass blades, rhizomes, and seeds

Chacma baboon
Papio ursinus

On alert The dominant male in a troop is always on the alert for challenges from bachelor bands.

GRASS–EATING GELADAS

The only surviving species of a genus once widespread throughout Africa, geladas are now restricted to the highlands of northwest Ethiopia. Here, they sleep on rocky cliffs beyond the reach of most predators, and forage in nearby grasslands by day. They survive almost entirely on grass, a degree of specialization that makes the species especially vulnerable as the local human population burgeons and requires ever larger areas of pasture for grazing livestock.

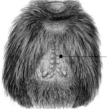

ring of red beading on female indicates she is ready to mate

Bleeding heart Both male and female geladas have bald chests, which alter in color and appearance according to the female's sexual cycle. On other baboons, such sexual advertising is conveyed on the rump. By appearing on the chest, it allows geladas to remain in a heat-conserving squatting position.

Social creatures The basic unit of gelada society comprises one male, several females, and their offspring, but several families form foraging bands of around 70 animals. At times, a number of bands may congregate in vast herds of 600 or more individuals.

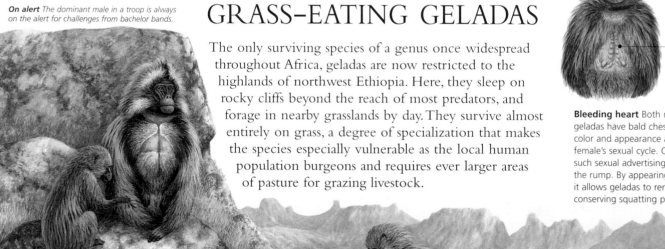

Long, slender, prehensile tail suits arboreal lifestyle

White-cheeked mangabey
Lophocebus albigena

Male is twice as large as female

Brightly colored rump with short tail

Drill
Mandrillus leucophaeus

Bright red and blue face on male, more subdued blue face on female and juvenile

Color of naked rump ranges from blue to purple

Mandrill
Mandrillus sphinx

Agile mangabey
Cercocebus galeritus

FACT FILE

Mandrill The largest of all monkeys, Africa's mandrills are instantly recognizable by their striking red and blue faces. During the day, they come down from their sleeping trees to search for fruit, seeds, insects, and small vertebrates on the rain-forest floor. Troops of up to 250 mandrills are made up of smaller multi-male groups, each with about 20 animals led by a dominant male who fathers most of the young.

Up to 30 in (76 cm)
Up to 3 in (7 cm)
Up to 55 lb (25 kg)
Family band, troop
Vulnerable

Equatorial W. Africa

Showing off
To threaten a rival or predator, a male mandrill will spread its arms wide and yawn, displaying its daunting teeth.

Attractive colors In addition to their vibrant faces, male mandrills have a yellow beard, mauve rump, red penis, and lilac scrotum. The skin colors are most intense on the dominant male—they seem to be linked to testosterone levels and may be advertising his virility.

CONSERVATION WATCH

Threatened drills and mandrills Both drills and mandrills are under threat as logging, farming, and human settlement continue to destroy much of their rain-forest habitat. Both species are also hunted for food, with their large groups and loud calls making them easy to find. Drills are now endangered, their numbers reduced by 80 percent over recent years. Mandrills, considered vulnerable, are expected to suffer a similar decline in the near future.

FACT FILE

Sykes' monkey Among this species, a single adult male dominates troops of 10–40 females and their offspring. The females help raise one another's young.

- Up to 26½ in (67 cm)
- Up to 33½ in (85 cm)
- Up to 26½ lb (12 kg)
- Family band, variable
- Locally common

C., E. & S. Africa

Vervet monkey Although it prefers to live in woodland along rivers, this adaptable monkey is found in many habitats, including human settlements.

- Up to 24½ in (62 cm)
- Up to 28½ in (72 cm)
- Up to 20 lb (9 kg)
- Herd, troop
- Declining

Sub-Saharan Africa

Diana monkey Spending their lives high in the trees, Diana monkeys live in single-male groups of 15 or more individuals. The young gain their arboreal skills through constant play.

- Up to 23½ in (60 cm)
- Up to 31½ in (80 cm)
- Up to 16½ lb (7.5 kg)
- Family band
- Endangered

Coastal W. Africa

Mona monkey Like many other Old World monkeys, this small primate stores fruit and insects in its cheek pouches while it forages.

- Up to 27½ in (70 cm)
- Up to 27½ in (70 cm)
- Up to 15½ lb (7 kg)
- Herd, troop
- Locally common

W. & C. Africa

MIXING SPECIES

Large groups of monkeys sometimes contain more than one species. In East Africa, for example, Sykes' and redtail monkeys form stable associations, traveling and feeding together. Such an arrangement reduces the risk of predation while avoiding the increased competition for food involved in a larger single-species group.

Sykes' monkey (blue monkey)
Cercopithecus mitis

Coat can be blue, reddish brown, or grayish brown

Vervet monkey
Chlorocebus aethiops

Male has turquoise-blue scrotum

Diana monkey
Cercopithecus diana

White stripe across forehead thought to resemble shape of goddess Diana's bow, inspiring this monkey's common name

Long white tufts on ears

Will freeze in position if it senses danger

Mona monkey
Cercopithecus mona

Redtail monkey
Cercopithecus ascanius

Grasping hands for
gripping branches
and collecting fruit

Allen's swamp monkey
Allenopithecus nigroviridis

Lives in swamp forests
and forages on ground
or in shallow water

Chestnut fur
on underside of
tail gave rise to
common name

Webbing between digits
helps with swimming

Patas monkey
Erythrocebus patas

Slender legs of equal
length allow monkey
to run at speeds of up
to 35 mph (55 km/h)

Red-eared monkey
Cercopithecus erythrotis

MONKEY SIGNALS

Sometimes referred to as guenons, the monkeys in the genus *Cercopithecus* all use a range of signals to communicate with other members of their species. While many of these signals are vocal, encompassing barks, grunts, screams, booms, and chirps, others are tactile or visual. Nose-to-nose contact is a form of friendly greeting used by many species. Tail position can indicate an animal's level of confidence. Staring, head-bobbing, and yawning are often used as a threat display to intimidate a potential opponent, while a display of clenched teeth is a fear grimace, employed as a gesture of appeasement.

On the nose *A nose-to-nose greeting between two redtail monkeys is often followed by grooming or play.*

Confident tail *Among vervets, tail position indicates whether the animal is fearful or not. When on all fours, a tail arched over the body conveys great confidence.*

Raising the alarm *To warn the troop of a predator, a vervet uses specific alarm calls: a "chutter" sound for snakes makes the monkeys stand up and check the grass; a double cough for eagles prompts them to look up in the air and take cover; and a barking call for leopards sends them running to the trees.*

⚡ CONSERVATION WATCH

Patas vulnerability This terrestrial monkey lives on the savannas of central Africa. Already vulnerable to rainfall fluctuations in this drought-prone region, more and more patas monkeys are being killed by hunters for their meat and by farmers because they feed on crops. Their habitat is also becoming increasingly fragmented by human activities.

APES

CLASS	Mammalia
ORDER	Primates
FAMILIES	2
GENERA	5
SPECIES	18

Like humans, apes are intelligent and quick to learn, form complex social groups, and spend years on the care of each young. They are divided into two families: the gibbons of Hylobatidae, and the great apes—orangutans, chimpanzees, gorillas—of Hominidae, which includes humans. Although apes and Old World monkeys have a similar nose shape and dental structure and are grouped together as catarrhine primates, they differ in many ways. Apes have skeletons suited to sitting or standing upright. They have no tail, their lowest vertebrae fused to form the coccyx instead. Their spines are shorter, their chests are barrel-shaped, and their shoulders and wrists are very mobile.

GIBBON SONGS

Gibbon pairs often begin the day with duets led by the female and punctuated by the male. While these songs may reinforce the pair bond, they are also territorial and act as spacing calls, helping the gibbons to avoid other pairs during their daytime foraging. Many gibbon species feature throat sacs that amplify their calls. Among the siamangs, the largest gibbons, both males and females possess enormous throat sacs. The sacs produce a booming sound as they are inflated, which is followed by a deafening bark or shriek.

Moving apes While all apes other than humans have arms longer than their legs, orangutans and gibbons are the only ones in which the arms are genuinely elongated compared to their trunk. The orangutan's head and body measure about 5 feet (1.5 m), while their arms have a spread of more than 7 feet (2.2 m). Gibbons move by brachiation, using their arms to swing from one branch to another. Orangutans do not brachiate, but clamber slowly through the trees using some combination of all four limbs. Chimpanzees spend up to three-quarters of their time on the ground, but will brachiate when in trees. Gorillas are largely terrestrial and rarely climb trees.

CLEVER APES

Ape societies are organized in various ways. Monogamous gibbons live in pairs with their offspring, making groups of up to six animals. Orangutans with overlapping ranges form loose associations and meet occasionally, but the male tends to be a solitary forager, and the female usually lives just with her single young. Chimpanzee communities involve 40–80 individuals, but these are rarely together at once and tend to forage in smaller groups. Gorillas live in harems, with one dominant male, possibly one or two lower-ranking adult males, several females, and their young.

The gibbons and the great apes evolved into distinct families at least 20 million years ago. Chimpanzees are believed to be the closest relatives

Parenthood All infant apes stay dependent on their parents for a long time. Female gorillas usually give birth to a single young, who takes up to 3 years to be weaned. Because more than a third of all infant gorillas die before this, most females take 6–8 years to produce a surviving offspring.

of humans, sharing a common ancestor until about 6 million years ago. The great apes appear to work through problems much as humans do. Chimpanzees and orangutans are known to fashion tools in the wild, while in research centers all the great apes have been taught to use implements. By recognizing themselves in mirrors, great apes show a concept of self, and some have been taught to recognize and use symbols such as sign language.

A flexible grip
The orangutan's strong hands and feet are hook-like, the thumb and big toe are short, and the other digits are long.

CONSERVATION WATCH

Extensive logging and clearing of tropical forest have placed most apes in jeopardy. The bushmeat trade has also taken a heavy toll. Of the 18 species of apes, 100% are listed on the IUCN Red List, as follows:

3	Critically endangered
7	Endangered
3	Vulnerable
4	Near threatened
1	Data deficient

Hanging around
Although it does hang under branches, the orangutan uses all its limbs to move through the trees.

Energy conservation
Long arms allow the orangutan to reach fruit with minimum exertion.

Kloss's gibbon
Hylobates klossii

White face rings,
hands, and feet
with reddish or
black coat

Lar gibbon
Hylobates lar

Throat sac bigger
than head

Siamang
Hylobates syndactylus

Elongated arm
with hook-like,
grasping hand

Hoolock
Hylobates hoolock

Males are black;
adult females are
golden or buff,
sometimes with
black patches

Black gibbon
Hylobates concolor

FACT FILE

Kloss's gibbon To move through the forest, the Kloss's gibbon brachiates and can hurl itself over 30 feet (10 m) between trees. It feeds mostly on fruit, especially sugar-rich figs, but will also eat flowers and insects.

- 🐾 Up to 25½ in (65 cm)
- 🦷 None
- ⚖ Up to 17½ lb (8 kg)
- 👫 Pair
- ⚡ Vulnerable
- 🏛 ☀

Mentawai I. (Indonesia)

Hoolock Found farther north and east than any other gibbon, this large species avoids competition with other primates by preferring especially ripe fruit. Its numbers are now decreasing, however, as hunting and habitat fragmentation take their toll.

- 🐾 Up to 25½ in (65 cm)
- 🦷 None
- ⚖ Up to 17½ lb (8 kg)
- 👫 Pair
- ⚡ Endangered
- 🏛 ☀

N.E. India, Bangladesh, S.W. China, Myanmar

Lar gibbon To find the ripe fruit and new leaves and buds that make up its entire diet, this gibbon swings to the edge of the tree canopy, where these foods are most abundant.

- 🐾 Up to 25½ in (65 cm)
- 🦷 None
- ⚖ Up to 17½ lb (8 kg)
- 👫 Pair
- ⚡ Near threatened
- 🏛 ☀

S. China, Myanmar, Thailand, Malaya, Sumatra

Black gibbon This gibbon is born with a golden or buff coat, which turns black at about 6 months of age. Males remain black, but when females mature they turn golden or buff again, sometimes retaining patches of black.

- 🐾 Up to 25½ in (65 cm)
- 🦷 None
- ⚖ Up to 17½ lb (8 kg)
- 👫 Pair
- ⚡ Endangered
- 🏛 ☀

S. China, N. Vietnam

Siamang The largest gibbon, the siamang spends 5 hours a day eating, often hanging by one arm as it feasts. While it consumes a lot of fruit and some insects and small vertebrates, up to half of its diet is made up of leaves.

- 🐾 Up to 35½ in (90 cm)
- 🦷 None
- ⚖ Up to 28½ lb (13 kg)
- 👫 Pair
- ⚡ Near threatened
- 🏛 ☀

Malaya, Sumatra

FACT FILE

Orangutan Asia's only great apes, orangutans are also the world's largest arboreal mammals. Most hardly ever descend to the forest floor, moving through the forest by swinging a tree back and forth until they can grasp the next one. Every night, an orangutan constructs an elaborate nest in the crown of a tree and covers itself with vegetation to sleep.

- 🐾 Up to 5 ft (1.5 m)
- 🦅 None
- 🏋 Up to 200 lb (90 kg)
- 👣 Solitary, pair
- ⚡ Endangered
- 🏛 ☀

Borneo, Sumatra

Western gorilla The largest of all primates, male gorillas grow until they are about 12 years old, developing a saddle of silvery-white hair on the back, hence the term "silverback" for a mature male. Gorillas spend most of their time on the ground, covering substantial distances on all fours.

- 🐾 Up to 6 ft (1.8 m)
- 🦅 None
- 🏋 Up to 400 lb (180 kg)
- 👣 Variable
- ⚡ Endangered
- 🏛

C. Africa

TOOL TIME

The ingenuity and manual dexterity of chimpanzees are demonstrated by their tool use. They strip twigs and grass stems to make wands for probing ant and termite nests. Specially selected stones are used to open nuts and hard-shelled fruit. During displays of strength or hunting, some chimps use sticks and rocks as missiles. Tool use is a socially learned tradition and varies from one chimp population to another.

- 🐾 Up to 3 ft (93 cm)
- 🦅 None
- 🏋 Up to 110 lb (50 kg)
- 👣 Large troop, herd
- ⚡ Endangered
- 🏛 ☀

C. & W. Africa

Chimpanzee
Pan troglodytes

Arms longer than legs, with fingers longer than those of humans

Powerful grip

Flexible arms and legs can swing in most directions

Orangutan
Pongo pygmaeus

Male has large cheek pads and throat pouch with beard and mustache

Western gorilla
Gorilla gorilla

Walks on soles of feet and knuckles of hands

Bonobo
Pan paniscus

Slimmer body and more slender limbs than those of common chimpanzee

Extinction Miss Waldron's red colobus monkey (*Procolobus badius waldroni*), once found in Ghana and Côte d'Ivoire, was the only primate to be documented as extinct during the 20th century. The extinction appears to have been caused by hunting for the bushmeat trade, exacerbated by logging operations that gave access to formerly remote forests. Many living primate species continue to face similar threats. While the live-animal trade in endangered species has been outlawed, some primates are still captured and sold illegally as pets or for medical research, and many are killed as bushmeat.

CONSERVING PRIMATES

According to Conservation International, 195 primate species and subspecies—about a third of all primate types—are at risk of extinction within the next few decades. About half of all colobus monkeys and gibbons are threatened, while in the family Hominidae, humans are the only secure species, with all of the great apes considered endangered. The trade in live animals as pets or for biomedical research has contributed to the declining numbers, as has the hunting of primates as food or pests. The greatest threat, however, is from habitat destruction through logging, land clearing, and collection of wood for fuel. Because primates reproduce slowly, their populations take a long time to recover. Almost all are tropical animals and live in poorer countries, so conservation efforts are complicated by the pressing needs of the growing human population.

Habitat destruction When an area of rain forest is cut down, several primate species can be affected at once and the damage is permanent. Rain-forest soil is thin and low in nutrients, but it supports lush plant growth because the nutrients are efficiently recycled by the ecosystem. Once the tree cover is lost, the soil is washed away by rain and the area soon becomes barren.

Orangutan rescue When primates being kept illegally as pets are rescued, they do not have the skills to survive in the wild. At the Sepilok Orangutan Rehabilitation Centre, on the island of Borneo, rescued orangutans are trained to fend for themselves before being released back into the forest. More than 100 orangutans have joined Sepilok's wild population after rehabilitation.

3. Outward bound school
The Centre's staff gradually reduce the amount of food and emotional support they offer, encouraging the orangutans to fend for themselves.

Asian primates About 45 percent of endangered primates are found in Asia, particularly in Indonesia (35 endangered primates), China, India, and Vietnam (15 each). This photograph shows Delacour's langur (*Trachypithecus delacouri*), one of the Vietnamese species at risk.

1. Quarantine All new arrivals are kept in quarantine for 3–6 months to prevent them transmitting any diseases to the other orangutans at the Centre.

2. Nursery Wildlife rangers train young orangutans (up to 3 years of age) in basic survival skills, from climbing trees to building sleeping nests and finding fruit and other food in the forest.

4. Survival training When an orangutan starts showing signs of independence, even less food is offered. Eventually, most rescued animals join Sepilok's wild orangutan population.

CARNIVORES

CLASS	Mammalia
ORDER	Carnivora
FAMILIES	11
GENERA	131
SPECIES	278

From massive polar bears to little weasels, speedy cheetahs to lumbering elephant seals, pack-living wolves to solitary tigers, members of the order Carnivora display remarkable diversity. Although they are commonly referred to as carnivores, a term also used for any meat-eating animal, some of them eat meat only rarely, if at all. The one thing members of Carnivora have in common is a predatory ancestor with four carnassial teeth—scissor-like molars that can shear through meat. Most carnivores retain the carnassial teeth, which sets them apart from other meat-eating mammals. In mainly insectivorous or herbivorous carnivores, the carnassial teeth have been modified for grinding.

Sweet tooth Originally classified as a primate, the kinkajou is a nocturnal, tree-dwelling carnivore. A prehensile tail allows it to hang upside down as it feeds on fruit or uses its long, narrow tongue to gather nectar or honey. It sometimes supplements this sweet diet with insect prey.

PRIME HUNTERS

As the dominant land predators on all continents except Antarctica, carnivores are built for hunting. They rely on their acute senses of sight, hearing, and smell to help them detect prey. The complex ear region, which often features more than one inner chamber, increases sensitivity to the frequencies that are produced by their prey species.

Intelligence, agility, and speed help carnivores stalk, chase, and catch their prey efficiently. Even apparently cumbersome species such as bears are capable of impressive sprints, while the cheetah is the fastest land animal in the world. All carnivores have fused bones in the forefeet, a feature that helps absorb the shock of running. A reduced collarbone increases the mobility of the shoulder muscles, allowing a longer stride and greater speed.

To kill their prey, carnivores generally use their strong jaws and sharp teeth. Weasels smash the prey's skull by biting into the back of its head. Cats strike small prey at the neck to snap the spinal cord, while dogs dislocate the neck by violently shaking the animal in their jaws.

Prowling for meat Like most animals that belong to the order Carnivora, the jaguar is a predator and usually eats meat it has caught itself. A solitary hunter, it relies on stealth and keen senses as it stalks prey. The large ears capture sound waves, while the large eyes provide excellent binocular vision by day and night.

Vegetarian carnivore While the giant panda may eat small mammals, fish, and insects if they are available, bamboo makes up more than 99 percent of its diet. A plentiful, year-round food source, bamboo is low in nutrition, so giant pandas must spend 10–12 hours a day feeding in order to satisfy their energy requirements.

Adaptable animals Carnivores are found in almost all of Earth's habitats. Polar bears, arctic foxes, and these gray wolves survive in the icy landscape of the Arctic; otters and seals spend most of their time in the water; big cats prowl both jungles and savanna; and jackals live in deserts.

Cooperative hunting allows wolves, lions, and other pack animals to tackle much larger prey such as buffalo and wildebeest.

Almost all the larger meat-eating carnivores hunt vertebrates. Smaller carnivores mostly eat invertebrates, which are easier to catch but can rarely sustain a large animal. Various carnivores concentrate on termites, worms, fish, and crustaceans, and some are largely vegetarian, with a preference for berries, other fruit, nuts, seeds, nectar, or bamboo, but all tend to be opportunistic feeders and will take advantage of any easy meal that presents itself.

About 50 million years ago, the order Carnivora split into two lineages. The cat-like carnivores include civets (family Viverridae), cats (Felidae), hyenas (Hyaenidae), and mongooses (Herpestidae). Dog-like carnivores include dogs (Canidae), bears (Ursidae), raccoons (Procyonidae), weasels (Mustelidae), and seals (Otariidae and Phocidae). Until recent years, seals were often treated as a separate order known as Pinnipedia, but genetic studies indicate that they share a common ancestry with the other carnivores.

Group living For many smaller carnivores, living in a group helps to reduce the risk of predation. In suricate troops, which are made up of two or three family units, members take turns to watch for danger.

Designed to hunt The skeleton of a cat displays many of the anatomical features that have made carnivores such effective predators. A flexible spine, long limbs, fused wrist bones, and reduced collarbone all contribute to the cat's speed and agility.

INTRODUCING CARNIVORES

The exceptional hunting abilities of carnivores have inspired many misguided attempts to use them for pest control in regions where they are not native. The consequences of such introductions have usually been disastrous. The native fauna of New Zealand is under threat from stoats (right), which were introduced in the 1880s to take care of a rabbit problem. In the Caribbean and Hawaii, the small Indian mongooses (*Herpestes javanicus*) imported to control rodents and snakes ended up spreading rabies instead. On a number of the world's far-flung islands, feral cats, which were supposed to get rid of rats, preferred the easier prey of flightless birds and destroyed their populations.

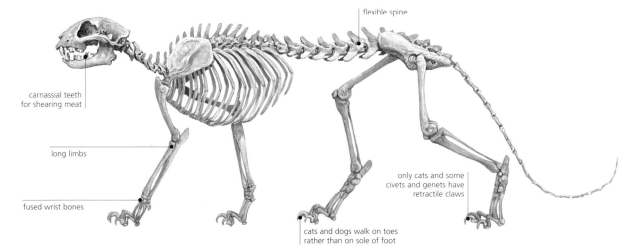

flexible spine

carnassial teeth for shearing meat

long limbs

fused wrist bones

only cats and some civets and genets have retractile claws

cats and dogs walk on toes rather than on sole of foot

THE DOG FAMILY

CLASS	Mammalia
ORDER	Carnivora
FAMILY	Canidae
GENERA	14
SPECIES	34

Perhaps no creatures have such an ambivalent relationship with humans as the dogs, wolves, coyotes, jackals, and foxes that make up the carnivore family Canidae. Domesticated at least 14,000 years ago, dogs were the first animals to enter a partnership with humans and have been used extensively for hunting, guarding, warmth, and companionship. At the same time, wild canids have been relentlessly persecuted, blamed for the loss of livestock and the spread of rabies and hunted for sport and fashion. While some species such as red foxes and coyotes have adapted and thrived in the midst of urban development, others such as red wolves are on the verge of extinction.

A wide distribution Originating in North America 34–55 million years ago, wild canids now occur on every continent except Antarctica, but are absent from some islands, including Madagascar, Hawaii, the Philippines, Borneo, and New Zealand. They were introduced to New Guinea and Australia in prehistoric times. The domestic dog is now found worldwide.

GRASSLAND CARNIVORES

Most canids live in open grasslands, where they capture their prey either by sudden pouncing or by extended pursuit. With their slender build, muscular, deep-chested bodies, and long, sturdy legs, they are capable of great endurance. In addition to the fused foot bones common to other carnivores, canid forelimb bones are locked to prevent them rotating as they run. A pointed muzzle houses the large scent organs that allow canids to track prey over long distances, while large, erect ears contribute to their acute hearing.

Opportunistic and adaptable, canids prefer to eat freshly killed meat but will take advantage of whatever food is locally available and may eat fish, carrion, berries, and human garbage. Their social organization is similarly flexible, varying between and within species and often reflecting their diet. Smaller species such as jackals and foxes mostly eat small animals and often live alone or in pairs. Larger species such as gray wolves and African wild dogs usually live and hunt in hierarchical social groups, cooperating to bring down prey larger than themselves. Canids that hunt especially large animals tend to live in the largest groups, while in areas where smaller prey are abundant, some gray wolves choose to live in pairs.

Group living confers benefits other than hunting advantages, however, and some canids live communally but hunt alone. These animals work together to care for the pack's young and defend their territory from rival packs.

Cooperative hunters Gray wolves usually live in family units of 5–12 dogs dominated by an alpha pair. The pack cooperates to snare larger prey such as deer. They most often target a young, old, or weak herd member, pursuing it until it is exhausted.

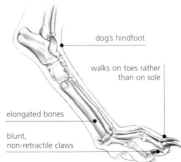

dog's hindfoot

walks on toes rather than on sole

elongated bones

blunt, non-retractile claws

Walking on tiptoes Members of the dog family have elongated feet and move by digitigrade locomotion: walking on just the toes rather than on the entire sole of the foot. As the claws cannot be retracted, they become blunt from wear. In a dog's forefeet, fused bones at the wrists help to absorb the impact of running.

FAMILY LIFE

Unusually among mammals, a lifelong monogamous pair bond forms the basis of the jackal social unit. Both parents take an active role in caring for the young, who are nursed for about 8 weeks and then fed regurgitated food for several weeks more. In many jackal families, one or two young stay with the parents for a year after reaching sexual maturity and help to raise the next litter.

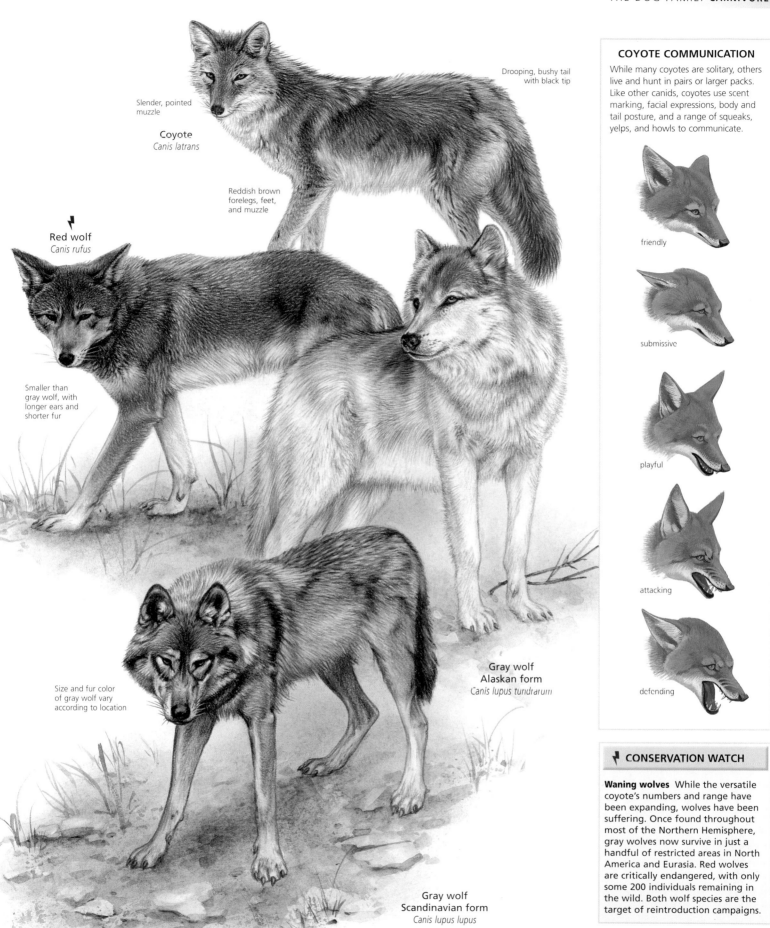

Slender, pointed muzzle

Coyote
Canis latrans

Drooping, bushy tail with black tip

Reddish brown forelegs, feet, and muzzle

Red wolf
Canis rufus

Smaller than gray wolf, with longer ears and shorter fur

Gray wolf
Alaskan form
Canis lupus tundrarum

Size and fur color of gray wolf vary according to location

Gray wolf
Scandinavian form
Canis lupus lupus

COYOTE COMMUNICATION

While many coyotes are solitary, others live and hunt in pairs or larger packs. Like other canids, coyotes use scent marking, facial expressions, body and tail posture, and a range of squeaks, yelps, and howls to communicate.

friendly

submissive

playful

attacking

defending

⚡ CONSERVATION WATCH

Waning wolves While the versatile coyote's numbers and range have been expanding, wolves have been suffering. Once found throughout most of the Northern Hemisphere, gray wolves now survive in just a handful of restricted areas in North America and Eurasia. Red wolves are critically endangered, with only some 200 individuals remaining in the wild. Both wolf species are the target of reintroduction campaigns.

FACT FILE

Side-striped jackal Rather than pursuing prey, this nocturnal jackal will quickly pounce on insects, mice, and birds, or scavenge the kills of other predators. Each family has a particular yipping call recognized only by its own members.

- Up to 32 in (80 cm)
- Up to 16 in (40 cm)
- Up to 26½ lb (12 kg)
- Pair
- Uncommon

C. & S. Africa

Golden jackal The most widely distributed jackal, this species has lived on the edge of human settlements since ancient times, when it featured prominently in Egyptian mythology.

- Up to 39½ in (100 cm)
- Up to 12 in (30 cm)
- Up to 33 lb (15 kg)
- Pair
- Common

N. Africa, S.E. Europe to Thailand, Sri Lanka

Black-backed jackal Near villages, this jackal is nocturnal, but elsewhere it may be active day or night. About half of its diet consists of insects, with small mammals and fruit making up the rest. Males and females form long-term pairs and share the care of their pups.

- Up to 35½ in (90 cm)
- Up to 16 in (40 cm)
- Up to 26½ lb (12 kg)
- Pair
- Locally common

E. & S. Africa

Ethiopian wolf This species is found only in a dozen isolated pockets in Ethiopia. With fewer than 500 adults remaining in the wild, it is one of the world's most endangered mammals.

- Up to 39½ in (100 cm)
- Up to 12 in (30 cm)
- Up to 42 lb (19 kg)
- Solitary, small group
- Critically endangered

Highlands of Ethiopia

Dingo Probably brought to Australia by Asian traders at least 3,500 years ago, the dingo became the dominant predator in many areas, cooperatively hunting large marsupials such as kangaroos and wallabies.

- Up to 39½ in (100 cm)
- Up to 14 in (36 cm)
- Up to 53 lb (24 kg)
- Solitary, small group
- Locally common

Mainland Australia

Side-striped jackal
Canis adustus

Shorter legs and ears than other jackals, with white and black side stripe on drab coat

Color can vary from brown-tipped yellow in rainy season to pale gold in dry season

Golden jackal
Canis aureus

Black fur runs from back of neck to tail

Ethiopian wolf (Simien jackal)
Canis simensis

Long, pointed muzzle for catching small mammals

Black-backed jackal
Canis mesomelas

Dingo
Canis lupus dingo

Dhole
Cuon alpinus

Short, broad muzzle suits almost exclusive diet of large vertebrate prey

Arctic fox winter coat
Alopex lagopus

Paws covered in dense fur during winter

Arctic fox summer coat
Alopex lagopus

Teeth include up to eight extra molars for grinding up termites, dung beetles, and other insects

Bat-eared fox
Otocyon megalotis

Cape wild dog (African wild dog, African hunting dog)
Lycaon pictus

Each Cape wild dog has a unique coat pattern

Molts twice a year as it grows a thick winter coat followed by a lighter summer coat

Raccoon dog
Nyctereutes procyonoides

FACT FILE

Arctic fox For winter, this fox grows a white coat to match its snowy habitat and feeds on marine mammals, sea birds, fish, and crustaceans, as well as on stored food. As summer approaches, its coat turns brown or black to blend in with the tundra vegetation.

- Up to 27½ in (70 cm)
- Up to 16 in (40 cm)
- Up to 20 lb (9 kg)
- Solitary
- Common

N. North America, N. Eurasia, Iceland, Greenland

Cape wild dog This canid is entirely carnivorous. After a kill, the healthy adult dogs will regurgitate food for any young, sick, or wounded pack members.

- Up to 35½ in (90 cm)
- Up to 16 in (40 cm)
- Up to 79½ lb (36 kg)
- Solitary, small group
- Endangered

E. & S. Africa

UNUSUAL CANID

The raccoon dog is the only canid to enter a dormant state in winter. While most other canids live in open grasslands, the raccoon dog prefers the dense undergrowth of forests. Originally from East Asia, it was introduced to Europe by the fur trade where it is now considered a pest.

Raccoon resemblance
The raccoon dog's black face mask, thick body, bushy tail, and ability to climb trees give it a great resemblance to the raccoon.

CONSERVATION WATCH

Of the 34 species of canids, 53% are listed on the IUCN Red List, as follows:

- 1 Extinct
- 2 Critically endangered
- 1 Endangered
- 2 Vulnerable
- 1 Near threatened
- 2 Conservation dependent
- 9 Data deficient

FACT FILE

Kit fox Found in arid regions, the kit fox avoids the heat of the day by resting in its underground den, coming out at night to hunt rabbits and kangaroo rats. This fox relies on the moisture in its prey for fluids and therefore kills more animals than are needed to meet its energy requirements alone.

🐾 Up to 20½ in (52 cm)
🐾 Up to 12½ in (32 cm)
🏋 Up to 6 lb (2.7 kg)
♟ Solitary
⚑ Conserv. dependent

S.W. USA & N. Mexico

THE SUCCESSFUL RED FOX

One of the most widely distributed species in the world, the red fox's versatile feeding habits have allowed it to thrive in forest, prairie, farmland, and suburban areas. Hunted for sport and bred for fur, this canid has been blamed for killing poultry and spreading rabies. Where it has been introduced, as in Australia, the red fox poses a major threat to native fauna.

🐾 Up to 19½ in (50 cm)
🐾 Up to 13 in (33 cm)
🏋 Up to 13 lb (6 kg)
♟ Solitary, pair
⚑ Common

🌳 🔺 🌿 🌵 🏞

North America, Europe, N. & C. Asia, N. Africa, Arabia; introd. Australia

Fox feast
Red foxes will eat almost anything, from rodents and rabbits to fruit and garbage.

⚡ CONSERVATION WATCH

Swift reintroduction Once ranging throughout the North American prairies, the swift fox lost habitat to agriculture and urbanization and was also hunted and poisoned. By 1978, it had disappeared from Canada, but reintroduction programs have established small populations in Alberta and Saskatchewan and the species has moved from endangered to lower risk status.

Tibetan fox
Vulpes ferrilata

Broad ears listen for rustling rodents

Corsac fox
Vulpes corsac

Blanford's fox
Vulpes cana

Displays cat-like movements

Kit fox
Vulpes macrotis

Pale fox
Vulpes pallida

Red fox
North American form
Vulpes vulpes fulva

Short reddish summer coat replaced by longer, thicker gray coat for winter

Swift fox
Vulpes velox

Bengal fox
Vulpes bengalensis

Red fox
Central European form
Vulpes vulpes crucigera

Gray fox
Urocyon cinereoargenteus

Strong, hooked claws
used for climbing trees

Black-tipped tail

Mane of erect
black hairs

Maned wolf
Chrysocyon brachyurus

Long legs help maned
wolf see above tall
grass of pampas

Crab-eating fox
(common zorro)
Cerdocyon thous

Argentine gray fox
Pseudalopex griseus

Small-eared zorro
Atelocynus microtis

Bush dog
Speothos venaticus

Webbed feet for
swimming after
aquatic prey

Culpeo fox
Pseudalopex culpaeus

Coat colors most
vivid in northern
part of range

Pampas fox
Pseudalopex gymnocercus

FACT FILE

Crab-eating fox An opportunistic feeder, this fox often eats crabs and other crustaceans during the wet season, but shifts to insects in the dry season. Its diet also features fruit, turtle eggs, small mammals, birds, reptiles, amphibians, fish, and carrion.

🐾 Up to 30 in (76 cm)
🦴 Up to 13 in (33 cm)
⚖ Up to 17½ lb (7.9 kg)
👫 Pair
🌡 Common
🌴🌱🌊

Colombia to Argentina except Amazon basin

Maned wolf This omnivorous canid eats large amounts of bananas, guavas, and other fruit as well as animals such as armadillos, rabbits, rodents, snails, and birds. It hunts at night in a fox-like manner, suddenly pouncing on its prey.

🐾 Up to 39½ in (100 cm)
🦴 Up to 16 in (40 cm)
⚖ Up to 53 lb (24 kg)
👫 Solitary, pair
🌡 Near threatened
🌴🌱🌊

Brazil to Paraguay & Argentina

Argentine gray fox This nocturnal fox usually lives in small groups made up of a mating pair, their offspring, and sometimes a second adult female who helps to raise the young. The group maintains a year-round territory.

🐾 Up to 26 in (66 cm)
🦴 Up to 16½ in (42 cm)
⚖ Up to 12 lb (5.4 kg)
👫 Solitary, pair
🌡 Locally common
🌱🌊

Chile & Argentina

Bush dog With its squat stature and short face, the bush dog looks less like a dog than any other canid. Packs of up to 10 animals forage together in forest undergrowth, keeping in touch via high-pitched peeps and whines.

🐾 Up to 29½ in (75 cm)
🦴 Up to 5 in (13 cm)
⚖ Up to 15½ lb (7 kg)
👫 Solitary to large group
🌡 Vulnerable
🏛🌴🌊

W. Panama to Paraguay & N. Argentina

Pampas fox When threatened by humans, the pampas fox freezes and may remain motionless if handled. Pairs live together only during the mating season and share the care of the young.

🐾 Up to 28½ in (72 cm)
🦴 Up to 15 in (38 cm)
⚖ Up to 17½ lb (7.9 kg)
👫 Solitary, pair
🌡 Locally common

E. Bolivia & S. Brazil to N. Argentina

THE BEAR FAMILY

CLASS	Mammalia
ORDER	Carnivora
FAMILY	Ursidae
GENERA	6
SPECIES	9

In spite of their fearsome reputation, bears tend to be the most herbivorous of the carnivores. Only one species, the polar bear, is primarily a meat-eater. Berries, nuts, and tubers make up the bulk of the American black bear's diet; the sloth bear feeds mostly on insects; and the giant panda eats almost nothing but bamboo. The first bear species emerged from the canid family 25–20 million years ago in Eurasia. About the size of a raccoon, these early creatures had a long tail and the shearing carnassial teeth common to most members of Carnivora. Over time, most bears became much bigger, their tails shortened, and their carnassials were flattened for grinding vegetable matter.

Northern diversity Most abundant in the Northern Hemisphere, bears live in Europe, Asia, and North and South America. The brown bear was also found in North Africa until the 1800s. Today, all but two bear species are in danger, victims of habitat loss and overhunting.

Fish feeder In the northwest coastal regions of North America, brown bears will wait at waterfalls to catch spawning salmon as they swim upstream. This annual glut of fish provides important protein before winter begins.

Full size Grizzly bears (*Ursus arctos horribilis*) will attempt to intimidate a rival or foe by rearing up on their hindfeet and even walking bipedally for a short distance. The upright stance increases their already impressive size. They may also growl and display their long canine teeth.

STRENGTH AND BULK

Although the red panda may weigh only about 6 pounds (3 kg), most bears classified in the Ursidae family are substantial animals, with the polar bear and brown bear vying for the title of the largest terrestrial carnivore. As they often spend more of their time foraging than hunting, bears are built for strength rather than speed, with a stocky, muscular body, thick legs, and a massive skull. An enlarged snout reflects their keen sense of smell. Vision and sound are less important, and their eyes and ears are relatively small.

Bears are found in the tropics, but it is in the cold northern lands that they are most numerous. Here, their great size allows them to put on fat deposits through spring and summer when food is abundant. When the weather cools, the bears retreat to a den or cave and enter a long sleep that can last half the year. During this dormant period, they live entirely on their body fat; they do not eat, urinate, or defecate,

and their heart and respiration rates drop. Unlike in true hibernation, however, their body temperature hardly falls. Remarkably, females give birth to young during the winter dormancy, maximizing the cubs' chance to grow and accumulate fat deposits before the next winter.

Most bears are solitary, although cubs often stay with the mother for 2–3 years. Rival males can be aggressive in the breeding season, with fights resulting in injury or even death.

DELIBERATE MOVEMENT

Bears usually move slowly and deliberately on all fours, but are capable of great bursts of speed when pursuing prey. They walk with a plantigrade gait, placing the entire sole on the ground. This not only supports their great bulk, but also allows them to stand up on their hindfeet. While mainly terrestrial, most bears are also agile climbers.

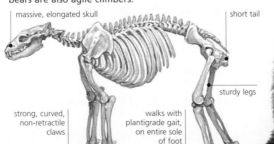

massive, elongated skull

short tail

strong, curved, non-retractile claws

walks with plantigrade gait, on entire sole of foot

sturdy legs

Himalayan brown bear
Ursus arctos isabellinus

Brown bear's coat can be brown, blonde, silver-tipped, or nearly black

Pronounced shoulder hump

American black bear
Ursus americanus

Black bear's coat can be black or brown

European brown bear
Ursus arctos arctos

Massive bulk helps polar bear withstand cold and store fat for times of scarcity

Polar bear
Ursus maritimus

Largest species of bear

Large, paddle-like paws for swimming

Kodiak bear
Ursus arctos middendorffi

Largest of all brown bear subspecies

Males twice as large as females

Asiatic black bear
Ursus thibetanus

FACT FILE

Brown bear This species once lived throughout Eurasia and North America and south to North Africa and Mexico. Its subspecies include the European brown bear (*Ursus arctos arctos*), the North American brown bear or grizzly (*U. a. horribilis*), the Kodiak bear (*U. a. middendorffi*), and the Himalayan brown bear (*U. a. isabellinus*).

- Up to 9 ft (2.8 m)
- Up to 8½ in (21 cm)
- Up to 1,320 lb (600 kg)
- Solitary
- Locally common

Pockets in N.W. North America, Wyoming, W. & N. Europe, Himalayas, Japan

American black bear Easily the most common bear, this species has adapted to a range of habitats and varies its omnivorous diet with the season.

- Up to 7 ft (2.1 m)
- Up to 7 in (18 cm)
- Up to 530 lb (240 kg)
- Solitary
- Locally common

Forested North America, nearby islands

Asiatic black bear This primarily herbivorous species readily climbs trees to gather fruit and nuts. To startle predators such as tigers, it will stand up and display its white chest mark.

- Up to 6 ft (1.9 m)
- Up to 4 in (10 cm)
- Up to 375 lb (170 kg)
- Solitary
- Vulnerable

Afghanistan & Pakistan to China, Korea & Japan

BEAR PAWS

The feet of bears reflect their varied habitats and diet. American black bears have hook-like claws for climbing trees and digging up roots. To grasp bamboo, giant pandas have an L-shaped pad, part of which covers a modified wrist bone that acts as a sixth digit.

American black bear   Giant panda

forefoot   hindfoot   forefoot   hindfoot

BAMBOO BEAR

As China's human population has burgeoned, most of the giant panda's habitat has been destroyed. Only about 1,000 pandas remain in the wild, restricted to isolated mountain pockets of bamboo forest. Widely recognized as a symbol of conservation, the giant panda is still poached for its skin.

⚡ CONSERVATION WATCH

Of the nine species of bears, seven are listed on the IUCN Red List, as follows:

- 2 Endangered
- 3 Vulnerable
- 1 Conservation dependent
- 1 Data deficient

Giant panda
Ailuropoda melanoleuca

Distinctive black and white markings make the giant panda one of the most widely recognized of all animal species

Spectacled bear
Tremarctos ornatus

Only bear species in South America

Giant panda's front paws have "pseudo-thumb," an extra opposable digit for grasping bamboo

Sloth bear
Melursus ursinus

Mobile snout with long tongue for capturing termites and ants

Shaggy coat may insulate from heat in tropical environment

Long tongue licks up larvae, insects, and honey

Smallest bear apart from red panda

Sun bear
Helarctos malayanus

Long, curved claws help this highly arboreal bear to climb trees

Red panda
Ailurus fulgens

Coat made up of long, coarse hairs and dense undercoat to insulate against the cold weather of its high-altitude habitat

Only bear with a long tail

A YEAR AS A POLAR BEAR

Adapted to the harsh climate of the Arctic, the polar bear lives near the ice-covered water that contains its main prey, the ringed seal. Unlike other bears in cold environments, this semi-aquatic carnivore tends to remain active through winter, but can enter a dormant state and live off its fat deposits at any time of the year if food becomes scarce. Its solitary existence is interrupted only during the breeding season or when adult males fast together in groups known as sloths.

Cub protection Male polar bears sometimes kill cubs, presumably to free up the female for breeding. A mother often stands guard over her young and will attack a much larger male to protect them.

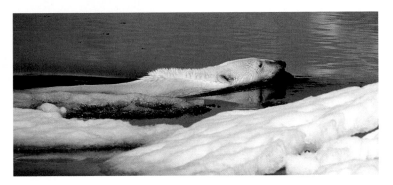

Seal hunter Polar bears will wait at a seal's breathing hole for hours, ready to pounce on the prey as it surfaces. They feed almost exclusively on seals and other marine mammals.

Expert swimmer Using its enormous forepaws as paddles, the polar bear can swim for several hours. On land, it is surprisingly agile and can reach speeds of 25 miles per hour (40 km/h). Dense fur and a layer of fat beneath the skin insulate against the cold.

April–July feeding Polar bears spend summer preying on the abundant and unwary pups of ringed seals. When the sea ice melts in late July, the bears come ashore and fast until it freezes once more.

April–May mating Female polar bears spend so long raising their young that they are available for mating only once every 3 years. This leads to intense competition among males for mates.

February–April emergence When the cubs are large enough to venture onto the sea ice, the mother leads them out of the den. Cubs stay with their mother for about 2½ years, learning the hunting skills that are crucial to their survival.

November–January birth While other polar bears remain active through winter, pregnant females retreat to a snow den, where they give birth to their young. Most litters contain two cubs, who are nursed until around late March.

MUSTELIDS

CLASS	Mammalia
ORDER	Carnivora
FAMILY	Mustelidae
GENERA	25
SPECIES	65

As a group, the weasels, otters, skunks, and badgers of the family Mustelidae are the most successful and diverse carnivores, with many more species than any other family. Mustelids are found in almost every type of habitat, including forests, deserts, tundra, and fresh and salt water, and may be arboreal, terrestrial, burrowing, semiaquatic, or fully aquatic. While a few species, such as sea otters and wolverines, can weigh more than 55 pounds (25 kg), most members of the family are medium-sized, with the smallest, the least weasel, weighing as little as 1 ounce (30 g). Highly carnivorous, mustelids are voracious hunters and will often tackle prey much larger than themselves.

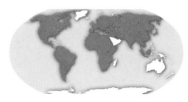

Widespread family Absent only from Australia and Antarctica, mustelids are found throughout Europe, Asia, Africa, and the Americas. Despite their prevalence, only a small number have been well studied. Mustelids have been introduced in many places, either accidentally when they have escaped from fur farms or deliberately to control rodents and rabbits.

Scented defense Almost all mustelids possess scent glands near the anus that produce musk, a foul-smelling liquid used to mark territory. In skunks, this feature has developed into a defense system, with a spray of noxious musk deterring all but the most determined predators.

RELENTLESS HUNTERS

With an elongated body and short legs, mustelids can pursue rodents and rabbits down burrows. Weasels tend to be slender and lithe, with a flexible spine that allows them to scamper and leap. Badgers, on the other hand, have squat bodies and shuffle along with a rolling gait. Many mustelids are good swimmers and climbers and readily exploit aquatic and tree-dwelling prey as well as terrestrial species.

The mustelid head has a low, flat skull and short face with small ears and eyes. Smell is usually the most important of the senses and is used to locate and track prey and for communication among members of a species, with territories marked

Leaping weasel Agile and remarkably strong, weasels can run carrying up to half their weight in food. The smallest of all mustelids, the least weasel will relentlessly pursue its prey of mice and voles through thick grass or under snow.

by scent. Most mustelids have long, curved, non-retractile claws that they use for digging. Aquatic and semiaquatic species often have webbing between the toes to help with swimming.

Mustelids have a double coat, with a layer of soft, dense underfur interspersed with longer guard hairs. This warm, water-repellent coat enables mustelids to hunt in water and stay active throughout cold winters, but it has also made many species the target of the fur trade.

A SOLITARY LIFE

Most mustelids tend to be fiercely solitary, coming together only during the breeding season. Mating is often violent and forced on the female by the male. Copulation can last for up to 2 hours and is the trigger for the female's ovulation, a process that almost guarantees fertilization. Once an egg is fertilized, it may remain in a dormant state for weeks or even months, becoming implanted in the uterus only when conditions are favorable. For example, the pine marten (pictured) mates in winter, but implantation does not occur until early spring, allowing the young to be born in April.

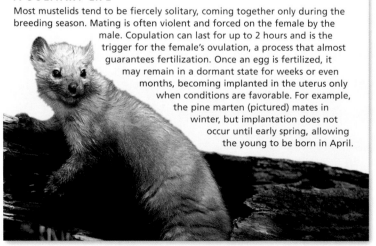

European otter
Lutra lutra

Glands at base of tail produce musk scent

Enters and leaves the water at fixed locations within its home territory

Smooth-coated otter
Lutra perspicillata

Neotropical otter
Lontra longicaudis

Fingers lack webbing and claws but have opposable thumb and are highly dextrous and sensitive

Cape clawless otter
Aonyx capensis

Sensitive whiskers help locate prey

Giant otter
Pteronura brasiliensis

Spotted-necked otter
Lutra maculicollis

Sea otter
Enhydra lutris

Uses stone as tool to crack open sea urchin

Broad, flipper-like back paws with webbing to the tips of the toes

Insulating layer of air trapped between long guard hairs and dense underfur

---

FACT FILE

Neotropical otter Much of this solitary otter's day is spent diving for fish. It eats small prey in the water but takes larger prey to the shore.

- Up to 32 in (81 cm)
- Up to 22½ in (57 cm)
- Up to 33 lb (15 kg)
- Solitary
- Data deficient

Mexico to Uruguay

Giant otter Family groups of several giant otters share a streamside burrow and may forage together. Overhunting has made this species the rarest otter.

- Up to 4 ft (1.2 m)
- Up to 27½ in (70 cm)
- Up to 75 lb (34 kg)
- Family band
- Endangered

S. Venezuela & Colombia to N. Argentina

Sea otter This often solitary species can spend its entire life in the ocean, sleeping on the surface and devoting up to 5 hours a day to foraging, but it may rest on shore in large sexually segregated groups. The only non-primate mammal known to employ tools, it will use a stone to dislodge abalone or crack open shellfish.

- Up to 4 ft (1.2 m)
- Up to 14 in (36 cm)
- Up to 99 lb (45 kg)
- Solitary, rests in group
- Endangered

North Pacific

AQUATIC PAWS

All otters have dextrous paws, but they vary in the degree of webbing and the presence or absence of claws. The paws of most river otters (such as those of the European otter, pictured) are webbed for swimming, clawed for digging, and rounded for walking on land.

⚡ CONSERVATION WATCH

Hunted otters By 1911, fur hunters had depleted sea otter populations to fewer than 2,000 individuals. Legal protection and reintroduction programs have helped increase their numbers to about 150,000 animals, but the species remains endangered, threatened by poaching, marine oil pollution, persecution by fishing crews, and predation by orcas.

FACT FILE

Hog badger Although the hog badger sometimes falls prey to leopards and tigers, it will put up a fight. When threatened, it arches its back, bristles its hair, and growls. It may also emit a noxious fluid from its anal glands.

Up to 27½ in (70 cm)
Up to 6½ in (17 cm)
Up to 31 lb (14 kg)
Not known
Not known

N.E. India to N.E. China & S.E. Asia

Eurasian badger While most badgers tend to be solitary, this species lives in extended family groups. A powerful digger, it lives in permanent burrow complexes known as setts, which are passed down through the generations.

Up to 35½ in (90 cm)
Up to 8 in (20 cm)
Up to 35½ lb (16 kg)
Family band
Locally common

Britain & W. Europe to China, Korea & Japan

American badger This solitary species spends much of its time busily digging for rodents such as prairie dogs and ground squirrels. It will rapidly burrow its way out of danger if threatened by a predator on the surface.

Up to 28½ in (72 cm)
Up to 6 in (15 cm)
Up to 26½ lb (12 kg)
Solitary
Locally common

N. Canada to Mexico

CLIMBING BADGER

The smallest badger, the Chinese ferret badger forages at night for worms, insects, frogs, small rodents, and fruit. By day, it takes refuge in a burrow or rock crevice, or may use its long claws to climb a tree and then nest in the branches.

Up to 17 in (43 cm)
Up to 9 in (23 cm)
Up to 6½ lb (3 kg)
Not known
Locally common

E. India, S.E. Asia, S. China, Taiwan

Sunda stink badger
Mydaus javanensis

May squirt foul secretion from anal glands when threatened

Hog badger
Arctonyx collaris

Elongated snout with pig-like nostrils

Eurasian badger
Meles meles

Powerful forelimbs and claws for digging

Chinese ferret badger
Melogale moschata

Long, bushy tail

American badger
Taxidea taxus

Burmese ferret badger
Melogale personata

Hooded skunk
Mephitis macroura

Longer, softer fur
than striped skunk

Striped skunk
Mephitis mephitis

Eastern hog-nosed skunk
Conepatus leuconotus

Long claws on
forefeet for digging

Spotted skunk
Spilogale putorius

Striped hog-nosed skunk
Conepatus semistriatus

No white stripe down
center of face

Patagonian hog-nosed skunk
Conepatus humboldtii

Andean hog-nosed skunk
Conepatus chinga

Bare, projecting nose

FACT FILE

Striped skunk This nocturnal creature is an opportunistic feeder and tends to consume a wide range of foods, from small mammals, insects, and fish to fruit, nuts, grains, and grasses. During winter, it becomes inactive and rarely emerges from its den.

Up to 31½ in (80 cm)
Up to 15½ in (39 cm)
Up to 14 lb (6.5 kg)
Solitary
Common

N. Canada to Mexico

Spotted skunk The only skunk that can climb, this species also tends to be more alert and active than other skunks. During the mating season in March and April, males may succumb to "mating madness," spraying any large animal they come across.

Up to 13 in (33 cm)
Up to 11 in (28 cm)
Up to 2 lb (900 g)
Solitary
Common

USA (E. of Rocky Mts)

Andean hog-nosed skunk This species dens in rocky crevices, hollow logs, or burrows abandoned by other animals. It pounces on insects and will also hunt small vertebrates such as rodents, lizards, and snakes. It has some resistance to the venom of pit vipers.

Up to 13 in (33 cm)
Up to 8 in (20 cm)
Up to 6½ lb (3 kg)
Solitary
Common

South America

SKUNK DEFENSE

Before a skunk shoots out foul-smelling musk from its anal glands, it gives an enemy fair warning, raising its tail, stamping its feet, pretending to charge, or even doing a handstand. The skunk's distinctive black and white markings also serve to warn predators that it is a meal best avoided.

Danger display
*When mortally threatened,
a striped skunk will present both
its head and rump to the enemy.*

FACT FILE

American marten This agile mustelid speeds through the trees in pursuit of red squirrels and other prey. It will also hunt birds and insects and forage for fruit, nuts, and carrion. Although primarily a tree-dweller, it is also at ease on the ground or in water.

- Up to 17½ in (45 cm)
- Up to 9 in (23 cm)
- Up to 3 lb (1.3 kg)
- Solitary
- Uncommon

Alaska & Canada to N. California & Colorado

Fisher The largest marten, the fisher will tackle a porcupine. While other predators are put off by the porcupine's quills, the fisher stands at the perfect height to bite the unprotected face. Once repeated bites send the porcupine into shock, the fisher will flip it over and feed on its soft belly.

- Up to 31 in (79 cm)
- Up to 16 in (41 cm)
- Up to 12 lb (5.5 kg)
- Solitary
- Uncommon

Alaska & Canada to N. California

COVETED FUR

A creature of the dense taiga forest of northern Asia, the sable hunts and dens on the forest floor. The species was once found as far west as Scandinavia, but so many animals have been trapped for the fur trade that its range and numbers have been substantially reduced.

- Up to 22 in (56 cm)
- Up to 7½ in (19 cm)
- Up to 4 lb (1.8 kg)
- Solitary
- Uncommon

N. Asia

Valuable fur
The sable's long, silky winter coat has made its pelt one of the most prized by the fur trade.

⚡ CONSERVATION WATCH

Of the 65 species of mustelids, 35% are listed on the IUCN Red List, as follows:

- 2 Extinct, or extinct in wild
- 7 Endangered
- 8 Vulnerable
- 2 Near threatened
- 4 Data deficient

American marten
Martes americana

Relatively large eyes and cat-like ears

Yellow-throated marten
Martes flavigula

Fisher
Martes pennanti

Long tail aids balance when climbing trees

Color varies from yellowish brown to dark brown

Japanese marten
Martes melampus

Sable
Martes zibellina

Beech marten
Martes foina

Pine marten
Martes martes

Soles of feet covered in fur in winter

Semiretractile claws used for climbing

Great variation in size, from 1–9 oz (35–250 g), depending on location

Coat becomes white in winter in northern part of range

Long-tailed weasel
Mustela frenata

Stoat (ermine) winter coat
Mustela erminea

Least weasel
Mustela nivalis

White winter coat helps stoat blend in with snow

Head paler than body

Malaysian weasel
Mustela nudipes

Stoat (ermine) summer coat
Mustela erminea

FACT FILE

Least weasel The smallest of all the carnivores, the least weasel often shares territory with its larger relative, the stoat, but concentrates on smaller prey such as mice and voles. Like the stoat, it can have a white winter coat.

- Up to 10 in (26 cm)
- Up to 3 in (8 cm)
- Up to 9 oz (250 g)
- Solitary
- Common

N. Northern Hemisphere; introd. New Zealand

Long-tailed weasel Females of this species give birth to an average of six young around May. The young learn how to hunt from their mother and can kill prey at 8 weeks of age.

- Up to 10 in (26 cm)
- Up to 6 in (15 cm)
- Up to 13 oz (365 g)
- Solitary
- Common

Canada to Peru & Bolivia

Stoat The stoat often sheds its brown summer coat as winter approaches, replacing it with a longer, thicker coat that is entirely white except for the black tail tip. The white fur has long been sought after by the fur industry.

- Up to 12½ in (32 cm)
- Up to 5 in (13 cm)
- Up to 13 oz (365 g)
- Solitary
- Common

Northern Hemisphere; introd. New Zealand

THE WOLVERINE

The largest terrestrial mustelid, the wolverine (*Gulo gulo*) lives in the northern coniferous forest and tundra of Eurasia and North America. It looks somewhat like a bear, but its behavior is definitely mustelid. Remarkably strong and ferocious for its size, it can take down reindeer and caribou, but will scavenge carrion if it is available. Any surplus food is stored in tunnels under the snow, and may be eaten up to 6 months later. The wolverine's massive head houses jaws and teeth that can crunch through large bones and frozen meat. Large feet and a plantigrade gait in which the entire sole is planted on the ground allow the wolverine to travel quickly over snow and outrun hoofed prey. This northern mustelid is also an agile climber and strong swimmer.

RELENTLESS CARNIVORES

Weasels will pursue prey underground or under snow and can carry up to half their own weight in meat as they run. While smaller weasels prefer mice and voles, and larger weasels favor rabbits, they all avail themselves of whatever animals they come across.

Black-footed ferret While most mustelids are opportunistic feeders, the black-footed ferret preys almost solely on prairie dogs and uses their burrows for shelter.

- Up to 18 in (46 cm)
- Up to 5½ in (14 cm)
- Up to 2½ lb (1.1 kg)
- Solitary
- Extinct in the wild

S. Canada to N.W. Texas (until late 1980s); reintrod. Montana, Dakota & Wyoming
- Former range

BATTLE OF THE MINKS

Both the European and American minks are versatile feeders that hunt in or near water. The European mink has been in decline ever since the American mink escaped from European fur farms and became a direct competitor in the wild.

American mink
- Up to 19½ in (50 cm)
- Up to 8 in (20 cm)
- Up to 2 lb (900 g)
- Solitary
- Common

North America; introd. Europe, Siberia
- Introduced range

Mink variation
While most American minks are brown, about 10 percent have blue-gray fur.

European mink
- Up to 17 in (43 cm)
- Up to 7½ in (19 cm)
- Up to 26 oz (740 g)
- Solitary
- Endangered

France & Spain; Finland to Romania & Georgia
- Former range

⚡ CONSERVATION WATCH

Ferret decline In 1920, more than 500,000 black-footed ferrets lived on the North American plains but, as humans exterminated their prairie-dog prey, ferret numbers fell until they were thought extinct. A small population found in the 1980s led to a captive-breeding program, but the species remains North America's most endangered mammal.

Oily guard hairs make coat water-repellent

Siberian weasel
Mustela sibirica

American mink
Mustela vison

Partially webbed toes for swimming

Black face mask

✝ **Black-footed ferret**
Mustela nigripes

Polecat
Mustela putorius

Males can weigh twice as much as females

Steppe polecat
Mustela eversmannii

Always has white patch on upper lip

European mink
Mustela lutreola

Tough skin is so loose that ratel can swing around to attack a predator that has bitten down on its neck

Ratel (honey badger)
Mellivora capensis

Foul-smelling liquid secreted from anal glands

Patagonian weasel
Lyncodon patagonicus

Tayra
Eira barbara

Large hindfeet with long claws

Grison
Galictis vittata

Stands on hind legs to search for prey

Saharan striped weasel
Ictonyx libyca

Striped polecat (zorilla)
Ictonyx striatus

African weasel
Poecilogale albinucha

Marbled polecat
Vormela peregusna

FACT FILE

Ratel This mainly terrestrial mustelid will climb trees to reach honey. It has developed a symbiotic relationship with the honey guide bird, which will sing a distinctive song to lead it to a bee-hive. After opening the hive with its powerful claws, the ratel eats most of the honey, but leaves the wax and bee larvae for the bird. The ratel's omnivorous diet also includes insects and both large and small vertebrates.

Up to 30½ in (77 cm)
Up to 12 in (30 cm)
Up to 28½ lb (13 kg)
Solitary
Uncommon

W. Africa, sub-Saharan Africa, Arabia, Iraq, Turkmenistan, Pakistan, India

Shaggy attack
The ratel sometimes preys on poisonous snakes. Its long, thick coat and tough skin make it difficult for a snake to bite the flesh.

PLAYING DEAD

When threatened, a striped polecat will fluff up its long tail and growl or scream. If that does not work, it then squirts the attacker with foul-smelling fluid from its anal glands. As a final resort, the polecat will pretend to be dead. Despite these various defense strategies, striped polecats do fall victim occasionally to predators such as domestic dogs and wild cats. More commonly, however, they are killed by cars. Once one animal has been hit, its family members do not move from the scene and thus often meet the same fate.

A repulsive meal
Although feigning death makes the striped polecat easier to attack, it gives the predator a chance to taste the anal gland secretions on the fur. These are so unpleasant that the predator may well decide to abandon the meal.

SEALS AND SEA LIONS

CLASS	Mammalia
ORDER	Carnivora
FAMILIES	3
GENERA	21
SPECIES	36

With flexible, torpedo-shaped bodies, limbs modified to become flippers, and insulating layers of blubber and hair, seals, sea lions, and walruses are superbly adapted to a life in water. They have not, however, completely severed their link with land and must return to shore to breed. Collectively known as pinnipeds, these marine mammals were once placed in their own order, but are now considered to be part of Carnivora. Most feed on fish, squid, and crustaceans, but some also eat penguins and carrion and may attack the pups of other seal species. They can dive to great depths in search of prey, with the elephant seal able to stay submerged for up to 2 hours at a time.

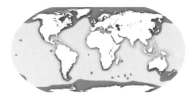

Cold-water creatures Although monk seals are found in warmer waters, most seals, sea lions, and walruses are restricted to the colder, highly productive seas of the world's polar and temperate regions. The fossil record shows that the three families all originated in the North Pacific. They are now most abundant in the North Pacific, North Atlantic, and Southern oceans.

Communal living Most pinnipeds are gregarious animals and tend to live in large colonies. Walrus herds can number in the hundreds or even thousands and may be single sex or mixed, with both body and tusk size determining rank.

THREE GROUPS

There are three pinniped families. The Phocidae are known as the true seals. They swim mainly with strokes of their hind flippers, which cannot bend forward to act as feet, making their movement on land particularly ungainly. Although their hearing, especially under water, is good, true seals lack external ears.

Sea lions and fur seals belong to the family Otariidae. These "eared seals" have small external ears. They rely mostly on their front flippers for swimming, and can bend their hind flippers forward when on land, allowing them to walk "four-footed" and sit in a semi-upright position.

The third family, Odobenidae, contains a single species, the walrus, instantly recognizable by the long canine teeth that form tusks on both sexes. Like true seals, walruses use their hind flippers for swimming and lack external ears. Like eared seals, however, walruses can bend their hind flippers forward.

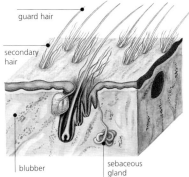

Insulating layers Pinnipeds have a thick layer of blubber that provides insulation, buoyancy, and a fat store. For further protection, all but the walrus have hairy bodies, and fur seals have dense secondary hairs that form a waterproof barrier.

BRINGING UP BABY

All pinnipeds return to land or ice to give birth and mate. Mating takes place just days after the usually single pup is born, but the fertilized egg does not become implanted in the uterus for months. This delayed implantation allows birthing, nursing, and mating to occur in one season so that the animals live on land, where they are most vulnerable, only once a year. Pups are dependent for varying lengths of time. Harp seals (right), for example, are nursed for only 12 days or so, while walruses stay with their mother for 2 years.

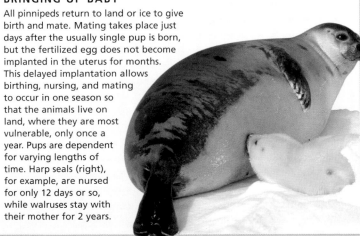

⚡ CONSERVATION WATCH

The commercial sealing operations that began in the 16th century had a devastating effect on pinniped populations. Of the 36 species of pinnipeds, 36% are listed on the IUCN Red List, as follows:

2	Extinct
1	Critically endangered
2	Endangered
7	Vulnerable
1	Near threatened

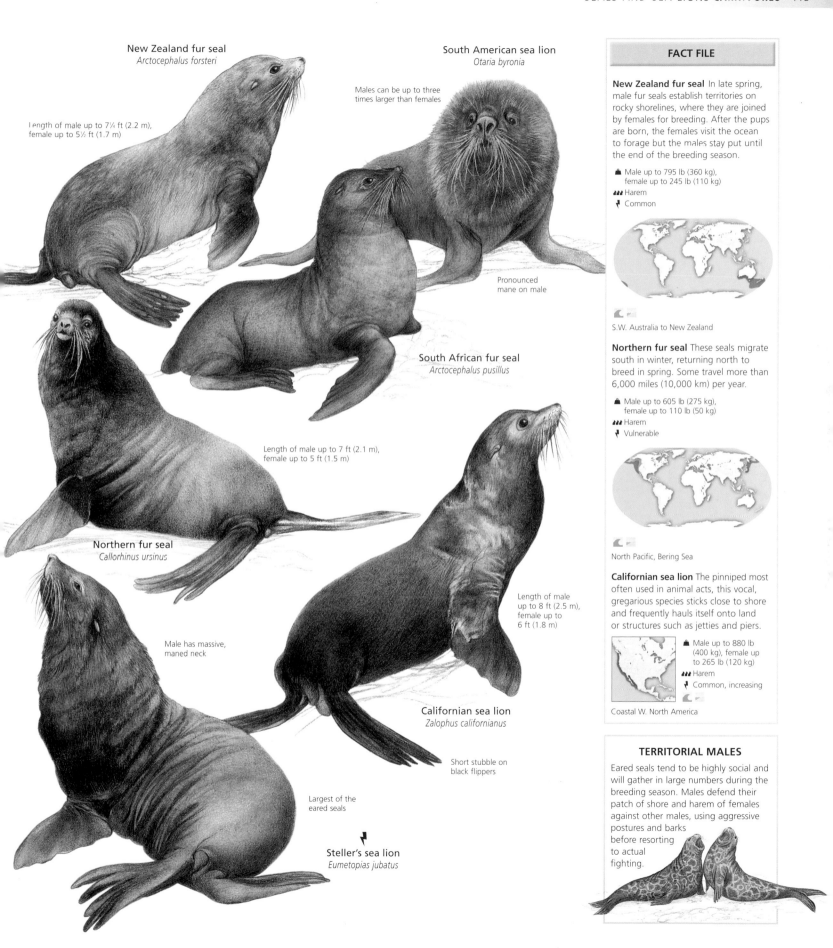

New Zealand fur seal
Arctocephalus forsteri

Length of male up to 7¼ ft (2.2 m),
female up to 5½ ft (1.7 m)

South American sea lion
Otaria byronia

Males can be up to three
times larger than females

Pronounced
mane on male

South African fur seal
Arctocephalus pusillus

Length of male up to 7 ft (2.1 m),
female up to 5 ft (1.5 m)

Northern fur seal
Callorhinus ursinus

Length of male
up to 8 ft (2.5 m),
female up to
6 ft (1.8 m)

Californian sea lion
Zalophus californianus

Short stubble on
black flippers

Male has massive,
maned neck

Largest of the
eared seals

Steller's sea lion
Eumetopias jubatus

FACT FILE

New Zealand fur seal In late spring, male fur seals establish territories on rocky shorelines, where they are joined by females for breeding. After the pups are born, the females visit the ocean to forage but the males stay put until the end of the breeding season.

Male up to 795 lb (360 kg),
female up to 245 lb (110 kg)
Harem
Common

S.W. Australia to New Zealand

Northern fur seal These seals migrate south in winter, returning north to breed in spring. Some travel more than 6,000 miles (10,000 km) per year.

Male up to 605 lb (275 kg),
female up to 110 lb (50 kg)
Harem
Vulnerable

North Pacific, Bering Sea

Californian sea lion The pinniped most often used in animal acts, this vocal, gregarious species sticks close to shore and frequently hauls itself onto land or structures such as jetties and piers.

Male up to 880 lb (400 kg), female up to 265 lb (120 kg)
Harem
Common, increasing

Coastal W. North America

TERRITORIAL MALES

Eared seals tend to be highly social and will gather in large numbers during the breeding season. Males defend their patch of shore and harem of females against other males, using aggressive postures and barks before resorting to actual fighting.

SNOW LAIRS

The ringed seal lives in waters that are covered in ice for at least part of the year. A pregnant female digs a cave into the snow above her breathing hole, which provides her pup with protection from both the extreme Arctic weather and hungry predators such as polar bears.

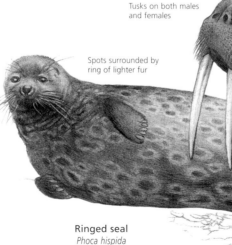

Bearded seal
Erignathus barbatus

Long, sensitive whiskers used to locate clams, snails, crabs, and shrimp

Baikal seal
Phoca sibirica

Common seal (harbor seal)
Phoca vitulina

Ribbon seal
Phoca fasciata

Length of male up to 6¼ ft (1.9 m), female up to 5½ ft (1.7 m)

Common name inspired by harp-shaped marking on back and sides of adult

White coats of pups shed by 3 weeks of age

Harp seal
Phoca groenlandica

Tusks on both males and females

Spots surrounded by ring of lighter fur

Walrus
Odobenus rosmarus

Ringed seal
Phoca hispida

Hooded seal
Cystophora cristata

Lining of left nostril inflated as part of mating display

Crabeater seal
Lobodon carcinophagus

Dark gray or brown back after January molt, becomes almost entirely blonde later in year

Gray seal
Halichoerus grypus

Swims with strokes of large flippers, while most other pinnipeds use tail

Weddell seal
Leptonychotes weddellii

Leopard seal
Hydrurga leptonyx

Can be colored brown, gray, or black

Mediterranean monk seal
Monachus monachus

Southern elephant seal
Mirounga leonina

Largest of all pinnipeds: length of male up to 20 ft (6 m), female up to 10 ft (3 m)

FACT FILE

Mediterranean monk seal This species was once common throughout Mediterranean coastal waters, but an ever-growing human presence has seen its numbers dwindle. Today, its main refuges are small, barren islands.

Up to 9 ft (2.8 m)
Up to 660 lb (300 kg)
Harem
Critically endangered

Coastal W. Africa, Aegean Sea

Southern elephant seal Males of this species can be more than six times heavier than the females. Only the largest 10 percent of males ever have the chance to mate. To attract females, a male inflates his trunk-like nose.

Male up to 8,160 lb (3,700 kg), female up to 1,320 lb (600 kg)
Harem
Locally common

Argentina, New Zealand, sub-Antarctic islands

KRILL EATERS

Rather than eating crabs as their name suggests, crabeater seals feed almost exclusively on the abundant supply of krill in Antarctic waters. They sieve the tiny crustaceans through their complex, knobbly cheek teeth.

INFLATED NOSE

When it is trying to attract a mate, or is threatened or excited, mature male hooded seals have the unusual ability to blow up their black hood, which is an extension of the nasal cavity. They can also make the lining of the left nostril inflate into a red bladder.

Blowing up *As part of its mating display, the male hooded seal may inflate either its red nostril bladder or its entire black hood.*

THE RACCOON FAMILY

CLASS	Mammalia
ORDER	Carnivora
FAMILY	Procyonidae
GENERA	6
SPECIES	19

Restricted to the New World, the family Procyonidae includes raccoons, coatis, kinkajous, ringtails, and olingos. All are medium-sized with a long body and tail, broad faces, and erect ears. Apart from the kinkajou, they also share mask-like markings on the face and alternating light and dark rings on the tail. Omnivorous feeding habits have enabled members of this family to thrive in habitats as varied as coniferous forest, tropical rain forest, wetlands, desert, farmland, and urban areas. Procyonids tend to be highly vocal, barking and squeaking to maintain complex social structures. Raccoons often sleep in communal dens, males may travel in groups, and females form "consortships" with one to four males. Male coatis are solitary, but bands of about 15 females groom one another, share the care of young, and fight off predators together. Kinkajous rest in groups of a female and her young plus two adult males.

Opportunistic omnivores Although their preferred habitat is woodland near water, raccoons have adapted to live alongside humans in rural and urban environments. They often visit North American backyards to raid trash cans for food scraps, and may den in old buildings, cellars, or attics.

FACT FILE

Kinkajou Originally classified as a lemur, the nocturnal kinkajou has a prehensile tail; large, forward-facing eyes; a primarily fruit-based diet; and a treetop lifestyle. It is nonetheless a carnivore, with genetic studies showing that it belongs in the Procyonidae family with raccoons and coatis.

🐾	Up to 21½ in (55 cm)
🦝	Up to 22½ in (57 cm)
⚖	Up to 7 lb (3.2 kg)
👥	Solitary, pair
⚡	Locally common

S. Mexico to Bolivia & Brazil

White-nosed coati Snuffling through the leaf litter on the forest floor by day, coatis use their flexible snouts and keen sense of smell to locate insect prey in crevices. They also consume large quantities of fruit and small vertebrates such as lizards and rodents. At night, they retreat to the treetops.

🐾	Up to 27 in (69 cm)
🦝	Up to 24½ in (62 cm)
⚖	Up to 10 lb (4.5 kg)
👥	Family band
⚡	Locally common

Arizona to Colombia & Ecuador

Raccoon These nocturnal masked creatures eat whatever is available, from small vertebrates, insects, and worms to fruit, nuts, and seeds. They prefer aquatic prey, such as fish, crustaceans, and snails, which they appear to wash with their dextrous hands.

🐾	Up to 21½ in (55 cm)
🦝	Up to 16 in (40 cm)
⚖	Up to 35½ lb (16 kg)
👤	Solitary
⚡	Common

North & Central America

Only New World carnivore with prehensile tail

Kinkajou
Potos flavus

Ringtail
Bassariscus astutus

⚡ CONSERVATION WATCH

Of the 19 species of procyonids, 63% are listed on the IUCN Red List, as follows:

1	Extinct
7	Endangered
3	Near threatened
1	Data deficient

Mobile tail used for balance

Raccoon
Procyon lotor

14–16 alternating black and white rings on tail

Forepaws are sensitive and dextrous

White-nosed coati
Nasua narica

HYENAS AND AARDWOLF

The four species in the family Hyaenidae—the aardwolf and the brown, striped, and spotted hyenas—look rather like dogs but are classified as cat-like carnivores because they are more closely related to the cats and civets. Between their long front legs and shorter back legs, the spine distinctively slopes downward to the tail. A relatively massive head with a broad muzzle houses powerful, bone-crunching jaws and teeth. Unlike most other mammals, hyenas can digest skin and bone. They often scavenge the kills of lions and other predators, but sometimes capture their own prey. Spotted hyenas are the most effective hunters and will cooperate to bring down large prey such as zebra and wildebeest. The aardwolf is primarily an insect-eater, using its long, sticky tongue and peg-like teeth to harvest up to 200,000 termites per night.

CLASS	Mammalia
ORDER	Carnivora
FAMILY	Hyaenidae
GENERA	3
SPECIES	4

African distribution The range of the striped hyena extends into the Middle East and South Asia, but the other Hyaenidae members are restricted to Africa. Hyenas and aardwolf are most often found in grassland or savanna habitats, where they take refuge in caves, thick vegetation, or abandoned burrows. Although no hyena species is endangered, they are often loathed and widely persecuted, and the spotted hyena depends on conservation measures for its survival.

Brown hyena
Hyaena brunnea

Striped legs

Aardwolf
Proteles cristatus

Mane erects during stress to make aardwolf look larger

Powerful jaws and teeth can crush bones of large ungulates

Sloping spine

Striped hyena
Hyaena hyaena

Dominating females Female spotted hyenas (*Crocuta crocuta*) are bigger than males, have large female genitals that look like a penis and scrotum, and outrank males in the clan. Mothers raise their young without any help from the father. When the cubs are a few months old, they join a communal den, where they remain until they are weaned at 15 months of age.

CLAN SOCIETY

All hyenas live in clans of several or more animals that share a home range, with spotted hyenas congregating in groups of up to 80 members. Elaborate scentmarking and greeting rituals help to maintain these complex social systems. When striped or brown hyenas meet, they erect their manes, sniff each other's head and body, and may engage in ritual fighting.

CIVETS AND MONGOOSES

CLASS	Mammalia
ORDER	Carnivora
FAMILIES	2
GENERA	38
SPECIES	75

The carnivore family Viverridae includes civets, genets, and linsangs. It also once included mongooses, but these have now been placed in their own family Herpestidae. Related to cats and hyenas, viverrids and herpestids tend to be medium-sized with a long neck and head, a long, slender body, and short legs. Their skeletal structure and teeth closely resemble those of the earliest carnivores, but the inner-ear region is highly developed. Viverrids are generally nocturnal, arboreal forest-dwellers with long tails, retractile claws, and erect, pointed ears. Many have scent glands near the genitals that in some species produce civet oil, once widely used as a perfume base. Mongooses tend to be found in more open country. Usually terrestrial and often diurnal, they have shorter tails, non-retractile claws, and small, rounded ears.

Old World families The civets, genets, and linsangs of Viverridae and the mongooses of Herpestidae are native to much of the Old World, with a number of species found only on the island of Madagascar. Famed as ratters, some mongooses have also been introduced on many islands in the New World, often with disastrous consequences. In the West Indies and Hawaii, for example, the introduced small Indian mongoose (*Herpestes javanicus*) is now a pest that attacks poultry and native fauna.

⚑ CONSERVATION WATCH

While a number of viverrids and mongooses are so successful that they are considered pests in areas, others are suffering as their habitat is destroyed. Deforestation is a critical issue on Madagascar, which has four endangered species from these families. Of the 75 species in Viverridae and Herpestidae, 32% are listed on the IUCN Red List, as follows:

- 1 Critically endangered
- 8 Endangered
- 9 Vulnerable
- 6 Data deficient

Social life While all viverrids and many herpestids usually live alone or in pairs, some mongoose species are gregarious and live in colonies. Suricates live in troops of up to 30 animals, which cooperate to care for the young and watch for danger. Nonbreeding members will babysit, and sentinel duties are rotated.

Coat is most striking, with stronger colors and more pronounced pattern, in wetter parts of range

Blotched genet (large-spotted genet)
Genetta tigrina

Angolan genet
Genetta angolensis

Fishing genet
Osbornictis piscivora

Naked palms to locate fish hiding in crevices

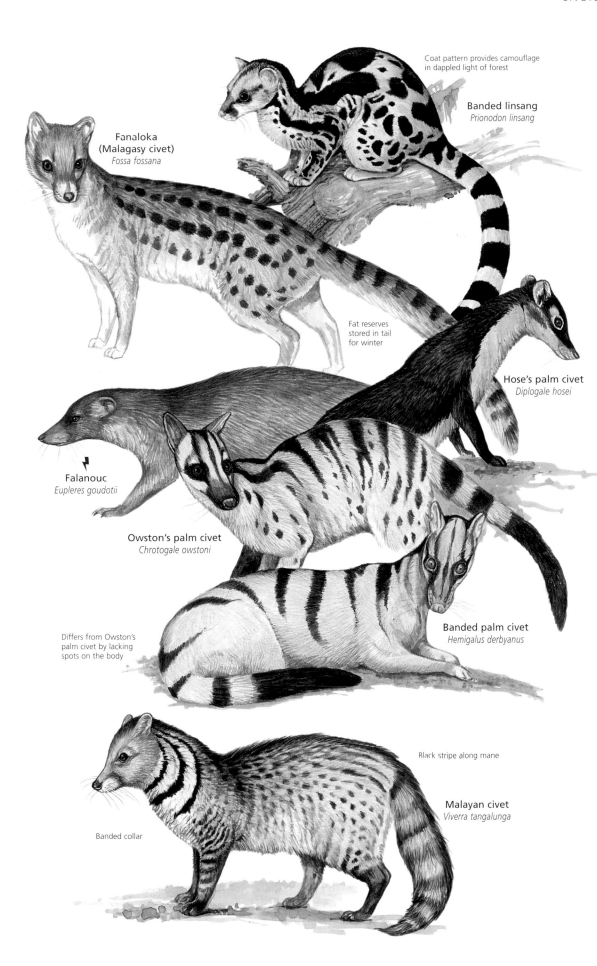

Coat pattern provides camouflage in dappled light of forest

Banded linsang
Prionodon linsang

Fanaloka
(Malagasy civet)
Fossa fossana

Fat reserves
stored in tail
for winter

Hose's palm civet
Diplogale hosei

Falanouc
Eupleres goudotii

Owston's palm civet
Chrotogale owstoni

Differs from Owston's
palm civet by lacking
spots on the body

Banded palm civet
Hemigalus derbyanus

Black stripe along mane

Malayan civet
Viverra tangalunga

Banded collar

THE FOSSA

The dominant predator on the island of Madagascar is the fossa (*Crytoprocta ferox*). This agile civet pursues lemurs through the trees, but will also hunt snakes, tenrecs, and guinea fowl on the ground. During the mating season, a female fossa waits high in a tree for males to congregate beneath her, then mates with a number of them for almost 3 hours.

Balancing act
The fossa's tail is about as long as its body and helps it to balance as it chases lemurs through the trees.

MASKED MAMMAL

The masked palm civet of China and Southeast Asia plays a key role in its ecosystem. Through an omnivorous diet, it keeps insect and small vertebrate populations under control and helps disperse fruit seeds. In turn, it is a prey species of tigers, hawks, and leopards. To discourage predation, this civet relies on the powerful odor produced by its anal glands. Its distinctive facial markings may serve to warn predators of this noxious scent.

Only viverrid with prehensile tail

Binturong
Arctictis binturong

Jerdon's palm civet
Paradoxurus jerdoni

Common palm civet (toddy cat)
Paradoxurus hermaphroditus

Brown palm civet
Macrogalidia musschenbroekii

African palm civet
Nandinia binotata

Masked palm civet
Paguma larvata

Three-striped palm civet
Arctogalidia trivirgata

Squirrels form part of civet's omnivorous diet, which also includes frogs, birds, insects, and fruit

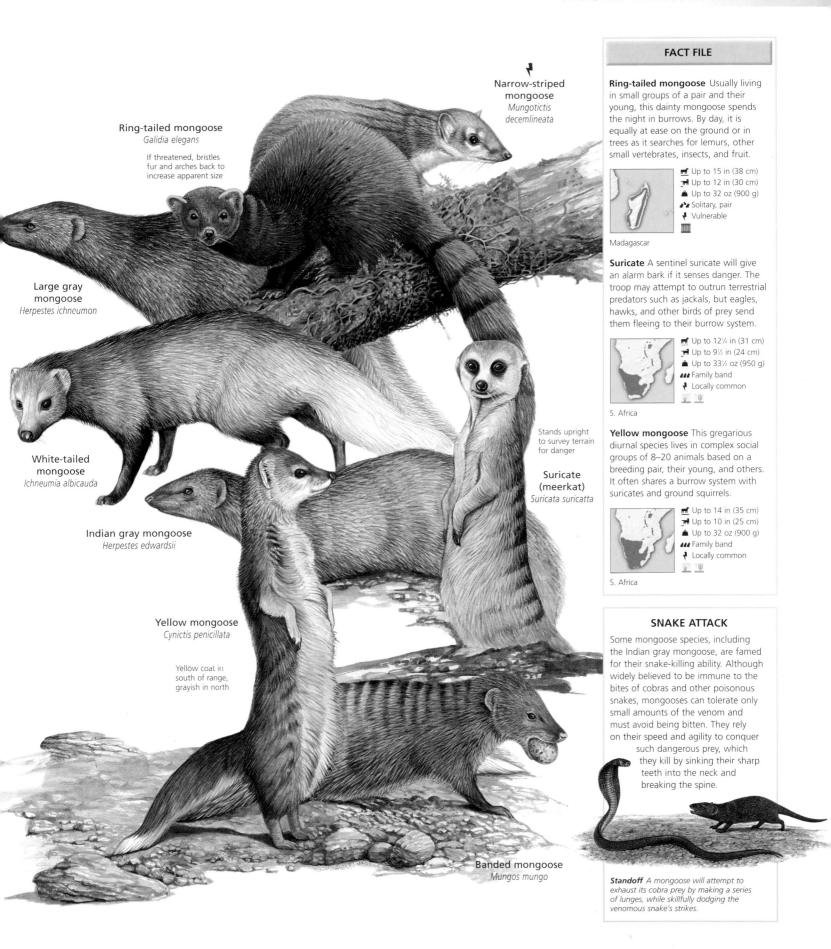

Ring-tailed mongoose
Galidia elegans

If threatened, bristles fur and arches back to increase apparent size

Narrow-striped mongoose
Mungotictis decemlineata

Large gray mongoose
Herpestes ichneumon

White-tailed mongoose
Ichneumia albicauda

Indian gray mongoose
Herpestes edwardsii

Stands upright to survey terrain for danger

Suricate (meerkat)
Suricata suricatta

Yellow mongoose
Cynictis penicillata

Yellow coat in south of range, grayish in north

Banded mongoose
Mungos mungo

SNAKE ATTACK

Some mongoose species, including the Indian gray mongoose, are famed for their snake-killing ability. Although widely believed to be immune to the bites of cobras and other poisonous snakes, mongooses can tolerate only small amounts of the venom and must avoid being bitten. They rely on their speed and agility to conquer such dangerous prey, which they kill by sinking their sharp teeth into the neck and breaking the spine.

Standoff A mongoose will attempt to exhaust its cobra prey by making a series of lunges, while skillfully dodging the venomous snake's strikes.

CATS

CLASS	Mammalia
ORDER	Carnivora
FAMILY	Felidae
GENERA	18
SPECIES	36

The ultimate hunters, cats eat very little other than meat, making them the most carnivorous of the carnivores. Their predatory expertise has placed them at the top of many food chains on all continents except Australia and Antarctica and in habitats ranging from deserts to Arctic regions. Within the family Felidae, there are considerable size differences but few variations in general form. All species have a strong, muscular body; a blunt face with large, forward-facing eyes; sharp teeth and claws; and acute senses and quick reflexes. They generally rely on stealth to capture prey, which they stalk or ambush. Although largely terrestrial, cats are agile climbers and often good swimmers.

Worldwide spread Wild felids are the dominant predators on most continents, and are absent only from Australasia, Madagascar, Greenland, and Antarctica. First domesticated in ancient Egypt thousands of years ago, the domestic cat has since spread everywhere except Antarctica, and feral populations have had a serious impact on native ecosystems.

Surprise attack Small cats such as bobcats, wildcats, and lynx tend to hunt smaller mammals such as rodents, lizards, and birds. They creep up, then suddenly pounce with a jack-in-the-box movement, killing the prey with a bite to the neck.

Roars and purrs A lion's roar usually advertises its control of territory. Only the big cats have a flexible-enough larynx to produce roars. All cats can purr, but big cats can purr only as they exhale, while small cats can produce a constant purr.

Open wide
Because they rarely eat vegetation, cats lack grinding teeth. Instead, their powerful jaws house blade-like teeth, with sharp stabbing canines and shearing carnassials. A rough tongue covered with tiny projections is used to rasp meat off bones and to groom the fur.

PRIME PREDATORS

Cats are split into three subfamilies: the big cats of Pantherinae include tigers, lions, leopards, and jaguars; the small cats of Felinae include pumas (which can be bigger than some "big cats"), lynx, bobcats, and ocelots; and cheetahs are on their own in Acinonychinae. The chief difference between the big and small cats lies in the flexibility of the larynx, which allows big cats to roar. Cheetahs are distinguished by their non-retractile claws and by their exceptional speed, which allows them to outrun fast prey such as gazelles over short distances.

The sense of smell is used for communication among cats, which scentmark their territory. When hunting, however, felids depend more on vision and sound. Forward-facing eyes provide binocular vision that helps with judging distances. A light-reflecting disk in the eye and rapidly adjusting irises enhance their night vision, which is up to six times sharper than that of humans. Large, mobile ears funnel sound to the sensitive inner ear, which can pick up the faint, high-pitched sounds of small prey such as mice.

The first felids began to evolve about 40 million years ago and led to today's species and to a branch that included the saber-toothed tiger, a massive creature with huge canines that disappeared only 10,000 years ago at the end of the last ice age. Cats were domesticated in the Middle East 7,000 years or so ago, a development that saw them spread to almost every part of the globe as companion animals.

⚑ CONSERVATION WATCH

Because they need a wide range to find an adequate supply of prey, felids are particularly affected by habitat loss. Hunting has also taken a heavy toll on most cat species. Of the 36 species of felids, 69% are listed on the IUCN Red List, as follows:

1	Critically endangered
4	Endangered
12	Vulnerable
8	Near threatened

Lion
Panthera leo

Male is 30–50 percent heavier than female

Some males have dark mane, but most have golden mane

Lionesses do most of the hunting, but the male will usually eat first

"King" cheetah

In some cheetahs, a recessive gene produces a blotchy coat pattern with stripes down the spine

Cheetah
Acinonyx jubatus

Cheetah cubs stay with mother until 13–20 months old

FACT FILE

Lion While most felids tend to be solitary, lions are famed for their close, enduring group relationships. Prides of 4–20 lionesses occupy a home range, cooperate to bring down large prey, and share care of the cubs. Males live alone or in coalitions with other males.

- Up to 7½ ft (2.3 m)
- Up to 39½ in (1 m)
- Up to 495 lb (225 kg)
- Family band
- Vulnerable

Sub-Saharan Africa, India

Cheetah With a burst of speed, the cheetah attempts to capture hoofed mammals such as Thomson's gazelle and wildebeest calves. Only about half such pursuits end in success. In turn, cheetahs are sometimes killed by lions.

- Up to 4½ ft (1.4 m)
- Up to 31½ in (80 cm)
- Up to 159 lb (72 kg)
- Solitary
- Vulnerable

Sub-Saharan Africa

LION INFANTICIDE

The cubs in a pride of lions are usually sired by a coalition of two or three adult males. This resident coalition's tenure is usually short-lived, lasting only a few years before invading males move in. The intruders kill all the smaller cubs, which frees up the females to breed.

Protective mother *Lionesses carry their cubs in the mouth and will try to protect them from invading males.*

FAST AS A FLASH

Reaching speeds of 60 miles per hour (95 km/h) in pursuit of prey, the cheetah is the fastest mammal on land. Such sprints can last for only 20–60 seconds before the cheetah overheats and must rest. Sometimes it is too out of breath to defend its kill from scavengers.

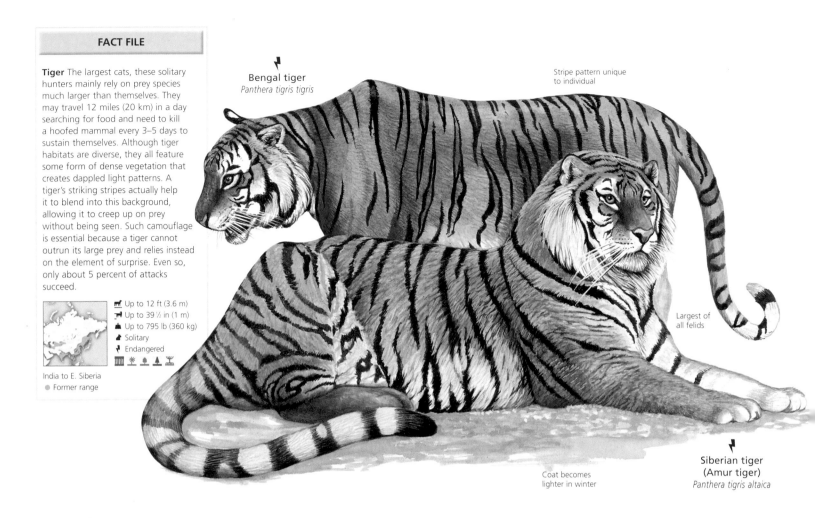

FACT FILE

Tiger The largest cats, these solitary hunters mainly rely on prey species much larger than themselves. They may travel 12 miles (20 km) in a day searching for food and need to kill a hoofed mammal every 3–5 days to sustain themselves. Although tiger habitats are diverse, they all feature some form of dense vegetation that creates dappled light patterns. A tiger's striking stripes actually help it to blend into this background, allowing it to creep up on prey without being seen. Such camouflage is essential because a tiger cannot outrun its large prey and relies instead on the element of surprise. Even so, only about 5 percent of attacks succeed.

Up to 12 ft (3.6 m)
Up to 39 ½ in (1 m)
Up to 795 lb (360 kg)
Solitary
Endangered

India to E. Siberia
● Former range

Bengal tiger
Panthera tigris tigris

Stripe pattern unique to individual

Largest of all felids

Coat becomes lighter in winter

Siberian tiger (Amur tiger)
Panthera tigris altaica

VANISHING TIGERS

At the beginning of the 20th century, there were about 100,000 tigers roaming the tropical jungles, savanna, grasslands, mangrove swamps, deciduous woodlands, and snow-covered coniferous forests of Asia, from eastern Turkey to far eastern Russia. Today, perhaps fewer than 2,500 breeding adults remain in the wild. The Bali, Caspian, and Javan tigers—three of the eight tiger subspecies—are now extinct. Of the remaining subspecies, South China tigers exist only as a remnant population of 20–30 animals, and merely 500 or so Siberian or Amur tigers and 500 Sumatran tigers survive. The largest populations are of the Bengal tiger (shown at left) and the Indochinese tiger, but even these are in serious danger of extinction.

For years, tigers have been shot or poisoned because they are considered pests; because their skins as well as their body parts (used in traditional Asian medicine) fetch good prices; and because they are prized as trophies by sport hunters. At the same time, a continuing increase in local human populations has led to the degradation and fragmentation of much tiger habitat, as well as the decimation of hoofed mammals, the tiger's main prey, by subsistence hunters.

Although the tiger is now protected in most countries, illegal poaching persists. Conservation measures include preserving tiger habitat and reintroducing tigers in some areas.

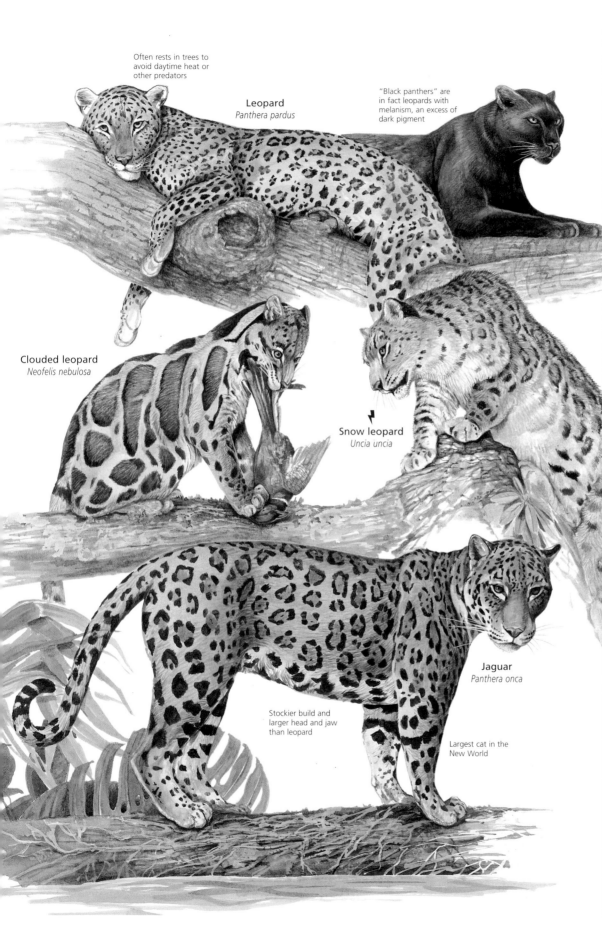

Often rests in trees to avoid daytime heat or other predators

Leopard
Panthera pardus

"Black panthers" are in fact leopards with melanism, an excess of dark pigment

Clouded leopard
Neofelis nebulosa

Snow leopard
Uncia uncia

Stockier build and larger head and jaw than leopard

Largest cat in the New World

Jaguar
Panthera onca

FACT FILE

Leopard The most widespread big cat, the leopard owes its success to a varied diet, which includes gazelles, jackals, baboons, storks, rodents, reptiles, and fish. An agile climber, it often drags its kill to the safety of high branches.

- Up to 7 ft (2.1 m)
- Up to 3½ ft (1.1 m)
- Up to 200 lb (90 kg)
- Solitary
- Locally common

Sub-Saharan & N. Africa; S., S.E. & C. Asia

Clouded leopard This largely arboreal cat will wait in a tree to ambush prey such as deer and pigs below. It will also seize primates and birds in the branches. The species is the smallest of the big cats and has only a soft roar.

- Up to 3½ ft (1.1 m)
- Up to 35½ in (90 cm)
- Up to 51 lb (23 kg)
- Solitary
- Vulnerable

Nepal to China, S.E. Asia

Jaguar This New World cat looks like the leopard, but fills a similar ecological niche to the tiger. It tends to live in dense vegetation near water and stalk large prey such as deer and peccaries. It also takes fish and other aquatic prey.

- Up to 6¼ ft (1.9 m)
- Up to 23½ in (60 cm)
- Up to 355 lb (160 kg)
- Solitary
- Near threatened

Mexico to Argentina

SNOWED IN

Adapted to high altitudes, the snow leopard lives in the remote mountains of Central Asia. It has a dense coat with very large, furry paws that act as snowshoes. Up to five cubs are born in a rocky den lined with the mother's fur.

FACT FILE

Bobcat Rare in some parts of its range but more common in others, the bobcat usually hunts small prey such as rabbits and rodents by night but will also eat carrion. It rests by day, often in a cave.

- Up to 41 in (105 cm)
- Up to 8 in (20 cm)
- Up to 68½ lb (31 kg)
- Solitary
- Locally common

Temperate North America to Mexico

Eurasian lynx Mostly found in remote forested areas frequented by its main prey of small deer, this species remains active throughout the winter months.

- Up to 4⅓ ft (1.3 m)
- Up to 9½ in (24 cm)
- Up to 84 lb (38 kg)
- Solitary
- Near threatened

France, Balkans, Iraq, Scandinavia to China

Puma This cat's once vast range is now largely restricted to remote mountains, where it hunts white-tailed deer, moose, and caribou. The puma hisses, growls, whistles, and purrs, but cannot roar.

- Up to 5 ft (1.5 m)
- Up to 38 in (96 cm)
- Up to 265 lb (120 kg)
- Solitary
- Near threatened

Canada to S. Argentina & Chile

Caracal The swiftest of the small cats, the caracal can leap 10 feet (3 m) to snatch birds from the air. It also pounces on rodents and antelopes.

- Up to 36 in (92 cm)
- Up to 12¼ in (31 cm)
- Up to 42 lb (19 kg)
- Solitary
- Uncommon

Africa, Middle East, India & N.W. Pakistan

JACKKNIFE CLAWS

Apart from the cheetah, all cats have retractile claws, which remain sharp because they are unsheathed only for capturing prey or climbing trees.

Bobcat
Lynx rufus

Canadian lynx
Lynx canadensis

Eurasian lynx
Lynx lynx

Coat can be mainly striped, mainly spotted, or plain

In winter, coat thickens and becomes paler, and furry feet help lynx to travel over soft snow

Largest of the small cats

Puma
(cougar, mountain lion)
Puma concolor

Tufts of black fur on long, slender ears

Caracal
Caracal caracal

Iberian lynx
Lynx pardinus

Coat color and pattern vary according to location; most commonly reddish brown or grayish with spots on lower flanks or all over

African golden cat
Profelis aurata

Jungle cat
Felis chaus

Long legs for chasing prey

Pallas's cat
Otocolobus manul

Chinese desert cat
Felis bieti

Black-footed cat
Felis nigripes

European wildcats tend to have darker coats than those in Africa

Soles of feet are black and covered in hair that protects them from hot sand

Sand cat
Felis margarita

Wildcat
Felis silvestris

FACT FILE

Sand cat This desert creature can survive in extremely arid conditions, gaining enough water from its prey of rodents, hares, birds, and reptiles so that it does not need to drink.

↥	Up to 21 in (54 cm)
⬓	Up to 12¼ in (31 cm)
⚖	Up to 7½ lb (3.5 kg)
♙	Solitary
⚑	Near threatened

Sahara Desert (N. Africa)

Wildcat This species looks like a large domestic tabby cat, but with a broader head and darker fur. A solitary creature, it hunts mainly at night for rodents, birds, small reptiles, and insects.

↥	Up to 29½ in (75 cm)
⬓	Up to 14 in (35 cm)
⚖	Up to 17½ lb (8 kg)
♙	Solitary
⚑	Locally common

Africa, Europe to W. China & N.W. India

FROM THE WILD

Cats were first domesticated in ancient Egypt when stores of grain attracted rats and mice to human settlements. The rats and mice drew wildcats, which were tolerated because they kept the rodents under control. The Romans spread domesticated cats throughout Europe. Today, there are more than 100 million domestic or feral cats in the United States alone.

Wild feline Although wildcats tend to be much more fierce than domestic cats, domestic cats retain the hunting instinct and readily revert to a feral state.

African wildcat Wildcats in Africa live in less densely wooded habitats than European wildcats and tend to be lighter in coat color.

⚡ CONSERVATION WATCH

Small cat status Most small cats suffered drastic losses during the 20th century. For some, such as the pumas of Florida, fragmentation of habitat has isolated populations and led to inbreeding. The fur trade also had a great impact, especially on the ocelot and Geoffroy's cat, but was gradually curtailed as consumers became aware of the problems.

FACT FILE

Marbled cat Resembling a smaller version of the clouded leopard, this highly arboreal species feeds mainly on birds. Hidden among the branches of dense tropical forests, it has rarely been seen and little is known of its behavior.

🐾 Up to 21 in (53 cm)
〰 Up to 21½ in (55 cm)
⚖ Up to 11 lb (5 kg)
🐾 Solitary
⚡ Vulnerable

Nepal, N.E. India, S.E. Asia

Asiatic golden cat This felid mostly preys on small mammals and birds, but will hunt in pairs to bring down larger quarry such as buffalo calves. Females give birth to one or two young in a den made in a hollow tree or among rocks. Unusually among cats, the male helps to raise the kittens.

🐾 Up to 41 in (105 cm)
〰 Up to 22 in (56 cm)
⚖ Up to 33 lb (15 kg)
🐾 Solitary
⚡ Vulnerable

Nepal to China, Indochina, Malaya, Sumatra

Leopard cat The swimming ability of the leopard cat may help to explain its presence on many islands in Asia. A subspecies, the Iriomote cat, is found only on the small Japanese islands of Iriomote and Ryukyu.

🐾 Up to 42 in (107 cm)
〰 Up to 17½ in (44 cm)
⚖ Up to 15½ lb (7 kg)
🐾 Solitary
⚡ Locally common

Pakistan & India to China, Korea & S.E. Asia

Bay cat This species is so rare that it was not photographed until 1998. It lives in jungles and among limestone outcrops near forests on the island of Borneo. The coat is most commonly chestnut red but can also be gray.

🐾 Up to 26½ in (67 cm)
〰 Up to 15½ in (39 cm)
⚖ Up to 9 lb (4 kg)
🐾 Solitary
⚡ Endangered

Borneo

Fishing cat This cat will tap the water surface to attract fish. It will also climb trees, then dive headfirst into water, grabbing aquatic prey in its mouth.

🐾 Up to 34 in (86 cm)
〰 Up to 13 in (33 cm)
⚖ Up to 31 lb (14 kg)
🐾 Solitary
⚡ Vulnerable

India, Nepal, Sri Lanka, S.E. Asia

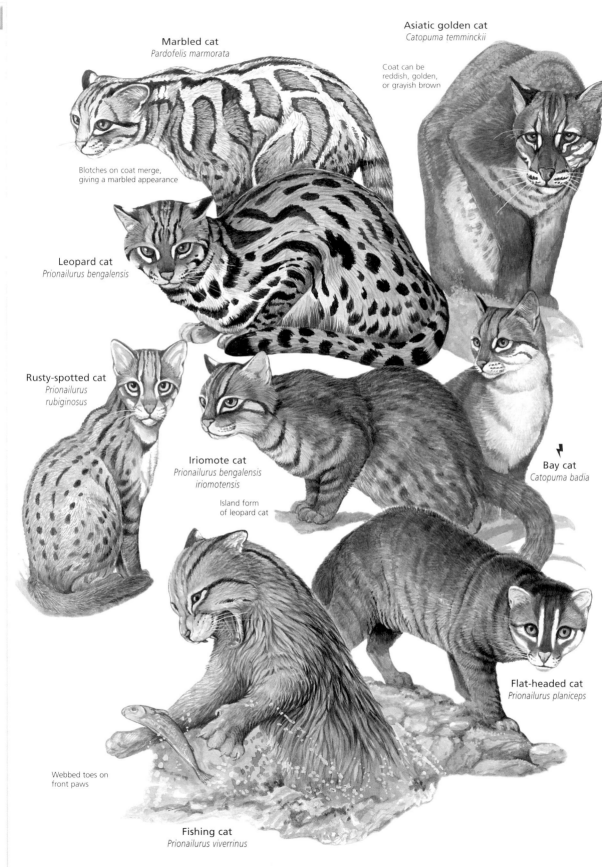

Marbled cat
Pardofelis marmorata

Blotches on coat merge, giving a marbled appearance

Asiatic golden cat
Catopuma temminckii

Coat can be reddish, golden, or grayish brown

Leopard cat
Prionailurus bengalensis

Rusty-spotted cat
Prionailurus rubiginosus

Iriomote cat
Prionailurus bengalensis iriomotensis

Island form of leopard cat

Bay cat
Catopuma badia

Flat-headed cat
Prionailurus planiceps

Webbed toes on front paws

Fishing cat
Prionailurus viverrinus

Elongated rather than rounded head

Jaguarundi
Herpailurus yaguarondi

Coat can be chestnut or brownish gray

Oncilla
Leopardus tigrinus

Ocelot
Leopardus pardalis

Margay
Leopardus wiedii

Pampas cat
Oncifelis colocolo

Kodkod
Oncifelis guigna

Geoffroy's cats have ocher coats in northern part of range, silvery gray coats in south

Geoffroy's cat
Oncifelis geoffroyi

Long, thick fur provides protection against exposed mountain environment

Andean cat
Oreailurus jacobita

FACT FILE

Jaguarundi This species is not closely related to the other South American felids and does not look like a typical cat. Sometimes called the weasel cat or otter cat, its long, slender body, short legs, and very long tail do resemble those of a mustelid. The jaguarundi is an agile climber and good swimmer.

Up to 25½ in (65 cm)
Up to 24 in (61 cm)
Up to 20 lb (9 kg)
Solitary
Uncommon

Arizona & Texas to S. Brazil & N. Argentina

Ocelot The wide variety of prey species taken by this opportunistic hunter has allowed it to live in a variety of densely covered habitats, from lush rain forests to semiarid brush. The ocelot's striking coat provides camouflage among thick vegetation, but has also made it a prime target for hunters. International trade in ocelot skins is now banned.

Up to 18½ in (47 cm)
Up to 16 in (41 cm)
Up to 26½ lb (12 kg)
Solitary
Locally common

S.E. Texas to N. Argentina

Geoffroy's cat This agile cat can walk upside down along a branch and hang from a tree by its feet. Its populations were decimated by the fur trade, with more than 340,000 skins exported from Argentina between 1976 and 1979.

Up to 26½ in (67 cm)
Up to 14½ in (37 cm)
Up to 13 lb (6 kg)
Solitary
Near threatened

S. Bolivia & Paraguay to Argentina & Chile

FELINE DEFENSE

Cats of the same species try to avoid conflict by marking their territory with scent, but hostile encounters can occur. Small cats are also at risk from larger cats. When threatened, cats will use a series of body and tail positions and facial expressions in an effort to avert what could be a costly attack.

Initial warning *A wide-eyed stare shows that the margay is prepared to defend itself.*

Last warning *With its ears folded back and mouth wide open to display its teeth, the margay gives the foe a last chance to retreat.*

HUNTING STRATEGIES

While some carnivores are chiefly foragers, surviving on carrion, easily captured invertebrate prey, or vegetation, most hunt vertebrates at least some of the time and many are capable of taking down an animal much larger than themselves. Those that target small mammals, birds, and reptiles tend to hunt alone, while larger prey often, but not always, encourages cooperative efforts. Group hunting is most common among dogs, lions, and spotted hyenas, while raccoons, civets, mongooses, mustelids, brown and striped hyenas, and most cats are more likely to be solitary predators. Dogs kill small prey by shaking it in their jaws to dislocate the neck, and defeat larger prey by disemboweling it or seizing the throat or nose. Almost all cats sink their canine teeth into the neck of their victim, while weasels, civets, mongooses, and jaguars are occipital crunchers, biting into the back of the head so the claws and teeth of the prey are kept out of the way. The larger carnivores usually need to make a substantial kill every few days. To find enough to eat, these predators often roam over extensive home ranges, which vary in size according to the abundance of prey. Lions and tigers, for example, have ranges of 8–200 square miles (20–500 sq. km) and may cover up to 12 miles (20 km) in a day.

Exception to the rule Most large carnivores need to eat vertebrates to support themselves. While insects make easy prey, they are small and can usually sustain carnivores no larger than a badger or aardwolf. The sloth bear, however, is at least five times larger than a badger but manages to survive mostly on a diet of invertebrates. Its muscular limbs and long, curved claws enable it to rip open termite mounds, releasing thousands of insects at a time.

Hyena variations Brown and striped hyenas depend largely on carrion, supplemented by invertebrates and small prey. Consequently, they tend to forage alone, as group foraging offers little advantage and would lead to aggressive competition. The larger spotted hyenas depend more on hunting and pursue larger prey, such as zebra, wildebeest, gemsbok, and impala. When the prey is substantially larger than themselves, hyenas rely on cooperation to bring it down. Even when the prey is a young, smaller animal and a single hyena could complete the task alone, the kill supplies enough food to feed several hyenas, so pack hunting avoids waste.

Family affair Spotted hyenas may live in clans of up to 80 animals, but their hunting packs are smaller and tend to be made up of closely related individuals. This ensures that a successful hunt benefits relatives rather than unrelated hyenas.

Hot pursuit Maintaining speeds of up to 35 miles per hour (60 km/h), hyenas will pursue their prey for up to 2 miles (3 km) until it tires and becomes vulnerable to attack. Only about a third of such pursuits end in success for the hyena pack.

The kill Hyenas tend to focus on young, weak, sick, or injured hoofed mammals, which they separate from the herd. When the target prey falters, the pack members will simultaneously bite the belly to disembowel it.

Moving in Even once a pack of spotted hyenas takes down an animal, they are not assured of a feast. Their main competitors are lions, which hunt the same prey and, attracted by the hyena's squabbling, may move in to steal the kill. While a pack of whooping hyenas advancing shoulder to shoulder may intimidate female or younger lions, they are no match for a male and usually surrender their meal.

Fast eaters *If undisturbed, spotted hyenas will gorge themselves, eating up to a third of their weight in meat at a time. They often hide part of a carcass in muddy water for later consumption.*

Making the most of a meal *When hyenas lose their kill to lions, they wait for the lions to finish eating and then return for the leftovers. A massive skull with a short, powerful jaw and immensely strong teeth allows hyenas to cut through the tough hides of their large prey and crush the bones to get to the marrow. Their acidic digestive system extracts all possible nutrition from the bones.*

Success and failure While predators are designed to outwit, outrun, or overpower their prey, the odds are not always in their favor. Most attempts at capture fail. The cheetah is capable of great bursts of speed in pursuit, but overheats in less than a minute and needs to rest. If the prey manages to stay ahead until this point, it will escape.

A broad hunter While some carnivores are highly specialized for capturing a particular kind of prey, others are generalists, pursuing any opportunity. The mink will hunt crustaceans and fish in water, take rabbits and birds on land, and chase small mammals down burrows. During times of scarcity, mink suffer from competition with more effective specialist predators, but can usually turn to an alternative source of food.

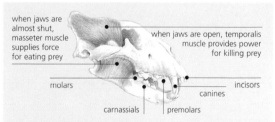

when jaws are almost shut, masseter muscle supplies force for eating prey

when jaws are open, temporalis muscle provides power for killing prey

molars

incisors

canines

carnassials

premolars

MEAT-EATING TEETH

Carnivore jaws and teeth are uniquely adapted to a diet of meat. Jaws tend to be extremely strong, able to suffocate or crush the bones of prey even when the mouth is wide open, and providing enough force to cut through flesh. Typically, carnivores have 44 teeth, with 3 incisors, 1 canine, 4 premolars, and 3 molars on each side of each jaw. The last premolar in the upper jaw and the first molar in the lower jaw form the carnassials, sharp-tipped cusps that act like scissors to shear through meat. In carnivores that primarily eat insects or plants, the equivalent teeth have flattened grinding surfaces, but their ancestors possessed carnassials. In some carnivores, particularly the cat family, the canines are especially large and are used for stabbing prey.

UNGULATES

CLASS	Mammalia
ORDERS	7
FAMILIES	28
GENERA	139
SPECIES	329

Some 65 million years ago, an order of hoofed mammals known as Condylarthra began to evolve into many diverse orders, of which seven remain. These surviving orders are all now referred to as ungulates, meaning "provided with hoofs." In fact, only two orders possess true hoofs: odd-toed ungulates (Perissodactyla) include horses, tapirs, and rhinoceroses, while even-toed ungulates (Artiodactyla) encompass pigs, hippopotamuses, camels, deer, cattle, sheep, and goats. The other five orders, each with its own specializations, are elephants (Proboscidea), aardvark (Tubulidentata), hyraxes (Hyracoidea), dugong and manatees (Sirenia), and whales and dolphins (Cetacea).

Head of the harem Like many other ungulates, zebras are territorial and live in harems of several mares dominated by a single stallion. The stallion will defend his harem from the attentions of other stallions by biting and kicking.

Mineral supplements Mountain goats, deer, and other ungulates may all converge on particular mineral-rich salt licks. It is thought that licking the rocks supplies them with nutrients that are lacking from their otherwise herbivorous diet.

HOOFS AND HERDS

Although less closely related to each other than to other members in the ungulate group, odd-toed and even-toed ungulates both stand on the tips of their toes, which are encased in hoofs. Together with their elongated metapodials (the hand and foot bones in humans), this unguligrade stance extends the leg, providing a longer stride and greater speed. As the dominant terrestrial herbivores, ungulates depend on their ability to run faster and farther than almost any large predator. They also have mobile ears, sharp, binocular vision, and a keen sense of smell to help them detect danger.

Another strategy for survival that is employed by many grassland ungulates is the formation of large herds. Living in a group increases the chance that a predator will be detected, and reduces any one individual's chance of being taken. Large herds are practical only on open plains, where many animals can remain in close contact. Many forest ungulates live in small family groups or are solitary.

Almost all ungulate species are herbivores, with teeth adapted for grinding. Their specialized digestive systems can break down cellulose, the usually indigestible component of plant cell walls. Food is fermented by microorganisms in the hindgut or in a special stomach chamber. Ruminants such as deer regurgitate the fermented food and chew it a second time, a practise known as "chewing the cud."

Elephants, hyraxes, and aardvarks lack true hoofs and do not have an unguligrade stance. While elephants have just the bones of their toes (encased in a fatty matrix) touching the ground, hyraxes and aardvarks walk on the entire foot.

Whales, dolphins, dugongs, and manatees have all evolved for life in the water, with a streamlined body and flippers. In fact, whales and dolphins were only recently classified as ungulates, when genetic studies showed that they are closely related to hippopotamuses. Some experts have even suggested placing them with even-toed ungulates in a single order called Certartiodactyla.

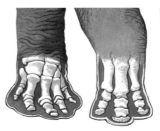
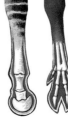

Elephant   Rhinoceros   Horse   Deer

Toes and hoofs Elephants have a broad foot with five toes encased in a fatty matrix. In the "true" ungulates, at least one toe has been lost and the remaining toes form a hoof. The hoofs of odd-toed ungulates have three toes (as in the rhinoceros) or a single toe (as in the horse), while even-toed ungulates have two or four toes, which may be fused to form a cloven hoof (as in deer).

Domestic ungulates Sheep and goats were domesticated by 7500 BC, and cattle soon followed. In all, about 15 ungulate species have been domesticated and are now found worldwide. Their success, however, has devastated much of Earth's surface and has been at the cost of wild ungulates—for example, four livestock species now account for more than 90 percent of Africa's savanna ungulates.

Browsers and grazers Ungulates may be browsers, feeding on woody vegetation such as trees and shrubs; grazers, feeding on grasses; or mixed feeders. African elephants concentrate on savanna grasses during the wet season, but switch to the woody parts of trees and shrubs when the grasses die back in the dry season.

Advanced young Although pigs have several piglets in a litter, most female hoofed mammals bear a single well-developed young, which can stand, see, and hear soon after birth. An impala will isolate herself to calve, but will rejoin the herd with her calf within a day or two.

Fermenting stomachs Ungulates rely on internal microorganisms to break down plant cellulose. Many even-toed ungulates, such as deer, cattle, and sheep, are ruminants. Their complex stomachs include a rumen, a chamber in which food is fermented by microorganisms before being regurgitated and chewed a second time. A ruminant's digestive process can take up to four days and gains maximum nutrition from food. Odd-toed ungulates, such as horses, rhinoceroses, and tapirs, ferment their food in the hindgut (the cecum and large intestine). The two-day digestive process is less efficient than that of ruminants, requiring odd-toed ungulates to consume greater quantities of food.

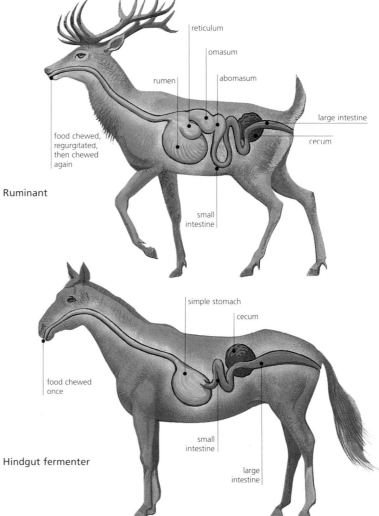

Ruminant

Hindgut fermenter

ELEPHANTS

CLASS	Mammalia
ORDER	Proboscidea
FAMILY	Elephantidae
GENERA	2
SPECIES	2

Weighing up to 7 tons (6.3 tonnes), elephants are the world's largest land animals. Their massive bulk is supported by four pillar-like legs and broad feet. An enormous head features immense fan-shaped ears and a long, flexible trunk. Full of blood vessels, the ears help to disperse the animal's body heat and will be flapped on hot days. The trunk, a union of the nose and upper lip, has more than 150,000 muscle bands and can both pick up twigs and lift heavy logs. Elephants can live for up to 70 years, longer than any land mammal apart from humans. As well as their longevity and strength, elephants are very social, intelligent, and quick to learn, traits that encouraged their domestication.

REMOVING THE THREAT
While both elephant species are threatened by habitat loss, the African elephant's handsome tusks have also made it the prime target of the ivory trade. In an attempt to halt the trade, the Kenyan government burned piles of poached tusks (below) and the international sale of ivory was temporarily banned.

Asiatic elephant   African elephant

Flexible trunk Used for caressing, lifting, feeding, dusting, smelling, as a snorkel, as a weapon, and in sound production, the elephant's trunk is superbly dextrous. Asiatic elephants have one finger-like projection at the tip, while African elephants have two.

Close relations Female elephants usually bear a single young after a gestation period of 18–24 months—the longest of any mammal. The calf is weaned very gradually, and may continue to take milk from the mother for up to 10 years. Females remain with their mother's herd, while males leave at around 13 years.

Shared care
The female elephants in a herd share the care of the young and will form a circle around them to protect them from danger.

Rapid growth *By the time it is 6 years old, a young elephant will weigh about 1 ton (1 tonne). Growth slows after about 15 years, but continues throughout its life.*

MATRIARCHS AND MUSTH

The order Proboscidea appeared about 55 million years ago and once included immense mastodons and woolly mammoths. Its members inhabited all kinds of habitat, from polar regions to rain forest, and at some time lived on all continents apart from Australia and Antarctica. Today's elephants are restricted to the forests, savanna, grasslands, and deserts of Africa and Asia.

To fuel their immense bodies, elephants spend 18–20 hours a day foraging or traveling toward food. An adult may eat up to 330 pounds (150 kg) of vegetation and drink 40 gallons (160 l) of water per day.

The basic social unit of elephants is a family group of related females and offspring, led by a matriarch. Adult males visit these groups only to mate, spending the rest of their time alone or in bachelor bands. A number of family groups may form larger herds. To maintain their social ties, elephants rely on a range of communication methods, primarily using touch (greeting one another by intertwining trunks, for example), sound (some vocalizations are much lower than human ears can hear and travel up to 2½ miles, or 4 km), and postures (a raised trunk, for instance, can be used as a warning).

Mature male elephants have periods of musth, a time of high testosterone levels when the musth gland between the eye and ear secretes fluid. The animals become more aggressive and more likely to win fights, and wander greater distances in search of females.

Humped or level back

Asiatic elephant
Elephas maximus

Skin color often masked by the dirt the animal throws over itself or the mud in which it wallows

Tusks usually found only on males

Runs from danger with tail held up, possibly as a signal to follow herd members

Tusks used to remove bark from trees, move fallen branches, mark trees, dig for water, and for fighting

Four nails on hindfoot

Larger ears than Asiatic elephant

Heavier and taller than Asiatic elephant

Concave back

Both males and females possess tusks

Trunk slightly floppier than that of Asiatic elephant

Young can follow mother a few days after birth

African elephant
Loxodonta africana

Three nails on hindfoot

FACT FILE

Asiatic elephant Smaller than the African elephant, this species is actually more closely related to the extinct woolly mammoth. The tusks are usually absent in the female. Females live in matriarchal herds of 8–40 mothers, daughters, and sisters. Males may spend much of their time alone or in temporary groups of up to seven males, but will join herds of females to mate. Elephants are vocal communicators, using low-frequency calls to maintain contact over distance; high-frequency calls to convey their mood; and loud trumpeting calls to raise the alarm.

  Up to 21 ft (6.4 m)
  Up to 10 ft (3 m)
  Up to 6 tons (5.4 t)
  Variable
  Endangered

India to S.W. China, S.E. Asia

African elephant Occupying deserts, forests, river valleys, and marshes as well as savanna, this species survives mainly in protected areas. Poaching has led to a rapid decline in numbers, with the Kenyan population dropping from 167,000 in 1970 to 22,000 in 1989. In open habitat and especially during the wet season, herds may come together to form temporary aggregations of hundreds of individuals. Elephants that inhabit forests tend to be smaller in size and live in small family groups.

  Up to 24½ ft (7.5 m)
  Up to 13 ft (4 m)
  Up to 7 tons (6.3 t)
  Variable
  Endangered

Sub-Saharan Africa

INSIDE THE HEAD

The elephant's massive skull contains pockets of air to minimize its weight. The tusks are elongated incisor teeth emerging from deep sockets. The molar teeth are replaced horizontally in a conveyor-belt fashion, with new teeth developing from behind and slowly moving forward to take the place of worn teeth.

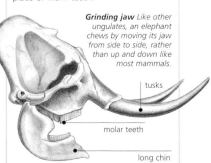

Grinding jaw Like other ungulates, an elephant chews by moving its jaw from side to side, rather than up and down like most mammals.

tusks

molar teeth

long chin

DUGONG AND MANATEES

CLASS	Mammalia
ORDER	Sirenia
FAMILIES	2
GENERA	3
SPECIES	5

Credited with inspiring the myth of the mermaid, the aquatic mammals of the order Sirenia are languid, docile creatures that never venture onto land. They are the only mammals to feed primarily on grasses and plants in shallow waters, a unique niche that may explain the order's lack of diversity, since seagrasses are much less varied than terrestrial grasses. The four living sirenian species are all found in the warm waters of tropical and subtropical regions. The dugong is restricted to the sea, while the Amazonian manatee is found only in the fresh waters of the Amazon River. African and Caribbean manatees live in freshwater, estuarine, and marine habitats.

Shaped for the water The dugong has a streamlined body, with paddle-like flippers instead of front legs. Its tail is fluked like a dolphin's, whereas a manatee's tail is more like that of a beaver. While sirenians usually conserve energy by moving slowly through the water, they are capable of swimming swiftly to escape danger.

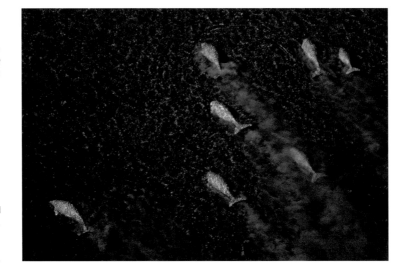

Slow mothers Sirenians have a very slow reproductive rate, which is a factor in their declining numbers. Females bear a single calf at a time, and wait at least 2 years and sometimes several before producing again. A calf nurses for up to 2 years, during which time it learns food sources and migration routes from its attentive mother.

Bristled feeder Like all sirenians, the Caribbean manatee swims slowly through the water, grazing on aquatic plants and seagrasses. It locates food with the aid of the sensitive, bristle-like hairs on its snout, and uses its muscular lips to grasp plants and pass them to the mouth.

Different skulls Manatees have a row of molar teeth, with new hind teeth constantly moving forward to replace the worn teeth. A dugong skull has an angled snout with only a few peg-like molars, which grow throughout life. In male dugongs, long incisors form tusks.

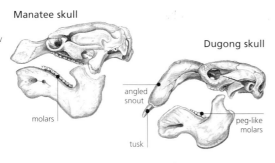

Manatee skull

molars

Dugong skull

angled snout

peg-like molars

tusk

GENTLE GRAZERS

Like other aquatic mammals, sirenians have a streamlined body, flippers, and flattened tail, and come to the surface to breathe through nostrils on top of the head. In keeping with a grazing lifestyle, the sirenian head is more like that of a pig and is used to root out grass rhizomes (underground stems) from the sediment. The angle of the dugong's snout restricts it to feeding from the bottom, but manatees can feed from all levels of the water.

The teeth of sirenians have become specialized in different ways for chewing great quantities of plant matter. The dugong uses rough horny pads in its mouth to crush its food, then grinds it with a few peg-like molars that continue to grow throughout its life. Manatees chew with their front molars, which are replaced by new teeth from behind when they wear out.

Sirenians have simple stomachs with extremely long intestines. Their plant food is broken down by microorganisms in the rear part of the digestive tract, making them hindgut fermenters like horses and other odd-toed ungulates. To counter the buoyancy provided by their gas-producing diet, sirenians have unusually dense, heavy bones.

Because their eyesight is generally poor, sirenians rely heavily on touch to find food. Their hearing is good underwater, with sounds transmitted through the skull and jaw bones. They emit squeaks to communicate, but how these sounds are produced is an enigma as they lack vocal cords.

Some sirenians live a solitary life, but more often, they are found in loosely structured groups of a dozen or so. Occasionally, such groups come together to form large herds of 100 or more. Social bonds are reinforced through playful nuzzling.

Because they have few natural predators, dugongs and manatees have developed no defenses other than their large size. This has made them easy targets for human hunters. Only about 130,000 individual sirenians remain, far fewer than in any other order of mammals.

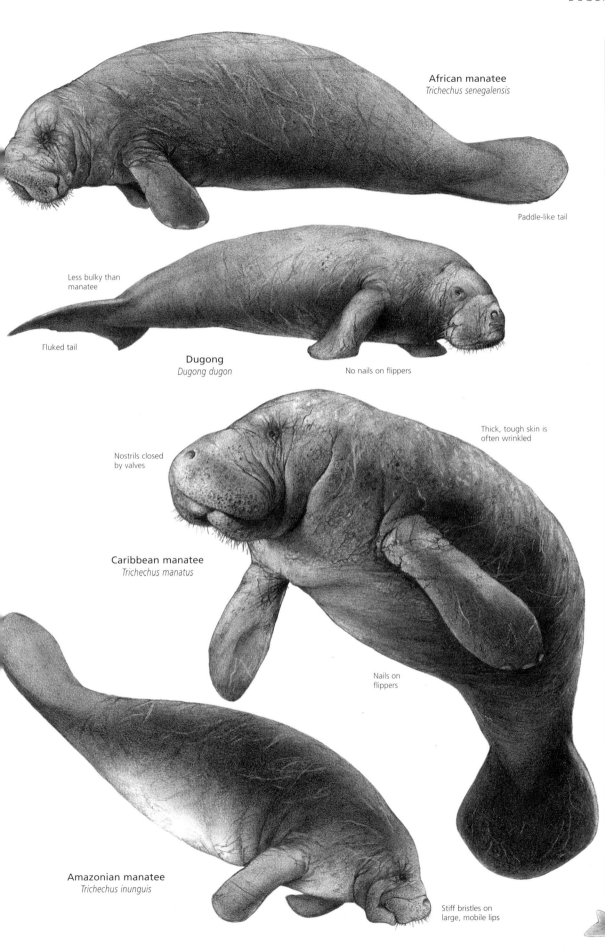

African manatee
Trichechus senegalensis

Paddle-like tail

Less bulky than manatee

Fluked tail

Dugong
Dugong dugon

No nails on flippers

Nostrils closed by valves

Thick, tough skin is often wrinkled

Caribbean manatee
Trichechus manatus

Nails on flippers

Amazonian manatee
Trichechus inunguis

Stiff bristles on large, mobile lips

FACT FILE

African manatee This poorly studied species is believed to be at least partly nocturnal. Found from coastal seas to rivers, it tends to feed from waters near or at the surface.

🐃 Up to 13 ft (4 m)
⚖ Up to 1,100 lb (500 kg)
🐾 Solitary, family group
⚡ Vulnerable

W. African coast, Niger River

Dugong Now much reduced, the original range of this marine species coincided with the distribution of seagrasses, its main food. The dugong grazes mostly on the ocean floor.

🐃 Up to 13 ft (4 m)
⚖ Up to 1,980 lb (900 kg)
🐾 Variable
⚡ Vulnerable

Red Sea to S.W. Pacific islands

Caribbean manatee This species moves freely between freshwater and marine habitats. When a female is ready to breed, a mating herd of up to 20 males will pursue her, competing for her attention for up to a month.

🐃 Up to 15 ft (4.5 m)
⚖ Up to 1,320 lb (600 kg)
🐾 Solitary
⚡ Vulnerable

Georgia & Florida to Brazil; Orinoco River

Amazonian manatee Few plants grow under the murky waters of the Amazon River, so this manatee feeds mainly on surface vegetation such as floating grasses and water hyacinths.

🐃 Up to 9 ft (2.8 m)
⚖ Up to 1,100 lb (500 kg)
🐾 Solitary
⚡ Vulnerable

Amazon basin

EXTINCT SEA COW

First sighted by Europeans in 1741, Steller's sea cow (*Hydrodamalis gigas*) became extinct in 1786, a victim of overhunting. It was the largest sirenian of all, weighing up to 11 tons (10 t).

HORSES, ZEBRAS, AND ASSES

CLASS	Mammalia
ORDER	Perissodactyla
FAMILY	Equidae
GENUS	1
SPECIES	9

The horses, zebras, and asses of the family Equidae rely on their large size, swift running style, and herding behavior to evade predation. An equid bears its weight on the tip of a single toe on each foot, a stance that provides a springy gait. The slender legs lock when at rest rather than relying on muscle contraction, a mechanism that minimizes the energy used during the many hours that the animal feeds. The teeth are highly specialized for a diet of grasses and other plants, with incisors to clip the vegetation, and complex, ridged cheek teeth for grinding. Plant cellulose is fermented in the hindgut, allowing equids to live on the abundant low-quality food of arid lands.

Wild and feral Wild equids live in grasslands, savanna, and deserts in Africa and Asia. They generally congregate in herds over large territories. Hunted for meat or hides and persecuted as competitors for grazing land, all wild equids have declined and most are at risk of extinction. Feral herds of the domestic horse can be found on every continent except Antarctica.

EVOLVING EQUIDS

All equids are covered in thick hair, with a mane along their long neck. Most species have single-colored coats, but zebras can be instantly recognized by their striking black and white stripes. Eyes at the side of the head provide good all-round vision by night and day, while erect, mobile ears with acute hearing listen out for danger. Equids tend to run away from predators, but will kick and bite to defend themselves if necessary. These highly social animals may whinny, bray, nicker, or squeal to communicate. Visual cues involving tail, ear, and mouth positions also play a role in equid communication, as does scent.

The first horse-like animal, a dog-sized mammal that walked on the soft pads of its feet, appeared about 54 million years ago. North America was the center of equid evolution, which resulted in a single-toed horse-like creature by at least 5 million years ago. Equids migrated to Africa and Asia, where modern species of zebras and asses later emerged. By the end of the last ice age, horses had vanished from North America, and were only reintroduced there by Europeans.

Humans first domesticated asses in the Middle East before 3000 BC, but within 500 years the faster and stronger domestic horse had arrived from Central Asia. Domestic horses revolutionized agriculture, transport, hunting, and warfare. Today, virtually all wild horses are feral populations of the domestic horse.

Harem of horses Wild horses, like common and mountain zebras, live in permanent groups of females and their young led by a harem male. The females are usually unrelated, having been abducted from their family group. Adult asses and Grevy's zebras form temporary associations.

The last wild horse The domestic horse is descended from the tarpan (*Equus ferus*). The only tarpan to survive into the modern era is Przewalski's horse (*E. f. przewalskii*), a subspecies that once roamed Mongolia, but is now found only in zoos and a few reintroduced populations.

Grooming together Both domestic and wild horses rely on mutual grooming to cement social bonds. Here, two foals nibble each other's shoulders and withers. The nose-to-tail stance allows them to continue to watch for predators.

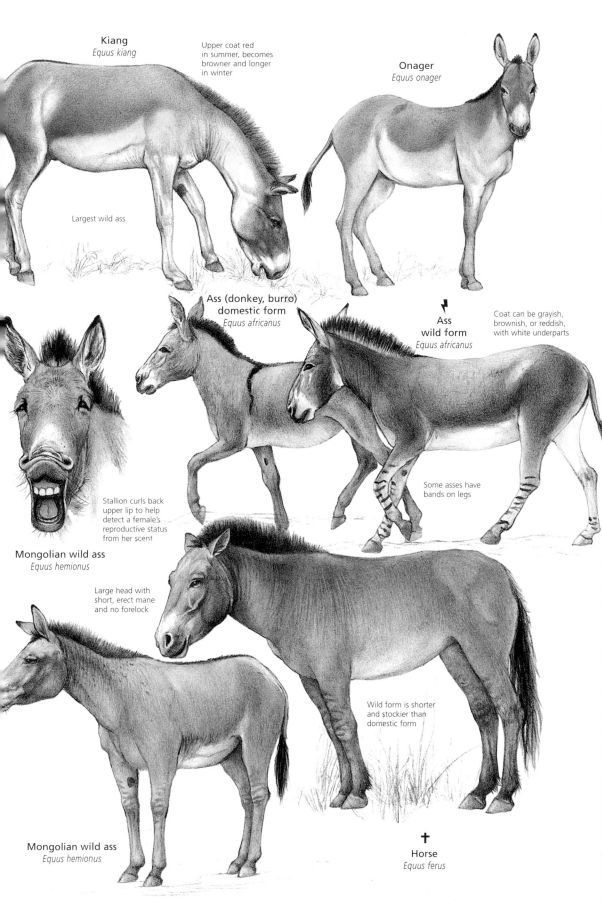

Kiang
Equus kiang

Upper coat red in summer, becomes browner and longer in winter

Largest wild ass

Onager
Equus onager

Ass (donkey, burro) domestic form
Equus africanus

Ass wild form
Equus africanus

Coat can be grayish, brownish, or reddish, with white underparts

Some asses have bands on legs

Stallion curls back upper lip to help detect a female's reproductive status from her scent

Mongolian wild ass
Equus hemionus

Large head with short, erect mane and no forelock

Wild form is shorter and stockier than domestic form

Mongolian wild ass
Equus hemionus

✝
Horse
Equus ferus

FACT FILE

Kiang Herds of up to 400 mares and offspring are led by an old female. Stallions usually live alone but several may live together during winter. In the summer mating season, stallions follow the large herds and fight one another for the right to mate.

🐎 Up to 8 ft (2.5 m)
🐎 Up to 4½ ft (1.4 m)
⚖ Up to 880 lb (400 kg)
🐾 Herd
⚡ Declining

Tibetan Plateau

Onager This wild ass is the fastest of the equids, reaching speeds of 40 miles per hour (70 km/h) in short bursts. It lives in arid environments, gathering in large, unstable herds with no lasting bonds between adults. Foals may be suckled for up to 18 months, but less than half survive their first year.

🐎 Up to 8 ft (2.5 m)
🐎 Up to 4½ ft (1.4 m)
⚖ Up to 575 lb (260 kg)
🐾 Herd
⚡ Rare

India, Iran; reintrod. in Turkmenistan

Ass In its wild form, the ass is rare, with only 3,000 individuals remaining. A surefooted animal, it was domesticated some 6,000 years ago and is still used as a beast of burden. The ass has great endurance and can survive for a long time in hot conditions with little food or water. Feral populations descended from domestic asses exist in several places. In the United States they are known as burros.

🐎 Up to 6½ ft (2 m)
🐎 Up to 4¼ ft (1.3 m)
⚖ Up to 550 lb (250 kg)
🐾 Harem
⚡ Critically endangered

Ethiopia, Eritrea, Somalia, Djibouti

⚡ CONSERVATION WATCH

The quagga *Equus quagga*, a brown zebra, became extinct in the 1870s. The horse *Equus ferus* is classified as extinct in the wild, with the last true wild subspecies, Przewalski's horse, not seen in its natural habitat since 1968. Of the nine species of equids, six are listed on the IUCN Red List, as follows:

1 Extinct
1 Extinct in the wild
1 Critically endangered
2 Endangered
1 Vulnerable

FACT FILE

Zebra Like all zebra species, this equid has a coat pattern of black stripes on a white background. Suggestions that this provides camouflage or confuses predators have been discounted. The likeliest explanation is that the stripes perform a social role, possibly helping individuals to identify each other.

ᵐ Up to 8 ft (2.5 m)
ᵐ Up to 5 ft (1.5 m)
▲ Up to 850 lb (385 kg)
♦♦♦ Harem
✦ Common

E. & S. Africa

STRIPES AND MOODS

Like all equids, zebras use a range of visual signals to express their moods. Competing stallions will shake their head, arch their neck, and stamp their feet before resorting to physical contests in which they bite each other's neck and legs. Both mares and stallions will attempt to deter a predator with a kicking display.

Prepared to bite
Stallions will display a bite threat before making physical contact.

Ready to kick
A threatened equid will kick out its back legs in a defense display.

Getting a whiff
By curling back the upper lip, a stallion directs the scent of a mare's urine to the Jacobson's organ in the roof of his mouth, which can detect whether she is ready to mate.

Largest of the wild equids

Grevy's zebra
Equus grevyi

Finely divided pattern of black on white

Zebra southern form
Equus burchelli

Shorter ears than those on other zebra species

Zebra northern form
Equus burchelli

Wide stripes on body

Mountain zebra
Equus zebra

Each individual zebra's pattern of stripes is unique

Stripes wider on rump than on body

Foals can walk within an hour of birth

Mountain zebra foal

TAPIRS

CLASS Mammalia
ORDER Perissodactyla
FAMILY Tapiridae
GENERA 1
SPECIES 4

Appearing in the fossil record before either horses or rhinoceroses, tapirs as a group have changed little in the past 35 million years. These reclusive tropical-forest browsers are about the size of a donkey, with a squat, streamlined body for moving through the thick undergrowth, and a sensitive, prehensile trunk that is used for grasping food, detecting danger through scent, and as a snorkel. Tapirs emerge from the shelter of thickets at night to feed on the leaves, buds, twigs, and fruit of low-growing plants—by distributing seeds in their feces, they play an important ecological role in the forest. Being good swimmers and fond of water, they also consume aquatic vegetation. While their small eyes provide poor vision, the senses of hearing and smell are acute. Usually solitary and sparsely distributed, tapirs communicate through high-pitched whistles and scentmarking. Following a 13-month gestation period, a female tapir generally bears a single young. While the mother is foraging, a newborn will hide among the thickets, its patterned coat providing effective camouflage in the dappled light of the forest. After a week, it will accompany the mother, eventually going off on its own by the time it is 2 years of age.

Reduced range Found at various times throughout much of North America, Europe, and Asia, tapirs are now restricted to three species in Central and South America and a single species in Southeast Asia.

Water refuge Never far from water, tapirs spend much of their time submerged, often with just the trunk appearing above the surface as a snorkel. Water provides cover from predators and relief from the heat.

FACT FILE

Brazilian tapir When this tapir plunges into water to escape a jaguar, it risks being taken by a crocodile. Its chief predator, however, is the human hunter, who follows its clear foraging trails.

🐾 Up to 6½ ft (2 m)
📏 Up to 3½ ft (1.1 m)
⚖ Up to 550 lb (250 kg)
♟ Solitary
⚡ Vulnerable

Tropical South America (E. of Andes)

Malayan tapir This species is the only living tapir in Asia. Courtship is marked by whistling pairs walking around in circles as they attempt to sniff each other's genitals.

🐾 Up to 8 ft (2.5 m)
📏 Up to 4 ft (1.2 m)
⚖ Up to 705 lb (320 kg)
♟ Solitary
⚡ Vulnerable

Myanmar, Thailand, Malaya, Sumatra

Short, bristly mane

Infant tapirs are mottled and striped to help camouflage them when their mothers are absent

Brazilian tapir
Tapirus terrestris

Disruptive pattern of black and white camouflages animal in its shady rain forest habitat

Malayan tapir
Tapirus indicus

⚡ CONSERVATION WATCH

Tapir numbers are in decline as their forest habitat is lost or fragmented, they are hunted for their meat, and livestock compete for their food. All four species are listed on the IUCN Red List, as follows:

2 Endangered
2 Vulnerable

RHINOCEROSES

CLASS	Mammalia
ORDER	Perissodactyla
FAMILY	Rhinocerotidae
GENERA	4
SPECIES	5

The snout of a rhinoceros features its most distinguishing characteristic—a great horn or two made up of fibrous keratin. Rhinoceroses use their remarkable horns to fight rivals, to defend their young against predators, to guide their young, and to push dung into piles as scented signposts. Although keratin is a common substance that is also found in human fingernails, rhino horns are attributed great potency in traditional Asian medicine. Such has been the demand that many thousands of rhinoceroses have been poached, and all five species are now at risk of extinction. Today, there are fewer than 15,000 wild rhinos in Africa, and no more than 3,000 in Asia.

Rhino standoff Both African rhino species use their horns to fight rivals, while Asian species use their sharp incisor or canine teeth. Before resorting to physical attack, rhinos will engage in a series of gestures, including pushing horns together, wiping horns on the ground, and spraying urine. Black rhinoceroses (pictured here) are especially aggressive, with half of all males and a third of females dying after fights.

High-speed charge The third heaviest of all mammal species (after the African and Asiatic elephants), the white rhinoceros is still capable of impressive bursts of speed when charging to scare off intruders.

MASSIVE HERBIVORES

The family Rhinocerotidae was once abundant, widespread, and diverse. The woolly rhinoceros, for example, roamed Europe until the end of the last ice age 10,000 years ago and appears in early cave art. A hornless rhinoceros, *Indricotherium*, was the largest animal ever to have lived on land. Today, only five species remain, two in Africa (the white rhinoceros and the black rhinoceros) and three in Asia (the Indian, the Javan, and the Sumatran).

Rhinoceroses have massive bodies supported by four stumpy legs. Three hoofed toes on each foot leave an "ace-of-clubs" print in their tracks. Their thick, wrinkled skin can be gray or brown, but its true color is often masked by dried mud, since rhinos like to wallow in muddy pools. Despite their names, there is no clear distinction in skin color between white and black rhinos: both are grayish, with the precise tinge determined by local soil color.

With a lifespan of up to 50 years, rhinos are slow breeders, a fact that has made them especially vulnerable to habitat loss and overhunting. After a gestation of about 16 months, a female bears a single young and nurses it for more than a year. Their association lasts for 2–4 years, until the next calf is born. Most adult rhinos are solitary, but breeding pairs may stay together for a few months, while females or immature males sometimes form temporary herds. White rhinos are known to form a circle around the young to protect them from predators.

Sharp hearing
Erect ears swivel to pick up faint sounds.

Cropped horn
To discourage poachers, the horn of this rhinoceros has been cropped.

Indian grazer
A prehensile upper lip helps gather tall grasses, but can be folded away for eating short grasses.

Dim sight
Small eyes at the side of the head provide poor vision.

Armor plating The Indian rhinoceros's distinctive dark gray skin falls into deep folds at the joints, resembling the plates of a coat of armor. This characteristic inspired Rudyard Kipling's famous story "How the Rhinoceros Got His Skin."

⚡ CONSERVATION WATCH

Coupled with extensive habitat loss, the trade in rhino horns (used in Asia for medicine and carvings) has had a devastating effect. Some conservationists advocate farming rhinos and cropping their horns to provide revenue for the local people and thus discourage poaching. All five rhinoceros species are listed on the IUCN Red List, as follows:

3	Critically endangered
1	Endangered
1	Near threatened

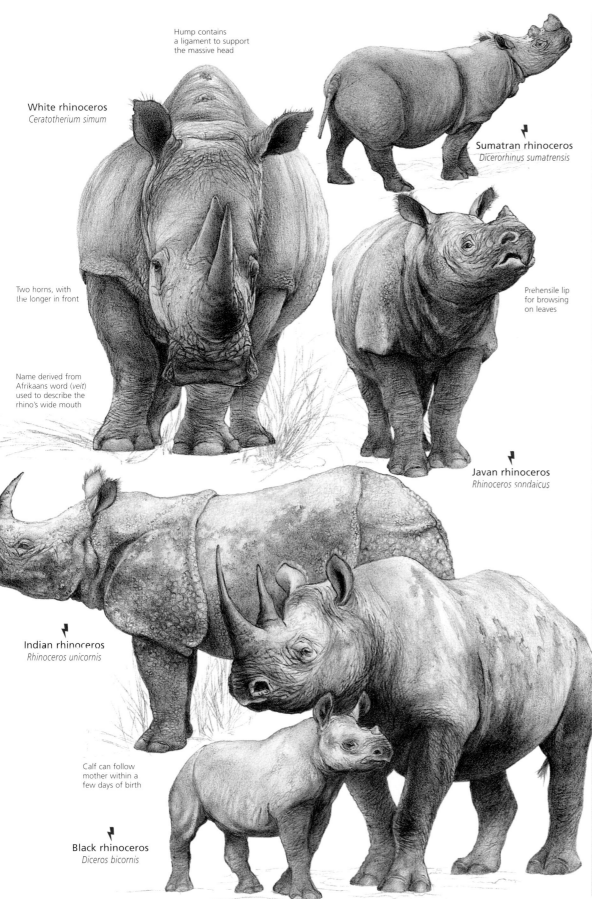

Hump contains
a ligament to support
the massive head

White rhinoceros
Ceratotherium simum

Two horns, with
the longer in front

Name derived from
Afrikaans word (*veit*)
used to describe the
rhino's wide mouth

Sumatran rhinoceros
Dicerorhinus sumatrensis

Prehensile lip
for browsing
on leaves

Javan rhinoceros
Rhinoceros sondaicus

Indian rhinoceros
Rhinoceros unicornis

Calf can follow
mother within a
few days of birth

Black rhinoceros
Diceros bicornis

FACT FILE

● Former range

White rhinoceros The largest surviving rhino, this species has a long head and squared upper lip for efficient cropping of short grasses. Despite its size, the white rhino is usually a placid animal.

  Up to 14 ft (4.2 m)
  Up to 6¼ ft (1.9 m)
  Up to 4 tons (3.6 t)
  Solitary, family group
  Near threatened

Sub-Saharan Africa

Sumatran rhinoceros The smallest of the rhinos, this is also one of the most threatened—only about 300 individuals survive in the wild. A browser that feeds mainly on saplings, it is the only Asian rhinoceros with two horns

  Up to 10½ ft (3.2 m)
  Up to 5 ft (1.5 m)
  Up to 2¼ tons (2 t)
  Solitary
  Critically endangered

Thailand, Myanmar, Malaya, Sumatra, Borneo

Javan rhinoceros This one-horned rhino has heavily folded skin resembling that of its Indian neighbor. The future of this species is uncertain: only about 60 wild individuals remain and they are restricted to two national parks.

  Up to 10½ ft (3.2 m)
  Up to 6 ft (1 8 m)
  Up to 2¼ tons (2 t)
  Solitary
  Critically endangered

Vietnam, Java

Indian rhinoceros The larger of the one-horned rhinos, this species prefers to graze on tall grasses, but will also browse shrubs, crops, and aquatic plants. It avoids the daytime heat by foraging late or early, or at night.

  Up to 12½ ft (3.8 m)
  Up to 6¼ ft (1.9 m)
  Up to 2½ tons (2.2 t)
  Solitary
  Endangered

Nepal, N.E. India

Black rhinoceros This browser has a prehensile upper lip to draw branches into its mouth. More aggressive than the white rhino, the black rhino will charge humans and vehicles.

  Up to 12½ ft (3.8 m)
  Up to 6 ft (1.8 m)
  Up to 1½ tons (1.4 t)
  Solitary
  Critically endangered

Sub-Saharan Africa

HYRAXES

CLASS	Mammalia
ORDER	Hyracoidea
FAMILY	Procaviidae
GENERA	3
SPECIES	7

About the size of a rabbit and looking rather like a large guinea pig, the hyraxes are often mistaken for rodents, but are in fact ungulates, with flattened hoof-like nails on their feet. Millions of years ago, hyraxes, some as large as tapirs, were the dominant grazing mammals of North Africa. They were displaced by larger ungulates such as antelopes and cattle. The surviving hyraxes are robust, agile creatures that scamper and leap along steep rocks and tree branches. The soles of their feet are uniquely equipped to provide traction, with soft pads kept moist by a glandular secretion, and muscles that retract the middle of the sole to form a suction pad. Hyraxes are gregarious animals, and some species live in colonies of up to 80 animals.

Africa to the Middle East Although they were once more diverse and widespread, hyraxes are now found only in Africa and the Middle East and there are just seven species in three genera. Rock hyraxes (*Procavia*) mostly live on rocky outcrops and cliffs in much of Africa and parts of the Middle East, but are also found in grassland and scrubby environments. Yellow-spotted hyraxes (*Heterohyrax*) occupy similar habitats, but are largely confined to East Africa. Tree hyraxes (*Dendrohyrax*) also make Africa their home, but tend to live in forests.

Warm huddle Most small mammals are nocturnal, but hyraxes are active by day. Unable to regulate their body temperature well, they conserve heat by huddling together and warm up by basking in the sun. Hyraxes live in family groups of several females and their offspring, headed by a territorial male. Females usually stay with their family for life, but males disperse at about 2 years of age. They may live on the edge of a family group, hoping to take over the territorial male's position.

Herbivorous hyraxes All hyrax species will feed both in trees and on the ground, and have been known to travel almost a mile (1.3 km) in search of food. Rock hyraxes mainly eat grasses, while yellow-spotted hyraxes and tree hyraxes tend to browse leafy plants. They rely on microorganisms in their multichambered stomach to digest the plant cellulose. Hyraxes are highly vocal creatures that sound like no other animal. The gregarious ground-dwellers chatter, whistle, and scream. At night, tree hyraxes begin a series of loud croaks that end in a scream. Hyrax vocabulary changes and expands throughout life. Young hyraxes utter long chatters that progressively intensify, but they make only a fraction of the sounds emitted by their adult relatives.

Tuft of hair covers scent gland on back

Southern tree hyrax
Dendrohyrax arboreus

Hoof-like nails

Yellow-spotted hyrax
Heterohyrax brucei

Rock hyrax
Procavia capensis

Large eyes provide sharp vision

Long upper incisors grow continuously

⚡ **CONSERVATION WATCH**

Hunted pelts Tree hyraxes are losing habitat as forests disappear. At least one species, the eastern tree hyrax (*Dendrohyrax validus*), is extensively hunted for its pelt. Of the seven species of hyraxes, three are listed on the IUCN Red List as vulnerable.

Standing guard Hyraxes are prey for eagles, pythons, and leopards. While a group is busy foraging or resting, at least one member will keep watch for danger. A loud warning cry will send the animals scurrying for cover among the rocks.

MIXED LIVING

Hyraxes include one of the few examples of two mammal species cohabiting. The yellow-spotted hyrax and the rock hyrax have been found living together on the same kopje (rocky outcrop), sharing holes for shelter by night and then huddling together to warm up by day. They do not interbreed, but females tend to give birth at the same time, and members of both species show great interest in the young. The two species avoid competing with each other by eating different foods.

Different diets While the yellow-spotted hyrax is a browser, feeding mainly on leaves, the rock hyrax is a grazer and concentrates on grasses.

AARDVARK

CLASS	Mammalia
ORDER	Tubulidentata
FAMILY	Orycteropodidae
GENERA	1
SPECIES	1

A medium-sized pig-like animal with a stocky body, long snout, and large ears, the aardvark is the only living member of the order Tubulidentata, which evolved from an early hoofed mammal. Solitary and nocturnal, this highly specialized creature emerges from its burrow after dark to search for ants and termites, taking up to 50,000 insects a night. A keen sense of smell helps the aardvark to detect prey, while its powerful, clawed feet can excavate a termite mound in a few minutes. The hair-lined nostrils can be contracted and the ears folded back to keep out dirt. A long, sticky tongue snatches the insects, which are usually swallowed without chewing and ground up in the animal's muscular stomach. With its thick skin and sharp claws, an adult aardvark is vulnerable to few predators other than hyenas and humans.

Aardvark
Orycteropus afer

Determined digger An aardvark uses the four shovel-shaped claws on each forefoot to dig out food and excavate burrows.

⚡ CONSERVATION WATCH

Specialized aardvarks Although the aardvark is not considered to be threatened, its highly specialized diet makes it vulnerable to habitat alteration. Grazing by both wild and domestic ungulates can benefit aardvarks, as termites flourish in the trampled ground. Crop farming, on the other hand, may cause a decline in aardvark numbers. Aardvarks are also hunted for their flesh.

THE CATTLE FAMILY

CLASS	Mammalia
ORDER	Artiodactyla
FAMILY	Bovidae
GENERA	47
SPECIES	135

The family Bovidae includes many millions of domesticated cattle, sheep, goats, and water buffalo. The 135 species of wild bovid are much more diverse, ranging from the dwarf antelope, just 10 inches (25 cm) tall and weighing as little as 5 pounds (2 kg), to massive animals such as bison, which can be more than 6 feet (2 m) high at the shoulder and weigh up to 1 ton (1 tonne). Cattle and their kin occur naturally throughout much of Eurasia and North America, and introduced species have formed feral populations in Australasia, but bovids reach their greatest numbers and variety in the grasslands, savanna, and forests of Africa.

Wide spread Bovids are distributed from hot deserts and tropical forests to arctic and alpine regions. There are no native bovids in Australia or South America, but domestic species are found worldwide. There are more than a billion domestic cattle in the world, and all are descended from aurochs, wild cattle that were once widespread but became extinct in 1627.

A DIVERSE FAMILY

The cattle, buffalo, bison, antelopes, gazelles, sheep, goats, and other members of Bovidae are ruminants, with a four-chambered stomach for fermenting plant cellulose. This efficient digestive system has allowed bovids to make the most of low-nutrient foods such as grasses and colonize a wide array of habitats, from arid scrublands to arctic tundra. Grazing bovids tend to have a substantial, stocky build to house their large stomachs. Antelopes and other slender bovids are often more selective browsers.

All male and many female bovids have horns made up of a bony core covered in a layer of keratin, which is never shed. Always unbranched with pointed tips, bovid horns vary in size and can be straight, curved, or spiral. They may be used in contests between males or to fend off predators. The legs of bovids are adapted for running away from danger. Bovids bear their weight on the two middle toes of each foot, which form a cloven hoof. The main bones in the feet are fused to form the cannon bone, which helps to absorb the impact of running.

While some bovids are solitary or live in pairs, most are gregarious. Some species live in harems led by a male, while others have herds made up of females and young, with males being largely solitary or associating in bachelor herds. Group living not only reduces the risk of predation, but also allows members to share information about feeding sites.

Cattle and sheep were first domesticated several thousand years ago. Since then, most wild bovids have declined. Extensively hunted for food, hides, and sport, wild species have also lost much of their natural range to agriculture.

Ringed horns
When male gazelles wrestle with their horns, the ridges prevent the horns slipping and causing serious injury.

Two-tone
The Thomson's gazelle's two-toned coat is interrupted by black markings on its face and along its side.

Safety in numbers Cape buffalo usually live in herds of 50–500 females and young but thousands, including males, may congregate during the wet season. Weak buffalo can survive within a herd, which will cooperate to drive off predators.

Ever alert As prey species, bovids such as gazelles rely on their sharp senses to detect danger. Most have large, mobile ears; eyes on the side of the head for all-round vision; and a keen nose. The striking coloration of many species may help to camouflage them by breaking up their outline.

☙ CONSERVATION WATCH

Of the 135 species of bovids, 83% are listed on the IUCN Red List, as follows:

4	Extinct
2	Extinct in the wild
7	Critically endangered
20	Endangered
25	Vulnerable
37	Conservation dependent
19	Near threatened

Abbott's duiker
Cephalophus spadix

Yellow-backed duiker
Cephalophus silvicultor

Duiker species vary in size but share distinctive body shape

Red-flanked duiker
Cephalophus rufilatus

Large gland beneath each eye produces secretion used in scentmarking

Common duiker
Sylvicapra grimmia

Banded duiker
(zebra duiker)
Cephalophus zebra

Short, conical horns

White band breaks up animal's outline

Ader's duiker
Cephalophus adersi

Ogilby's duiker
Cephalophus ogilbyi

FACT FILE

Duikers Duikers are small, short-horned antelopes that browse at the forest edge, occasionally supplementing their diet with insects and small vertebrates. The name *duiker*—an Afrikaans word for "diver"—was inspired by this shy animal's habit of diving into the underbrush when frightened.

Banded duiker This muscular species is easily identified by the striking stripes of its coat. As in zebras, each banded duiker's pattern of stripes is unique. Banded duikers are diurnal creatures that usually live in pairs, with the pair bond reinforced by mutual grooming.

- Up to 35½ in (90 cm)
- Up to 19½ in (50 cm)
- Up to 44 lb (20 kg)
- Solitary, pair
- Vulnerable

Liberia

Common duiker This nocturnal antelope lives at higher altitudes than any other African hoofed mammal. It relies on remarkable speed and stamina to escape its predators, which include big cats, dogs, baboons, pythons, crocodiles, and eagles.

- Up to 45½ in (115 cm)
- Up to 19½ in (50 cm)
- Up to 46½ lb (21 kg)
- Solitary
- Common

Sub-Saharan Africa except rain-forest zone

Ader's duiker Active by day, this species tends to live in territorial pairs. It feeds mainly on flowers, fruit, and leaves from the forest floor, taking advantage of scraps discarded by monkeys and birds in the trees above. Like many other duikers, Ader's duiker has a soft, silky coat with a reddish crest on its head.

- Up to 28½ in (72 cm)
- Up to 12½ in (32 cm)
- Up to 26½ lb (12 kg)
- Solitary, pair
- Endangered

Zanzibar, coastal S.W. Kenya

⚡ CONSERVATION WATCH

Dazzled prey Prized by the bushmeat trade and as trophies, duikers make easy targets at night when they are dazzled by the lights of hunters. The IUCN Red List classifies a total of 16 duiker species as threatened. The rarest of these species is the endangered Ader's duiker, which has fewer than 1,400 individuals remaining in the wild.

FACT FILE

Lichtenstein's hartebeest Males of this savanna species are territorial, marking their claim in the ground with their horns. Rivals will fight for the right to mate, with the victor leading a harem of 3–10 females and their young. Weaker males live alone or form loose bachelor bands.

- Up to 7 ft (2.1 m)
- Up to 4¼ ft (1.3 m)
- Up to 375 lb (170 kg)
- Small group
- Conserv. dependent

S. Africa

Hunter's hartebeest One of the world's rarest mammals, this species declined from 14,000 to 300 animals in the wild between 1976 and 1995. A selective grazer, it eats only short, newly sprouting grasses and moves to another area if the grasses grow long or are disturbed by other grazers. Many scientists believe that Hunter's hartebeest represents the evolutionary link between true hartebeests and the genus *Damaliscus*, making its survival of the utmost importance to the study of antelope evolution.

- Up to 6½ ft (2 m)
- Up to 4¼ ft (1.3 m)
- Up to 355 lb (160 kg)
- Herd
- Critically endangered

Kenya–Somalia border region

Topi and tsessebe These large grazing antelopes breed once a year, usually calving at the end of the dry season. In a large herd, the calves are likely to be followers, protected within a group of adults. In smaller herds, the calves may be hiders, concealed in dense vegetation while the adults forage.

- Up to 8½ ft (2.6 m)
- Up to 4 ft (1.2 m)
- Up to 310 lb (140 kg)
- Herd
- Conserv. dependent

Savanna zone of sub-Saharan Africa

Common hartebeest With its sloping back, this large animal can appear awkward, but it is capable of reaching speeds of 50 miles per hour (80 km/h). It lives on open plains, preferring edge habitats near forest. Hartebeest may join other antelopes and zebras to form large aggregations.

- Up to 6¼ ft (1.9 m)
- Up to 4¼ ft (1.3 m)
- Up to 330 lb (150 kg)
- Herd
- Conserv. dependent

Sahel, Serengeti, Namibia to Botswana

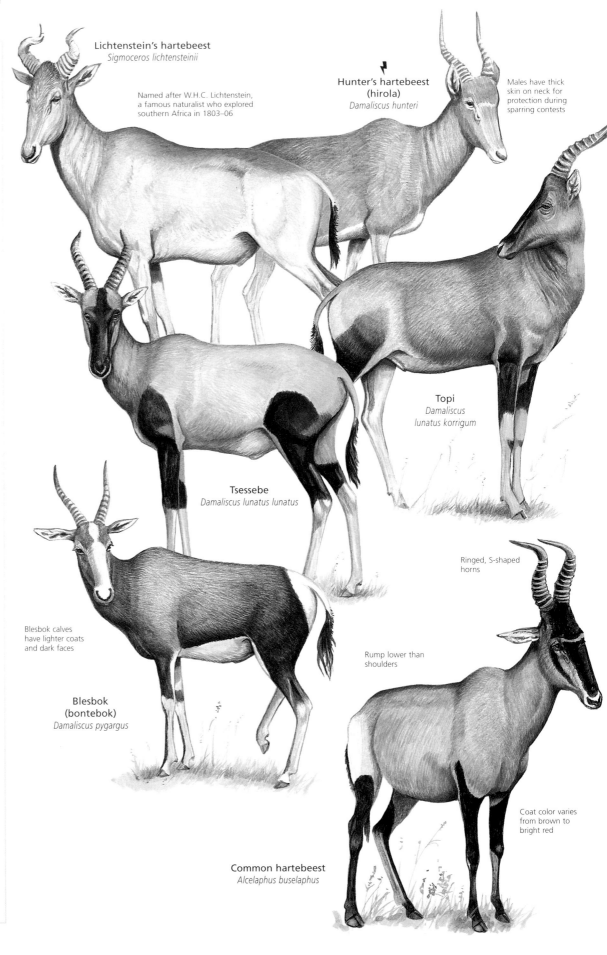

Lichtenstein's hartebeest
Sigmoceros lichtensteinii

Named after W.H.C. Lichtenstein, a famous naturalist who explored southern Africa in 1803–06

Hunter's hartebeest (hirola)
Damaliscus hunteri

Males have thick skin on neck for protection during sparring contests

Topi
Damaliscus lunatus korrigum

Tsessebe
Damaliscus lunatus lunatus

Ringed, S-shaped horns

Blesbok calves have lighter coats and dark faces

Blesbok (bontebok)
Damaliscus pygargus

Rump lower than shoulders

Coat color varies from brown to bright red

Common hartebeest
Alcelaphus buselaphus

Horns of a male
gemsbok can be up
to 5 feet (1.5 m) long

Gemsbok
Oryx gazella

Black-tufted tail

Dark markings on legs,
flanks, and face

Impala
Aepyceros melampus

S-shaped, ridged
horns only on male

Can leap up to 10 feet
(3 m) off the ground

Scent glands
beneath patches
of black hair on
rear feet

Wildebeest
Connochaetes taurinus

Vertical stripes
of longer hair
on back

**White-tailed gnu
(black wildebeest)**
Connochaetes gnou

FACT FILE

Gemsbok This species usually lives in herds of about 40 individuals, but hundreds may congregate during the wet season. During dry periods, the gemsbok can go without drinking for several days, surviving on the moisture content of fruit and roots.

 Up to 5¼ ft (1.6 m)
 Up to 4 ft (1.2 m)
 Up to 530 lb (240 kg)
 Herd
 Conserv. dependent

E. & S.W. Africa

Impala Mainly a grazer during the wet season, when it feeds on lush new grasses, the impala switches to browsing woody plants in the dry season. When threatened, this animal usually attempts to outrun the danger but may also try to confuse a predator by leaping in random directions.

 Up to 5 ft (1.5 m)
 Up to 35½ in (90 cm)
 Up to 110 lb (50 kg)
 Herd
 Conserv. dependent

Savanna zone of E. & S. Africa

Wildebeest Most wildebeest young are born within a single 3-week season, following a gestation of about 8 months. Within a few minutes of its birth, a calf can stand and nurse. About 40 minutes later, it can run.

 Up to 7½ ft (2.3 m)
 Up to 5 ft (1.5 m)
 Up to 550 lb (250 kg)
 Herd
 Conserv. dependent

E. & S. Africa

RUTTING SEASON

During the mating season, which usually occurs at the end of the wet season, male impalas go into rut and will strongly defend their territory with scentmarking, defensive postures, and physical contests. Territoriality breaks down during the dry season, when impalas extend and overlap their ranges.

A noisy display
The male impala's roaring display begins with a few explosive snorts, followed by several resonant deep grunts.

FACT FILE

Saiga Apart from its ridged horns and the long, mobile nose that hangs over its mouth, this antelope resembles a small sheep. The breeding season takes a harsh toll on male saigas. Relying on stores of fat rather than grazing, males expend great energy defending their harem of several or more females against the attentions of other males. By the end of the season, up to 90 percent will have died in battle or from starvation or predation. Thousands of saigas may then form mixed herds to migrate to summer pastures.

⬆	Up to 4½ ft (1.4 m)
📏	Up to 31½ in (80 cm)
⬛	Up to 152 lb (69 kg)
▲▲▲	Herd
🌱	Critically endangered

Russia, Kazakhstan

PRONKING

Gazelles sometimes leap repeatedly, keeping their back arched and legs stiff and landing on all fours—a habit known as "pronking" or "stotting." This behavior may occur when an animal is excited or alarmed and possibly distracts predators or warns them that they have been detected.

Leaping springbok
Named after its habit of pronking, the springbok erects the white crest on its back as it leaps up to 13 feet (4 m) in the air.

🗲 CONSERVATION WATCH

Dangerous horns Prized in Chinese medicine as a cure for fevers, the horns of the male saiga are eagerly traded on the black market. Since the breakup of the Soviet Union in 1990, conservation measures have weakened and poaching has dramatically increased. Hunters target only males, so the surviving males are defending ever-larger harems and cannot impregnate all the females. Over the past 10 years or so, saiga numbers have declined by about 80 percent.

Gerenuk
Litocranius walleri

Beira antelope
Dorcatragus megalotis

Can stand on hindlimbs to browse on leaves that are out of reach of most antelopes

Chiru
(Tibetan antelope)
Pantholops hodgsonii

Springbok
Antidorcas marsupialis

Blackbuck
Antilope cervicapra

Saiga
Saiga tatarica

Large, fleshy nose filters dust from air in summer and warms air in winter

Dibatag
Ammodorcas clarkei

Oribi
Ourebia ourebi

Scent gland
beneath eye

Steenbok
Raphicerus campestris

Short, spike-like horns
on males

Klipspringer
Oreotragus oreotragus

Guenther's dik-dik
Madoqua guentheri

Peg-like hoofs for
traveling over rocks

Waterbuck
Kobus ellipsiprymnus

Bohor reedbuck
Redunca redunca

Reedbucks usually
live near water

Mountain reedbuck
Redunca fulvorufula

FACT FILE

Steenbok Exclusively a browser, this swift antelope prefers nutritious new growth such as young leaves, flowers, fruit, and shoots. It is the only bovid known to scrape the ground before and after urinating and defecating.

🦌 Up to 33½ in (85 cm)
📏 Up to 19½ in (50 cm)
⚖ Up to 24½ lb (11 kg)
🐾 Solitary, pair
🌿 Common

E. & S. Africa

Klipspringer This sure-footed cliff dweller has a thick, moss-like coat that protects it from bumps and scrapes. It lives in small family groups in which one member acts as sentinel, giving a shrill whistle to warn of danger.

🦌 Up to 35½ in (90 cm)
📏 Up to 23½ in (60 cm)
⚖ Up to 28½ lb (13 kg)
🐾 Pair, family band
🌿 Conserv. dependent

Mountain & rocky areas in E. & S. Africa

Guenther's dik-dik The long, mobile snout of this shy antelope is thought to help control the animal's temperature, with blood diverted to the snout being cooled before it travels to the brain.

🦌 Up to 25½ in (65 cm)
📏 Up to 15 in (38 cm)
⚖ Up to 12 lb (5.5 kg)
🐾 Pair
🌿 Common

N.E. Africa

Waterbuck Old, weak herd animals are usually easy targets for predators. As a waterbuck ages, however, the secretions released by its sweat glands gradually impart an unpleasant taste to the flesh, encouraging predators to look elsewhere for a meal.

🦌 Up to 8 ft (2.4 m)
📏 Up to 4½ ft (1.4 m)
⚖ Up to 660 lb (300 kg)
🐾 Herd
🌿 Conserv. dependent

Savanna zone of sub-Saharan Africa

Mountain reedbuck This species can breed at any time, taking advantage of favorable conditions whenever they occur. Like many antelopes and deer, it has a white patch under the tail that is displayed as it runs away from danger.

🦌 Up to 4¼ ft (1.3 m)
📏 Up to 28½ in (72 cm)
⚖ Up to 66 lb (30 kg)
🐾 Harem
🌿 Conserv. dependent

Mountains of C., E. & S. Africa

Cushioned fights
Sand gazelles sometimes have "air-cushion" fights, with the rivals charging at each other headfirst but stopping about 12 inches (30 cm) apart. If neither admits defeat after a series of such charges, physical fighting ensues.

Locking horns
Like other gazelles, sand gazelles fight by lowering the head, locking horns, and then twisting and pushing until one gives up and moves away.

MALE COMPETITION

During the breeding season, male gazelles will defend their territory and harem against challengers. Males mark their territory with secretions from the glands beneath each eye, as well as with urine and feces. Threat displays begin with the head raised so the horns lie along the back, and progress to the head tucked in with the horns vertical. Head lowered with horns pointed at the opponent is usually the last display before physical contact.

Time out
Gazelles may interrupt a fight for a spot of feigned grazing before resuming the contest.

Dangerous games
While bachelor gazelles will practice their fighting skills in harmless sparring bouts, territorial males sometimes inflict serious injury.

FACT FILE

Thomson's gazelle With 90 percent of its diet consisting of grass, this species is almost exclusively a grazer. Thousands of individuals congregate for annual migrations, moving to woodland in the dry season and to grassland in the wet. Mature males establish territories, which are crossed by small, loosely structured groups of foraging females and offspring.

🦌 Up to 3½ ft (1.1 m)
📏 Up to 25½ in (65 cm)
⚖ Up to 55 lb (25 kg)
🐾 Herd
🌱 Conserv. dependent

E. Africa

Grant's gazelle This large species has a unique courting ritual in which the male makes sputtering sounds as he follows the female with his head and tail raised. Highly adapted to its hot, dry environment, Grant's gazelle can stand on its hindlimbs to reach moisture-rich leaves.

🦌 Up to 5 ft (1.5 m)
📏 Up to 37½ in (95 cm)
⚖ Up to 175 lb (80 kg)
🐾 Herd
🌱 Conserv. dependent

E. Africa

Dama gazelle
Gazella dama

Thomson's gazelle
Gazella thomsonii

Male horns are thicker and longer than those of female

Grant's gazelle
Gazella granti

Spanish ibex
Capra pyrenaica

West Caucasian tur
Capra caucasica

Coat becomes
redder in summer

Long outer coat
protects warm,
dense underfur

Mountain goat
Oreamnos americanus

Flexible hoof
pads to grip
uneven ground

Chamois
Rupicapra rupicapra

Serow
Capricornis sumatraensis

Takin
Budorcas taxicolor

FACT FILE

Spanish ibex Once abundant on the Iberian Peninsula, the Spanish ibex has suffered a dramatic decline in modern times, mainly because of overhunting. Fewer than 30,000 ibex remain and some subspecies are extinct.

🐐	Up to 4½ ft (1.4 m)
🐐	Up to 29½ in (75 cm)
⚖	Up to 175 lb (80 kg)
🐾	Herd
↯	Near threatened

Spain

West Caucasian tur This high-altitude creature lives in stable groups of a few dozen animals, which sometimes form herds of up to 500 animals. It migrates to higher ground for a diet of grasses in summer, switching to tree and shrub foliage from lower slopes in winter.

🐐	Up to 5½ ft (1.7 m)
🐐	Up to 3½ ft (1.1 m)
⚖	Up to 220 lb (100 kg)
🐾	Herd
↯	Endangered

W. Caucasus Mts

Mountain goat This animal can ascend rocky slopes with speed and agility as it searches for food such as grass, lichens, and woody plants.

🐐	Up to 5¼ ft (1.6 m)
🐐	Up to 4 ft (1.2 m)
⚖	Up to 310 lb (140 kg)
🐾	Family band
↯	Locally common

W. North America

DEFENDERS AND GRAZERS

Sheep, goats, musk oxen, and their kin are collectively called goat-antelopes. They belong to the subfamily Caprinae, which first appeared in the tropics, but gradually moved into extreme locations such as deserts and mountains. Today's species range from resource defenders, such as serows, which live in productive habitats, to grazers, such as chamois, which tend to be gregarious, wide-ranging, and adapted to harsh conditions.

Alpine life *Living above the treeline in Europe and Western Asia, chamois announce danger with foot stamping and whistles and flee across uneven ground in great leaps until they reach an inaccessible spot.*

FACT FILE

Himalayan tahr During the summer rutting season, competing males walk with their mane erect and head down to display their horns, with the stronger blocking the other's path or chasing it away. The contest rarely escalates to head wrestling.

🐂 Up to 4½ ft (1.4 m)
🐂 Up to 3¼ ft (1 m)
⬛ Up to 220 lb (100 kg)
🐾 Herd
⚡ Vulnerable

Himalayas

Nilgiri tahr Vast herds of this species once roamed the grass-covered hills of southern India, but hunting and habitat loss reduced its numbers to only about 100 animals. As a result of conservation efforts, the total population has now risen to about 1,000 animals. The Nilgiri tahr has a coarse coat, with a short, bristly mane.

🐂 Up to 4½ ft (1.4 m)
🐂 Up to 3¼ ft (1 m)
⬛ Up to 220 lb (100 kg)
🐾 Herd
⚡ Endangered

Nilgiri Mts (S. India)

Markhor This animal has suffered from excessive hunting and now survives only in fragmented populations in isolated, rugged terrain above the treeline. Its spiraling horns are prized both by trophy hunters and in Chinese medicine. Competition with domestic goats for food is also taking its toll.

🐂 Up to 6 ft (1.8 m)
🐂 Up to 3½ ft (1.1 m)
⬛ Up to 245 lb (110 kg)
🐾 Herd
⚡ Endangered

Turkmenistan to Pakistan

Saola Until the 1990s, no new large mammal species had been scientifically described for decades. Then in 1992, the saola was discovered in Vietnam, a country where a protracted war and limited international contact had impeded study of its fauna. Considered one of the world's rarest mammals, the saola is a nocturnal, forest-dwelling ox found only in remote mountainous regions. It travels in small groups of a few animals and appears to be a browser, feeding on fig leaves and other rain-forest vegetation.

🐂 Up to 6½ ft (2 m)
🐂 Up to 35½ in (90 cm)
⬛ Up to 220 lb (100 kg)
🐾 Solitary, family band
⚡ Endangered

Laos, Vietnam

Male has thick mane of fur around neck and shoulders

Nilgiri tahr
Hemitragus hylocrius

Himalayan tahr
Hemitragus jemlahicus

Arabian tahr
Hemitragus jayakari

Horns can be 5 feet (1.5 m) long

Inside edge of horns is sharp

Markhor
Capra falconeri

Bezoar (wild goat)
Capra aegagrus

Saola (Vu Quang ox)
Pseudoryx nghetinhensis

Male's horn size determines rank

Female horns have the same shape as male horns but are smaller

Bighorn sheep
Ovis canadensis

Aoudad (Barbary sheep)
Ammotragus lervia

Ventral mane of long white hair

Dall sheep
Ovis dalli

Siberian bighorn sheep
Ovis nivicola

Male horns almost meet at top of head in a "boss;" female horns are smaller with no boss

Musk ox
Ovibos moschatus

Long guard hairs can almost reach the ground

FACT FILE

Aoudad Originating in the hills of the Sahara, the aoudad was introduced to Europe in the 1800s and to the southwest United States in the 1950s. Before mating takes place, the female aoudad licks the flanks of the male, and the pair may touch muzzles.

- Up to 5½ ft (1.7 m)
- Up to 3½ ft (1.1 m)
- Up to 320 lb (145 kg)
- Herd
- Vulnerable

N. Africa; introd. Europe & USA

Bighorn sheep To win the right to mate, male bighorn sheep will fight head to head, with contests sometimes lasting more than 24 hours. As well as their massive horns, which can weigh up to 30 pounds (14 kg), these sheep have a reinforced skull that is linked to the spine by a thick tendon.

- Up to 6 ft (1.8 m)
- Up to 4 ft (1.2 m)
- Up to 300 lb (135 kg)
- Herd
- Conserv. dependent

W. North America

ARCTIC SURVIVORS

Musk oxen must survive long winters with subzero temperatures and little light. Their long guard hairs shield a dense underfur that is shed in spring. To reach grasses and sedges under the snow, musk oxen clear circular feeding patches with their horns and feet. A herd will crowd around a young musk ox to protect it from a predator.

- Up to 7½ ft (2.3 m)
- Up to 5 ft (1.5 m)
- Up to 905 lb (410 kg)
- Herd
- Uncommon

Arctic Canada & Alaska; Greenland

FACT FILE

Anoa Usually solitary, this species lives in lowland forests and wetlands. It feeds on the plants of the understory.

- Up to 5½ ft (1.7 m)
- Up to 3¼ ft (1 m)
- Up to 660 lb (300 kg)
- Family band
- Endangered

Sulawesi

Bison North America was once home to about 60 million bison, but the species now survives in the wild only in two national parks. Bison live in groups of females, offspring, and a few older males. Other mature males may live alone or form bachelor bands.

- Up to 11½ ft (3.5 m)
- Up to 6½ ft (2 m)
- Up to 1 ton (1 t)
- Herd
- Conserv. dependent

Canada, N.W. USA

Gaur Herds of females and juveniles led by a single male emerge from the forest early in the day to graze on nearby grassy slopes. They return to the forest at night to sleep.

- Up to 11 ft (3.3 m)
- Up to 7¼ ft (2.2 m)
- Up to 1 ton (1 t)
- Herd
- Vulnerable

India to Indochina & Malaya

Yak While domesticated yaks are found throughout much of Asia, wild yaks are restricted to uninhabited alpine tundra and cold steppe regions.

- Up to 11 ft (3.3 m)
- Up to 6½ ft (2 m)
- Up to 1 ton (1 t)
- Herd
- Vulnerable

Tibet

CONSERVATION WATCH

Wild cattle and buffalo Hunting, habitat loss, and domestic livestock (which interbreed with wild species, pass on diseases, and compete for food) have had a devastating effect on wild cattle and buffalo species. Today, most depend on protected reserves for their survival and a few, including the kouprey and tamaraw, are near extinction. Conservation programs have had some success, notably with the wisent (European bison), which was declared extinct in the wild in 1919, but has since been reintroduced from zoo stocks.

Mountain anoa
Bubalus quarlesi

Anoa
Bubalus depressicornis

Horns can be held flat along back to avoid becoming entangled in forest undergrowth

Tamaraw
Bubalus mindorensis

Hump of raised muscle

Bison
Bison bison

Hair longer at front than at rear of body

Large lungs and high red blood cell count allow yaks to flourish at high altitudes

Gaur (seladang)
Bos frontalis

Yak
Bos grunniens

Wild males are three times heavier than wild females, and two to three times heavier than domestic males

Kouprey
Bos sauveli

Nilgai
Boselaphus tragocamelus

Largest Asian antelope

Lesser kudu
Tragelaphus imberbis

11–14 vertical stripes branch off one long stripe along spine

Four-horned antelope
Tetracerus quadricornis

BOVID HORNS

All bovids have hollow, unbranched horns made up of a layer of keratin surrounding a bony core. Unlike tusks, horns leave the mouth free for grazing. Horns are sometimes used for defense, although bovids generally prefer to flee a predator if they can. The bovid species with the most elaborate horns are those that feature territorial or harem males, which must compete with one another in order to mate.

Eland
Taurotragus oryx

Dewlap may help to dissipate heat

The most horns
The four-horned antelope is the only bovid with four horns.

Greatest span
The African buffalo (*Syncerus caffer*) has a horn span of 50 inches (1.3 m).

Greater kudu
Tragelaphus strepsiceros

Spiral design
The spiral shape of the kudu's horns helps them to lock during contests, preventing them from slipping and gouging the rival.

Male horns can grow to 4 feet (1.2 m) in length

Corkscrew horns
The eland of Africa's savanna has tightly twisted horns with sharp points.

Bongo
Tragelaphus eurycerus

Giant eland
Taurotragus derbianus

INCREDIBLE JOURNEYS

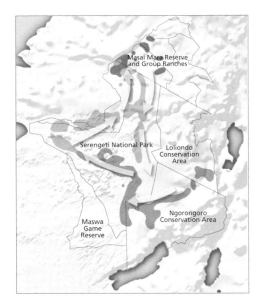

Among the most astounding sights in nature are the seasonal migrations of large, hoofed grazers such as caribou in Canada and Alaska, gazelles in Mongolia, kob in southern Sudan, and wildebeest, zebras, and gazelles in East Africa. Migrating herds number in the thousands, and are prompted by changes in the weather to begin their mass movement. In colder climates, caribou and gazelles travel north to summer ranges, and south to winter ranges. In Africa, herd movement relates to the succession of wet and dry seasons. The greatest of all today's migrations is that of roughly 1.3 million wildebeest, accompanied by about 200,000 zebras and gazelles, from the Serengeti in Tanzania to the Masai Mara in Kenya—a clockwise route of more than 1,800 miles (2,900 km) per year. Some incredible journeys no longer take place, as ungulate numbers have dwindled and the land crossed by their migration routes has been developed. Hundreds of thousands of springbok once migrated over a vast range in southern Africa. In North America, as many as 4 million bison once traveled en masse through the Great Plains to reach the fresh grasses of their northern summer and southern winter ranges.

MOVING CLOCKWISE

Early in the year, thousands of wildebeest give birth and then spread out on the plains of the Serengeti, which offer rain-ripened, mineral-rich short grasses. By the end of May, as the wet season comes to an end, these plains are depleted and the animals travel west and north in small groups to a transitional zone, where they mate. During the rutting season of May to June, this region resounds with deep lowing as each dominant male defends a harem against the attentions of other males. By July, many thousands of animals have formed a single great herd that makes its way to the Masai Mara, where they feast on new grass growth and drink from permanent rivers through the dry season. They begin the return journey to their breeding grounds in late November.

● Wet season
● Transitional zone
● Dry season

River crossing The most dangerous part of the great wildebeest migration is the crossing of the Mara River, which bisects the Masai Mara savanna. Swollen by the recent rains, the river can be a raging torrent. The migrating herd gathers at the banks until forced by the surge of animals to cross. Many wildebeest break their legs after leaping onto the rocky bottom. Others drown or are swept away by the powerful currents. Enormous crocodiles await, relying on the wildebeest prey for their main meal of the year. The animals that survive the crossing must then dodge the hungry lions on the other side.

Swimming caribou Each spring in Alaska and Canada, herds containing thousands of caribou migrate from their wintering grounds to their calving grounds farther north, traveling through deep snow and across icy rivers. After giving birth, the mothers feed on the tundra's nutritious new plant growth, which helps them produce rich milk. The calving grounds become cold and windswept as winter approaches, prompting the caribou to return south. In Europe, the same species has been domesticated and is known as the reindeer. The Sami herders follow the animals' natural migration routes.

Winter herd The world's largest remaining expanses of temperate grassland are found in eastern Mongolia. These steppes are home to the Mongolian gazelle (*Procapra gutturosa*). During summer, male and female gazelles form separate herds, and females give birth. Large mixed herds of several thousand animals gather for the winter migration, covering up to 180 miles (300 km) a day until they reach their southern mating grounds. Overall numbers of the species appear to be in decline. The impact of fires, epidemics, and other natural disasters has been exacerbated by such disruptions to the gazelles' migration routes as fencing along the border with China and a new railroad in Mongolia.

Annual cycle *The wildebeest mating season occurs in May to June. By the time of the perilous river crossing that occurs around July, more than 90 percent of all the adult female wildebeest may be pregnant.*

Fellow travelers *Zebras travel with or ahead of the great wildebeest herd, grazing on the tough longer grasses and exposing the sweet new growth for the wildebeest. Gazelles tend to follow the wildebeest herd.*

Survival of the fittest *Only the strongest members of the wildebeest herd make it from one side of the river to the other. They are rewarded by an abundance of lush green grass and spend their time building up reserves for the slow journey back to the Serengeti plains.*

Perilous journey About 400,000 wildebeest are born every year in the Serengeti during a 6-week period beginning in late January. Of these calves, two out of three will perish on their first migration to the Masai Mara, but enough will survive to replenish East Africa's great wildebeest herds.

Plenty for predators *The presence of the great herd in the Masai Mara attracts large numbers of predators. Crocodiles feast during the river crossing, while lions and hyenas target any stragglers.*

DEER

CLASS	Mammalia
ORDER	Artiodactyla
FAMILIES	4
GENERA	21
SPECIES	51

The largest family in the deer group, Cervidae contains deer and their allies, including moose, caribou, and elk. In many ways, deer resemble antelopes, with long bodies and necks, slender legs, short tails, large eyes on the side of the head, and high-set ears. They are distinguished, however, by the often spectacular antlers borne by the males of most species (and also by female caribou). Unlike horns, which are permanent and made of keratin, antlers are made of bone and are shed once a year. Growing antlers are covered in skin known as "velvet," which dies and is rubbed off once the antlers reach full size. Antlers can be small, simple spikes or enormous, branched structures.

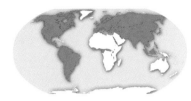

Deer distribution Deer never moved into sub-Saharan Africa, but they occur naturally in northwest Africa, Eurasia, and the Americas, and some have been introduced elsewhere. The species in the family Cervidae fall into two groups according to their ancestry: Old World deer first evolved in Asia, while the New World group began in the Arctic.

Lying up Until they are strong enough to join the herd, newborn fawns such as this mule deer spend their days hiding among vegetation. The newborn of many deer species have a dappled coat to break up their outline and provide camouflage. The mother visits regularly to suckle the fawn.

Northern habitats Most deer are found in temperate or tropical forest, but some species have adapted to more extreme conditions. The moose (right) dwells in northern wetlands, where its summer diet includes the roots of aquatic plants. The caribou lives on the treeless arctic tundra.

LARGE AND SMALL

The family Cervidae ranges from the southern pudu, weighing as little as 17½ pounds (8 kg), to the moose, at 1,760 pounds (800 kg). A moose's antlers can have a span of 6½ feet (2 m), though even these are dwarfed by the antlers of the extinct Irish elk (*Megaloceros*), which spanned 12 feet (3.5 m). One cervid species, the Chinese water deer, has no antlers at all, but its elongated canine teeth form knife-like tusks. Southeast Asia's muntjaks have only spikes for antlers but also bear tusks.

As prey species, deer have evolved various escape strategies. Some leap and dodge into a hiding spot. Others rely on great speed and stamina to outrun the threat. The moose can easily trot over obstacles that slow down its shorter predators.

All deer are ruminants with a four-chambered stomach, but, unlike bovids, they are not adapted to a diet of coarse grasses and rely on more easily digested food such as shoots, young leaves, new grasses, lichens, and fruit. Even those species that do graze on grasses need large amounts of high-quality browse as well.

The deer group is comprised of Cervidae and three other families of ungulates that superficially resemble them. These include the chevrotains of Tragulidae and the musk deer of Moschidae, which both have long canine teeth rather than antlers. North America's pronghorn is in its own family, Antilocapridae.

Group grazers While some smaller deer species live alone or in small family groups, larger species such as fallow deer tend to form herds. Living in a group offers a better chance of avoiding predation, as predators are more likely to be detected and tend to target only the weakest members. In New Zealand and other places, deer have been introduced and are bred commercially.

Siberian musk deer
Moschus moschiferus

Muscular hindlegs allow animal to perform agile jumps

Like other members of the family Moschidae, this species lacks antlers but males have long canine teeth

Extensively hunted for musk produced by gland between navel and sex organs

Chinese water deer
Hydropotes inermis

Only species of Cervidae in which males lack antlers

Indian spotted chevrotain
(Indian mouse deer)
Moschiola meminna

Water chevrotain
Hyemoschus aquaticus

Greater Malay chevrotain
Tragulus napu

Lesser Malay chevrotain
Tragulus javanicus

Spotted and striped coat helps camouflage animal amid forest foliage

FACT FILE

Indian spotted chevrotain The varied diet of this nocturnal animal includes both vegetation and small animals.

🐾 Up to 24 in (60 cm)
📏 Up to 12 in (30 cm)
⚖ Up to 6 lb (2.7 kg)
🐾 Solitary
⚑ Uncommon
🏛

India, Sri Lanka

Water chevrotain Entirely nocturnal, this solitary animal hides in the dense undergrowth of the tropical forest by day. It usually lives near water and will enter water to avoid predators, but cannot swim for long periods.

🐾 Up to 37½ in (95 cm)
📏 Up to 16 in (40 cm)
⚖ Up to 28½ lb (13 kg)
🐾 Solitary
⚑ Data deficient
🏛

Tropical W. Africa

Greater Malay chevrotain Because this species breeds at any time of year and will mate within a couple of hours of giving birth, females spend most of their life pregnant.

🐾 Up to 24 in (60 cm)
📏 Up to 14 in (35 cm)
⚖ Up to 13 lb (6 kg)
🐾 Solitary
⚑ Uncommon
🏛 ☀

Indochina, Thailand to Malaya, Sumatra, Borneo

Lesser Malay chevrotain The smallest of all even-toed ungulates, this animal has legs about as thick as a pencil. It may live alone or in small family groups and feeds on fallen fruit and leaves.

🐾 Up to 19 in (48 cm)
📏 Up to 8 in (20 cm)
⚖ Up to 4½ lb (2 kg)
🐾 Solitary, small group
⚑ Uncommon
🏛 ☀

Indochina, Thailand to Malaya & Indonesia

CHEVROTAINS

Also known as mouse deer, chevrotains are small, even-toed ruminants, but unlike true deer and cattle they lack horns or antlers. The males have long, continually growing canines. Shy and usually nocturnal, chevrotains tend to be solitary forest dwellers. They are classified in the family Tragulidae.

canines

FACT FILE

Sambar Native to Asia but introduced to Australia, New Zealand, and the United States, this nocturnal deer is most often found on forested hillsides. While several females with young may live together, males are usually solitary and aggressively defend their territories during the breeding season, when they mate with the females in their range.

- 🐾 Up to 8 ft (2.5 m)
- 📏 Up to 5¼ ft (1.6 m)
- ⚖ Up to 575 lb (260 kg)
- 🐾 Solitary, harem
- 🏃 Locally common
- 🏛 ☀ ☘ ⚘

India & Sri Lanka to S. China & S.E. Asia

IN A RUT

Known as wapiti or elk in North America and as red deer in Europe, *Cervus elaphus* is the noisiest of all deer species. After beginning courtship with a bugling call, males collect a harem, which they vigorously defend against other males throughout the rutting, or mating, season.

Vocal assault *A harem male and his challenger will roar at each other for several minutes before engaging in a physical contest.*

Antler lock *After performing a ritual parallel walk, competing males will lock antlers and wrestle until one is pushed back and flees.*

⚡ CONSERVATION WATCH

Of the 51 species in the four "deer" families, 76% are listed on the IUCN Red List, as follows:

- 1 Extinct
- 1 Critically endangered
- 7 Endangered
- 11 Vulnerable
- 7 Near threatened
- 12 Data deficient

Antlers can be up to 3 feet (1 m) long

Sambar
Cervus unicolor

Barasingha
Cervus duvaucelii

When tail is raised, the white underside acts as a "follow me" signal

Eld's deer
Cervus eldii

Rusa
Cervus timorensis

Fawn is spotted for camouflage

Roosevelt elk
Cervus elaphus roosevelti

Critically endangered Chinese deer; disappeared from the wild around AD 200, but survived because a captive herd was maintained by the Chinese royal family and breeding pairs were reared in Europe; reintroduced into two Chinese national parks in the 1980s

Mesopotamian fallow deer
Dama mesopotamica

Chital
Axis axis

Père David's deer
Elaphurus davidianus

Palm-shaped antlers have numerous points

Philippine hog deer
Axis calamianensis

Fallow deer
Dama dama

Tufted deer
Elaphodus cephalophus

Tuft of hair hides male's antlers

Giant muntjak
Megamuntiacus vuquangensis

Tusk-like canine teeth on male

Indian muntjak
Muntiacus muntjak

FACT FILE

Chital This deer is mainly a grassland grazer, but will enter nearby forests to browse fallen fruit and leaves. Herds of females and young are followed by dominant males in the breeding season.

Up to 6 ft (1.8 m)
Up to 3¼ ft (1 m)
Up to 245 lb (110 kg)
Herd
Common

Sri Lanka, India, Nepal

Fallow deer Most populations have been translocated from their natural range. Adaptable foragers, fallow deer have been introduced to diverse habitats, from the tropics to mountains.

Up to 6 ft (1.8 m)
Up to 3½ ft (1.1 m)
Up to 220 lb (100 kg)
Herd
Locally common

Originally Mediterranean to S.W. Asia

Tufted deer The male tufted deer has simple, spiked antlers and long, tusk-like upper canines. The antlers are often hidden by the hair on its forehead.

Up to 5¼ ft (1.6 m)
Up to 27½ in (70 cm)
Up to 110 lb (50 kg)
Solitary
Data deficient

E. Tibet & N. Myanmar to S.E. China

Giant muntjak First recorded in 1994, this secretive creature is about the size of a large dog, almost twice as big as the Indian muntjak.

Up to 3¼ ft (1 m)
Up to 27½ in (70 cm)
Up to 110 lb (50 kg)
Solitary
Not known

Vietnam

Indian muntjak Also called the barking deer, this species may bark for more than an hour if it senses a predator. It is omnivorous, using kicks of its forelimbs and bites to subdue small prey.

Up to 3½ ft (1.1 m)
Up to 25½ in (65 cm)
Up to 61½ lb (28 kg)
Solitary
Uncommon

Sri Lanka, India, Nepal to S. China, S.E. Asia

ANTLER CYCLE

Antlers are used in contests between male deer, but the reason they grow so large appears to be that they advertise the male's healthy genes to females. In deer species with the largest antlers, much of the courtship routine involves elaborate antler displays.

Spring
In temperate species, new antlers begin growing in late spring. They are covered in sensitive skin known as "velvet."

Summer
By late summer, the antlers are fully grown and have hardened. The velvet begins to dry and loosen.

Fall
The male rubs the velvet off on shrubs and small trees. The antlers are now ready for the contests and displays of the mating season.

Winter *Following the mating season, the two antlers are shed within days of each other.*

Male's massive antlers may have up to 20 points

Largest of all deer species; known as moose in North America and elk in Europe

Moose (elk)
Alces alces

Marsh deer
Blastocerus dichotomus

Female caribou is only female deer to possess true antlers

Male caribou has larger antlers than female

Clicking sound made during walking when tendons snap across bones in the feet

Caribou (reindeer)
Rangifer tarandus

Broad, flat feet can cross both snow and spongy tundra vegetation

Pampas deer
Ozotoceros bezoarticus

Mule deer (black-tailed deer)
Odocoileus hemionus

White-tailed deer
Odocoileus virginianus

Roe deer
Capreolus capreolus

Red brocket
Mazama americana

Both male and female bear horns, but the male's horns are longer and forked

Black markings only on male

Pronghorn
Antilocapra americana

Little red brocket
Mazama rufina

Appears on Chile's coat of arms

Peruvian guemal
Hippocamelus antisensis

Andean guemal
Hippocamelus bisulcus

Northern pudu
Pudu mephistophiles

Southern pudu
Pudu puda

Smallest of all deer in Cervidae family

FACT FILE

Red brocket An elusive creature that most often lives in dense, tropical forest, this small deer can disappear into undergrowth or swim to escape predators. It lives alone or in pairs and feeds on fruit, leaves, and fungi.

- Up to 5 ft (1.5 m)
- Up to 31½ in (80 cm)
- Up to 106 lb (48 kg)
- Solitary
- Data deficient

S. Mexico to N. Argentina

Southern pudu The smallest of all true deer species, the southern pudu will stand on its hindlegs to reach the leaves of trees or test the wind. Solitary except during the mating season, this territorial animal follows well-marked trails to its feeding and resting spots. Listed as vulnerable, this species suffers predation from domestic dogs, and competition for food from introduced species such as fallow deer.

- Up to 32½ in (83 cm)
- Up to 17 in (43 cm)
- Up to 28½ lb (13 kg)
- Solitary
- Vulnerable

S. Chile, S.W. Argentina

THE PRONGHORN

The sole species classified in the family Antilocapridae, the pronghorn is able to reach speeds of 40 miles per hour (65 km/h), making it one of the fastest mammals on land. It is distinguished by its unusual forked horns, which are made from keratin surrounding a bony core, like the horns of antelope. As with the antlers of deer, however, the keratin is shed annually.

- Up to 5 ft (1.5 m)
- Up to 3¼ ft (1 m)
- Up to 154 lb (70 kg)
- Herd
- Locally common

W. North America

Unique horns The head of a pronghorn buck features pronged horns, protruding eyes with long eyelashes, and a "mask" of black hair.

GIRAFFE AND OKAPI

CLASS	Mammalia
ORDER	Artiodactyla
FAMILY	Giraffidae
GENERA	2
SPECIES	2

With its head hovering up to 18 feet (5.5 m) above the ground, the giraffe is the tallest animal in the world. Along with its only close relative, the okapi, it is classified in the family Giraffidae. Both the giraffe and the okapi have a long neck, tail, and legs, with the forelimbs longer than the hindlimbs, creating a sloping back. Their small, constantly growing horns consist of bone covered by furred skin and are unique among mammals. The lips of giraffids are thin and mobile; the tongue is long, prehensile, and black; and the eyes and ears are large. Both species are found only in sub-Saharan Africa, where their strikingly patterned coats help them blend into their habitat—the giraffe's blotches mimic the dappled light of savanna woodland, while the okapi's rear stripes break up its outline amid the dense vegetation of the rain forest.

Dangerous drinking A giraffe gets most of the water it needs from its food, but will drink water when it is available. It must splay its forelegs to reach the water, making it vulnerable to predators at this time.

Necking rivals To establish rank, young male giraffes engage in ritualized necking contests. Much like arm wrestles, these involve two giraffes intertwining necks and pushing each other until one gives way. Older male giraffes head-butt each other in an attempt to push over the opponent. Competing okapi bulls also neck-wrestle before progressing to more aggressive contact.

STRIPED BEHIND

The okapi was first described only in 1901, when a British explorer went in search of a horse-like animal hunted by the local people. At first glance, the okapi looks more like a zebra than a giraffe. It shares distinctive features with the giraffe, however, including unusual fur-covered horns, specialized teeth and tongue, and a ruminating, four-chambered stomach. The stripes on the rump probably act as a "follow me" signal and allow a young okapi to keep track of its mother. With the stripes on the forelimbs, they also break up the animal's outline amid the dense vegetation of the forest.

DIFFERENT LIFESTYLES

Beyond their similarities, giraffes and okapi differ significantly. The most obvious contrast is in size and shape, with the okapi appearing rather horse-like, while the extreme elongation of the giraffe makes it instantly identifiable. The giraffe has only seven vertebrae in its neck, the same number as almost all other mammals, but each vertebra is lengthened. A specialized circulatory system powerfully pumps blood all the way up to its brain, but a series of valves adjusts the pressure when the animal leans down to drink.

The giraffe's extraordinary stature has allowed it to fully exploit the resources of its savanna woodland home. Because it is able to reach the leaves of tall acacia trees throughout the dry season, a giraffe can grow to a dramatic height and reproduce year-round. It is most vulnerable to lions and other predators when lying down or drinking. To avoid predation, a giraffe depends on its acute senses of vision, smell, and hearing. It may run away at speeds of more than 30 miles per hour (50 km/h) or deliver sharp kicks to the foe with its forefeet.

Living in dense, dark tropical forest, the okapi has poor vision but sharp hearing and a good sense of smell. It is extremely wary and will disappear into thick cover at the first hint of danger. Mostly solitary, this species marks its territory with urine or by rubbing its neck on trees.

The more open savanna habitat has encouraged giraffes to be social, and most live in small, loose herds of about a dozen animals. Young males may live in bachelor bands but tend to become solitary as they age. Males may fight each other for the right to mate, repeatedly swinging their long neck to deliver powerful head-butts to the rival's underbelly. A reinforced skull usually absorbs the impact of these blows, but occasionally an animal is knocked unconscious.

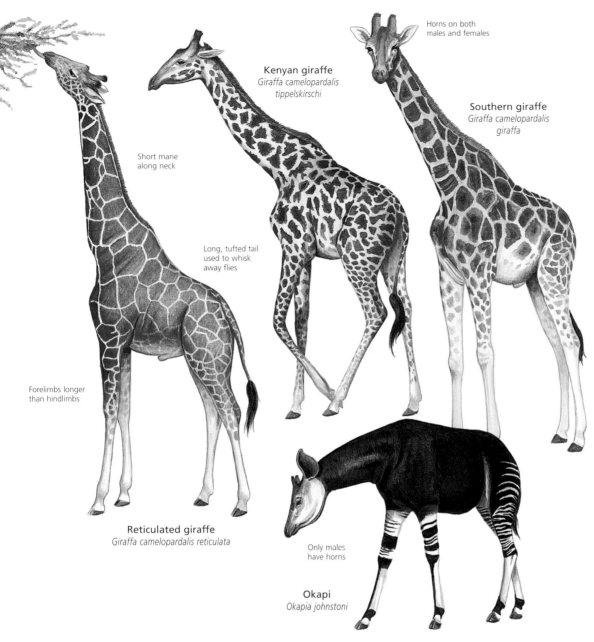

Horns on both males and females

Short mane along neck

Kenyan giraffe
Giraffa camelopardalis tippelskirschi

Southern giraffe
Giraffa camelopardalis giraffa

Long, tufted tail used to whisk away flies

Forelimbs longer than hindlimbs

Reticulated giraffe
Giraffa camelopardalis reticulata

Only males have horns

Okapi
Okapia johnstoni

SPECIALIZED BROWSERS

The giraffe and the okapi are almost exclusively browsers. They both have thin, muscular lips and a long, black tongue that is dextrous enough to pluck foliage or pull branches to the mouth. The tongue of the giraffe (right) is especially long and can measure up to 18 inches (46 cm). Both species strip leaves from branches using their unique lobed canine teeth, and then grind them with their molars. A four-chambered, ruminating stomach helps them gain maximum nutrition from their food, which is regurgitated and chewed a second time. Unlike other ruminants, giraffes can walk as they chew the cud, allowing them to spend more time feeding. A giraffe may spend between 12 and 20 hours a day feeding, consuming up to 75 pounds (34 kg) of vegetation in that time.

Giraffes can cope with a wide variety in the quality of their food. They prefer new growth, flowers, and fruit, but are able to switch to twigs and dried leaves. Their staple diet is acacia trees, which have chemical defenses that make the leaves toxic and unpalatable. In response, giraffes carefully select the least toxic foliage to eat and have thick, sticky saliva and a specialized liver function. Both the giraffe and the okapi appear to supplement their diet with minerals from other sources: the giraffe eats soil and chews bones discarded by scavengers, while the okapi licks the clay of riverbanks and eats charcoal from burned trees.

THE CAMEL FAMILY

CLASS	Mammalia
ORDER	Artiodactyla
FAMILY	Camelidae
GENERA	3
SPECIES	6

Famed for their humps and the ability to survive for long periods without drinking, the two species of camel are the single-humped dromedary, now found only in domesticated populations in northern Africa and the Middle East, and the Bactrian camel, domesticated in northern Asia, but also found in small numbers in the wild. Their relatives in the family Camelidae are the four camelids of South America—the wild guanaco and vicuña, and the domesticated llama and alpaca. Camelids first appeared some 45 million years ago in North America, but disappeared from there about 10,000 years ago at the end of the ice age. By then, they had dispersed to other parts of the world.

Old and new The two Old World camels occur in northern Africa and central Asia. The four South American species range from the foothills to the alpine meadows of the Andes Mountains. Domesticated camelids have been introduced in many places, including Australia, where feral dromedaries roam the central desert.

Precocious young In all camelid species, a single, well-developed young is born after a long gestation period, which lasts 11 months in South America's guanaco. A newborn guanaco can follow the mother within about 30 minutes of its birth.

ROBUST CAMELIDS

All camelids are adapted to arid or semiarid regions. A complex, three-chambered ruminating stomach extracts maximum nutrition from their main food of grasses. Their feet are unique among hoofed mammals in that only the front of the hoof touches the ground, and the animal's weight rests instead on a fleshy sole-pad. In camels, the feet are broad, helping it to travel over soft sand without sinking. The four South American species have a narrower foot for walking securely up rocky slopes. A thick double coat insulates against both heat and cold.

While Old World camelids are distinguished from the New World species by their much larger size and prominent humps, the overall anatomy is similar. All species have long, slender legs, a short tail, a long, curved neck, and a relatively small head with a split upper lip. When camelids walk, the front and back legs on the same side of the body move in unison, a distinctive gait known as pacing. Camelids are social animals and tend to live in harems of females and young led by a dominant male. Males without a harem may form bachelor bands.

By herding camelids, which provide meat, milk, wool, fuel, and transport, humans have been able to make a living in extreme locations, from the hot Sahara Desert to the cool high plains of the Andes. There are more than 20 million camelids in the world, but roughly 95 percent are domestic animals.

Water wise Dromedaries were introduced to northern Africa from Arabia several thousand years ago as domestic animals. Their hump stores fat, not water, but they can survive for months without drinking by feeding on desert plants. When water is available, however, they may gulp down the equivalent of a quarter of their weight.

DOMESTIC AND WILD

Until recently, both the domestic llama (right) and the domestic alpaca were assumed to be descendants of the wild guanaco. Molecular studies suggest, however, that the alpaca may be a cross between the llama and the wild vicuña. Both llamas and alpacas have been herded for many hundreds of years and there are now no wild individuals of these species. They vastly outnumber the wild guanaco and vicuña, but all South American camelids have been eclipsed by the introduced domestic sheep. Camelids were first domesticated in South America 4,000–5,000 years ago, and the llama was central to the success of the Inca Empire. Llamas and alpacas have now been introduced elsewhere, and are used for wool, to guard sheep, as pack animals for hikers, and as pets.

Bactrian camel
Camelus bactrianus

Fat stored in humps is used when food is scarce, causing humps to shrink

Long winter coat shed in summer

Narrow nostrils can close during dust storms

Long eyelashes keep desert dust out of eyes

Thick, tough lips can handle thorny vegetation

Dromedary
Camelus dromedarius

Guanaco
Lama guanicoe

Vicuña
Vicugna vicugna

FACT FILE

Bactrian camel Along with the dromedary, this species is unique among mammals because its blood cells are oval rather than round. This shape may help the cells travel through thick, dehydrated blood.

🐪 Up to 11½ ft (3.5 m)
🐪 Up to 7½ ft (2.3 m)
🐪 Up to 1,540 lb (700 kg)
🐫 Herd
⚡ Critically endangered

Kazakhstan to Mongolia

Dromedary Although domesticated, many dromedary herds are unattended during the mating season, when they revert to living in harems.

🐪 Up to 11½ ft (3.5 m)
🐪 Up to 7½ ft (2.3 m)
🐪 Up to 1,430 lb (650 kg)
🐫 Herd
⚡ Extinct in wild: domestic & feral only

N. Africa to India; introd. Australia

Guanaco Male guanacos, like all male South American camelids, have some sharp, hooked teeth that are used as weapons during fights with rival males.

🐪 Up to 6½ ft (2 m)
🐪 Up to 4 ft (1.2 m)
🐪 Up to 265 lb (120 kg)
🐫 Family band
⚡ Locally common

S. Peru to E. Argentina & Tierra del Fuego

Vicuña Strictly a grazer, this small camelid has sharp, constantly growing incisors for snipping short grasses.

🐪 Up to 6¼ ft (1.9 m)
🐪 Up to 3½ ft (1.1 m)
🐪 Up to 143 lb (65 kg)
🐫 Family band
⚡ Conserv. dependent

S. Peru to N.W. Argentina

PIGS

CLASS Mammalia
ORDER Artiodactyla
FAMILY Suidae
GENERA 5
SPECIES 14

Unlike most other ungulates, which are strictly herbivorous, the pigs, hogs, boars, and babirusa in the family Suidae are omnivores with a diet that includes insect larvae, earthworms, and small vertebrates, as well as a wide array of plants. The nostrils on a pig's prominent snout are enclosed in a disk of cartilage. Supported by a unique prenasal bone, this disk helps locate food by shoveling through leaf litter or dirt. The upper and lower canines in both males and females of most species form sharp tusks, which can be used as weapons. Occurring naturally in the forests of Africa and Eurasia, wild pigs have also been introduced in North America, Australia, and New Zealand.

Status symbols Thought to display status, the curved tusks of the male babirusa are elongated canine teeth. The upper tusks grow through the skin of the face.

Family ties Male wild pigs tend either to live alone or to belong to a bachelor band, while females and their offspring live in close-knit family groups that are known as sounders. These young warthogs are following their mother as she grazes.

⚡ CONSERVATION WATCH

Feral pigs now threaten native fauna, including other pig species, in many places. Habitat loss has also contributed to the decline of some pigs. Of the 14 species in the family Suidae, 43% are listed on the IUCN Red List, as follows:

- 2 Critically endangered
- 1 Endangered
- 2 Vulnerable
- 1 Data deficient

Wild boar
Sus scrofa

Female has smaller tusks than male

Weighs 13–20 pounds (6–9 kg), making it the smallest species in Suidae

⚡ **Pygmy hog**
Sus salvanius

Piglets striped for camouflage; stripes fade with age

Warthog
Phacochoerus africanus

Bush pig
Potamochoerus larvatus

Padded knees allow for
kneeling during feeding

Giant hog
Hylochoerus meinertzhageni

Upper tusks can grow to
14 inches (35 cm) long

Large folds and
wrinkles in skin

Red river hog
Potamochoerus porcus

Mane and ear tassels can
be fluffed out to increase
the animal's apparent size

Lower canines
used in fighting

Babirusa
Babyrousa babyrussa

PECCARIES

CLASS	Mammalia
ORDER	Artiodactyla
FAMILY	Tayassuidae
GENERA	3
SPECIES	3

Although they resemble the pigs of Suidae in many ways, the three species of peccary in the family Tayassuidae can be distinguished by their long, slender legs, a more complex stomach, and a scent gland on the rump. They are omnivorous like pigs, but prefer fruit, seeds, roots, and vines, with the Chaco peccary depending largely on cacti. These gregarious animals live in herds ranging from 2–10 Chaco peccaries to 50–400 white-lipped peccaries. Social bonds are reinforced by herd members rubbing their cheeks on each other's scent glands. A few white-lipped peccaries will stay behind to fight a predator, allowing the rest of the herd to flee.

American pigs While pigs occur naturally only in Africa and Eurasia, peccaries are restricted to the Americas, where they range from southwest United States to northern Argentina. The collared peccary and white-lipped peccary are found in tropical forest, wooded savanna, and thorn scrub. The Chaco peccary is found mainly in semiarid thorn forest.

Twin peccaries A peccary litter most often contains two young, but can include up to four. Young collared peccaries depend on their mother for about 6 months.

⚡ CONSERVATION WATCH

Multiple threats Coupled with hunting for the bushmeat trade and diseases from introduced species, the rapid destruction of South America's tropical forests is having a serious impact on the three species of peccaries, which depend on large home ranges. The Chaco peccary, with only about 5,000 individuals remaining, is listed as endangered on the IUCN Red List.

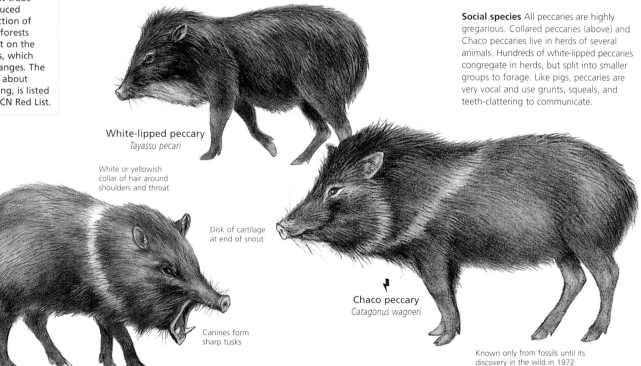

White-lipped peccary
Tayassu pecari

White or yellowish collar of hair around shoulders and throat

Disk of cartilage at end of snout

Social species All peccaries are highly gregarious. Collared peccaries (above) and Chaco peccaries live in herds of several animals. Hundreds of white-lipped peccaries congregate in herds, but split into smaller groups to forage. Like pigs, peccaries are very vocal and use grunts, squeals, and teeth-clattering to communicate.

Collared peccary (javelina)
Pecari tajacu

Canines form sharp tusks

Chaco peccary
Catagonus wagneri

Known only from fossils until its discovery in the wild in 1972

HIPPOPOTAMUSES

CLASS Mammalia

ORDER Artiodactyla

FAMILY Hippopotamidae

GENERA 2

SPECIES 4

Now known to be more closely related to whales than to other ungulates, the two surviving species of hippopotamus lead a semiaquatic life, spending the day resting in water and emerging at night to forage on land. Their thick skin has only a thin outer layer, which rapidly dries out and cracks unless regularly moistened. Both species have large heads, a barrel-shaped body, and surprisingly short legs. There is, however, an enormous size disparity, with the grassland-grazing common hippopotamus being seven times heavier than the forest-foraging pygmy hippo. Because their weight is often borne by water, hippos conserve energy and need relatively little food.

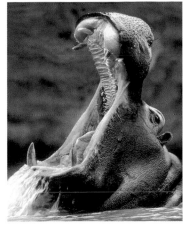

Underwater ungulate Lacking sweat glands, the common hippopotamus relies on water to stay cool. It is a good swimmer and diver, and the density of its body allows it to walk along a river or lake bed and stay submerged for about 5 minutes at a time. It can float by filling its lungs with air. A hippo's feet are webbed; the nostrils and ears can close underwater; and the eyes, ears, and nostrils are positioned so that it can see, hear, and breathe with just the top of the head emerging above the surface. Young are born and suckled underwater. Herds of up to 40 hippos may spend the day together in water, devoting most of their time to sleeping or resting. At night, they leave the water to feed on land for about 6 hours.

Open wide Hinged far back in the skull, a hippo's jaw can open remarkably wide, achieving a gape of 150 degrees, more than 100 degrees wider than the human gape. A male's large lower canines are used as weapons in battles for mating rights.

FACT FILE

Hippopotamus Several females and their young spend the day together in water, but forage alone on land at night. Dominant males are territorial and mate with the females that enter their length of riverbank or lake shore. This species mainly eats grasses.

🐃 Up to 14 ft (4.2 m)
🐃 Up to 5 ft (1.5 m)
⚖ Up to 2¼ tons (2 t)
🐾 Herd
✦ Locally common

Tropical & subtropical Africa

Pygmy hippopotamus Usually solitary, the pygmy hippo may spend the day hidden in a swamp or retreat to an otter's burrow in a riverbank. Its varied diet includes roots and fruit.

🐃 Up to 6½ ft (2 m)
🐃 Up to 35½ in (90 cm)
⚖ Up to 605 lb (275 kg)
🐾 Solitary, pair
✦ Vulnerable

W. Africa

⚡ CONSERVATION WATCH

Hippo habitats While abundant in some areas, the common hippo is rare in western Africa. Its tendency to gather in large herds makes it easy prey for human hunters. Threatened by habitat loss and poaching, the pygmy hippo is listed as vulnerable on the IUCN Red List. Its dense habitat and solitary nature prevent an accurate tally of numbers.

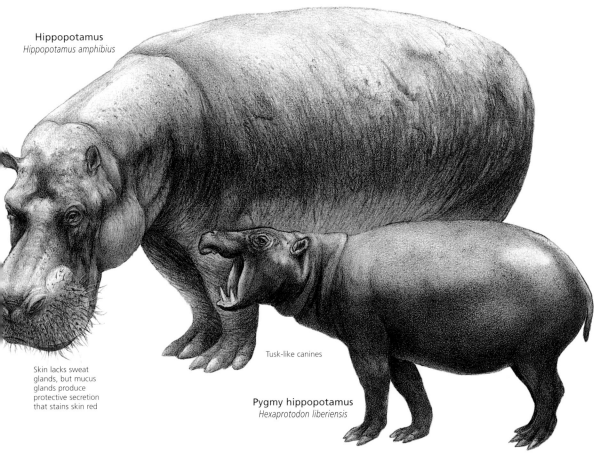

Hippopotamus
Hippopotamus amphibius

Skin lacks sweat glands, but mucus glands produce protective secretion that stains skin red

Tusk-like canines

Pygmy hippopotamus
Hexaprotodon liberiensis

CETACEANS

CLASS	Mammalia
ORDER	Cetacea
FAMILIES	10
GENERA	41
SPECIES	81

With their entirely aquatic lifestyle, the whales, dolphins, and porpoises of the order Cetacea are perhaps the most specialized of all mammals. They feed, rest, mate, give birth, and raise young in the water, yet they are warm-blooded and breathe air like other mammals. Gregarious and intelligent, cetaceans appear to be descended from the same land mammal that led to hippopotamuses, but their ancestors adapted to a watery life some 50 million years ago. Over time, they became as streamlined as fish, losing their hair and hindlimbs, modifying their arms into flippers, and developing a powerful fluked tail that makes some species the fastest creatures in the sea.

Ready to blow When a cetacean surfaces to breathe, it expels air and condensed moisture through nostrils modified to form a single or double blowhole on the top of the head. The blowhole closes underwater.

Staying warm and cool Being virtually hairless, a cetacean relies on a layer of blubber beneath the skin for insulation. A network of arteries and veins in the blubber, known as *retia mirabilia*, helps the animal to regulate its temperature.

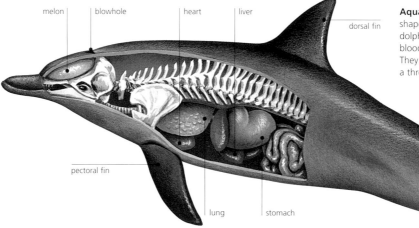

melon | blowhole | heart | liver | dorsal fin

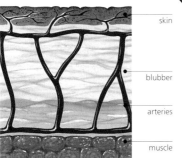

skin
blubber
arteries
muscle

pectoral fin | lung | stomach

Aquatic mammal Although their body shape is highly modified for life in water, dolphins and other cetaceans are warm-blooded and breathe air through lungs. They have a four-chambered heart and a three-chambered stomach.

A double fluke Like other cetaceans, the sperm whale propels itself with powerful up-and-down strokes of its fluked tail. The flippers are used for steering.

Bonded young After a long gestation period, a single calf is born tail-first underwater. Its mother and sometimes other members of the pod nudge it to the surface to take its first breath. Nourished by rich milk, the calf grows rapidly but stays with the mother for some years.

CETACEAN RECORDS

Cetaceans are found in all of the world's oceans and seas, and in some rivers and lakes. They are split into two living suborders: the toothed whales of Odontoceti, and the baleen whales of Mysticeti. Toothed whales, which include dolphins, porpoises, and sperm whales, have simple, conical teeth that can keep a firm grip on their slippery food of fishes and squids. Baleen whales include blue whales, humpbacks, gray whales, and right whales. They are filter feeders, straining great quantities of tiny plankton, other invertebrates, and small fish through bristled horny plates that hang from the roof of the mouth.

With water supporting their weight, some cetaceans have been able to reach enormous sizes. The blue whale is the largest animal that has ever lived, with a record weight of 209 tons (190 tonnes)— roughly equivalent to the weight of 35 elephants—and a record length of 110 feet (33.5 m).

Another cetacean, the sperm whale, boasts the deepest and

longest dives of any mammal. Sperm whales are believed to descend to at least 10,000 feet (3,050 m), and their dives can last for more than 2 hours. When a cetacean dives, its heart rate slows by 50 percent and blood is directed away from the muscles to the vital organs, allowing the animal to survive on very little oxygen until it ascends to breathe.

Cetaceans have little or no sense of smell. Their relatively small eyes provide reasonable vision both above and beneath the water's surface. All species lack external ears, but their hearing is highly sensitive, allowing them to pick up distant calls from members of their species. To find prey and avoid obstacles, toothed whales use echolocation, emitting a series of clicks and whistles, and then analyzing the reflected sounds.

Sound is critical in cetacean communication. Blue whales and fin whales emit low-frequency pulses that carry across vast stretches of ocean and can reach 188 decibels— the loudest sound made by an animal. Male humpbacks produce

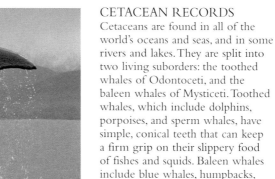

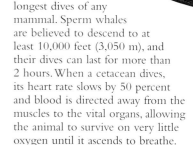

Clear breach Humpback whales may leap from the water a hundred or more times in a row. Such breaching appears to be used to communicate with other whales, but may also have other purposes.

the longest and most complex songs in the animal kingdom.

Because cetaceans spend most of their time underwater, accurate population statistics are difficult to compile. Nevertheless, it is certain that human activities have devastated cetacean numbers. Commercial whaling (now largely banned, but still pursued by Norway and Japan), driftnet fishing (which inadvertently traps cetaceans), and water pollution have all taken a heavy toll.

Social animals Almost all cetaceans are gregarious to some extent. Toothed whales tend to form larger groups than baleen whales and have more complex social structures. Hundreds or sometimes thousands of common dolphins travel together, swimming with great speed and leaping clear of the water. Members of a group usually feed at the same time and may hunt cooperatively, herding fish into clusters.

Great migration Gray whales breed during winter in warm waters near the Equator. Calves rely on their mother's rich milk to build up strength for the long swim to the whales' summer feeding grounds in plankton-rich polar waters. Because they do not eat during the 3- to 5-month journey, the adult whales rely on their blubber and fat for energy and may lose up to half their body weight.

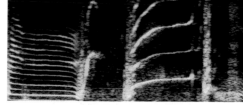

Orca song Each orca pod has a distinct dialect, a repetitive pattern of sounds used during travel and feeding that probably helps the animals to coordinate their activities. The calls become more varied during socializing.

Humpback song Male humpback whales sing complex songs that can be made up of nine themes and last half an hour. All males in an ocean basin sing the same song, but it may gradually change over time.

TOOTHED WHALES

CLASS	Mammalia
ORDER	Cetacea
FAMILIES	6
GENERA	35
SPECIES	68

About 90 percent of all cetaceans are toothed whales belonging to one of the six families in the suborder Odontoceti. In contrast to the enormous baleen whales, toothed whales tend to be medium-sized, although the largest of them, the sperm whale, is a massive creature. Their brains are relatively large, making them the most intelligent mammals other than primates. While some species are solitary, most are highly social and tend to be very vocal and playful. Members of a group may hunt cooperatively and help care for each other's young. Most toothed whales feed on fishes or squids, but one species, the orca, actively pursues warm-blooded prey such as seals and other whales.

Killer teeth Toothed whales have sharp, conical teeth. In fish-eating dolphins, these are small and numerous. Orcas, which hunt marine mammals, have fewer but larger teeth (above). Squid-eating beaked whales have just a single tooth per jaw.

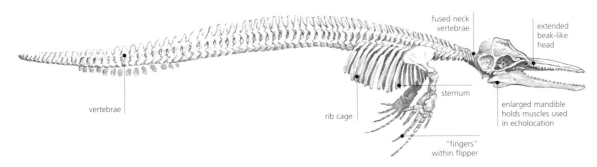

fused neck vertebrae

extended beak-like head

vertebrae

rib cage

sternum

enlarged mandible holds muscles used in echolocation

"fingers" within flipper

Long and narrow The skeleton of a toothed whale has been greatly modified from that of its land mammal ancestor. The hindlimbs have disappeared, while the forelimbs have become flippers, although the bones for five fingers remain. The head is usually long and narrow, forming a beak.

Serious playtime Dolphins, such as this dusky dolphin (*Lagenorhynchus obscurus*), may leap to impress mates, to herd fish, or simply for fun. Playful displays help to reinforce the social bonds among group members, providing the familiarity needed for successful cooperative hunting.

SOCIAL CETACEANS

The diverse members of Odontoceti include sperm whales; narwhals and belugas; beaked whales; dolphins, orcas, and pilot whales (grouped together in the family Delphinidae); porpoises; and river dolphins. Most have an elongated, beak-like head with sharp, conical teeth that can firmly seize prey but cannot chew it. Because there is only a single blowhole, the skull is asymmetrical. It supports a fluid-filled organ called the melon, which is thought to focus the clicks used in echolocation and communication. In sperm whales, the melon is greatly enlarged and filled with an oil known as spermaceti. This spermaceti organ may also help to focus sounds.

There is considerable variety in the social organization of toothed whales. Most groups are centered on the females, with males leaving the group at puberty. Orcas and pilot whales, however, never leave their birth group. River dolphins tend to form small groups or even live alone. Coastal dolphins form larger groups because their prey is concentrated in particular areas and they face more predators. In the deep ocean, small, closely related groups may form temporary herds containing thousands of dolphins.

Despite their reputation for being gentle and playful, dolphins do fight. Group living often involves rivalry for food or mates, and this may lead to physical clashes. Many toothed whales bear tooth rake marks as scars of such encounters.

Gregarious species Sperm whales live in closeknit groups of about a dozen related females and their young. The adults look after each other's young and will protect an injured member from predators. Young males leave to form bachelor groups, but become less social as they age.

> ⚡ **CONSERVATION WATCH**
>
> Of the 68 species of toothed whales, 82% are listed on the IUCN Red List, as follows:
>
> | | |
> |---|---|
> | 2 | Critically endangered |
> | 2 | Endangered |
> | 4 | Vulnerable |
> | 10 | Conservation dependent |
> | 38 | Data deficient |

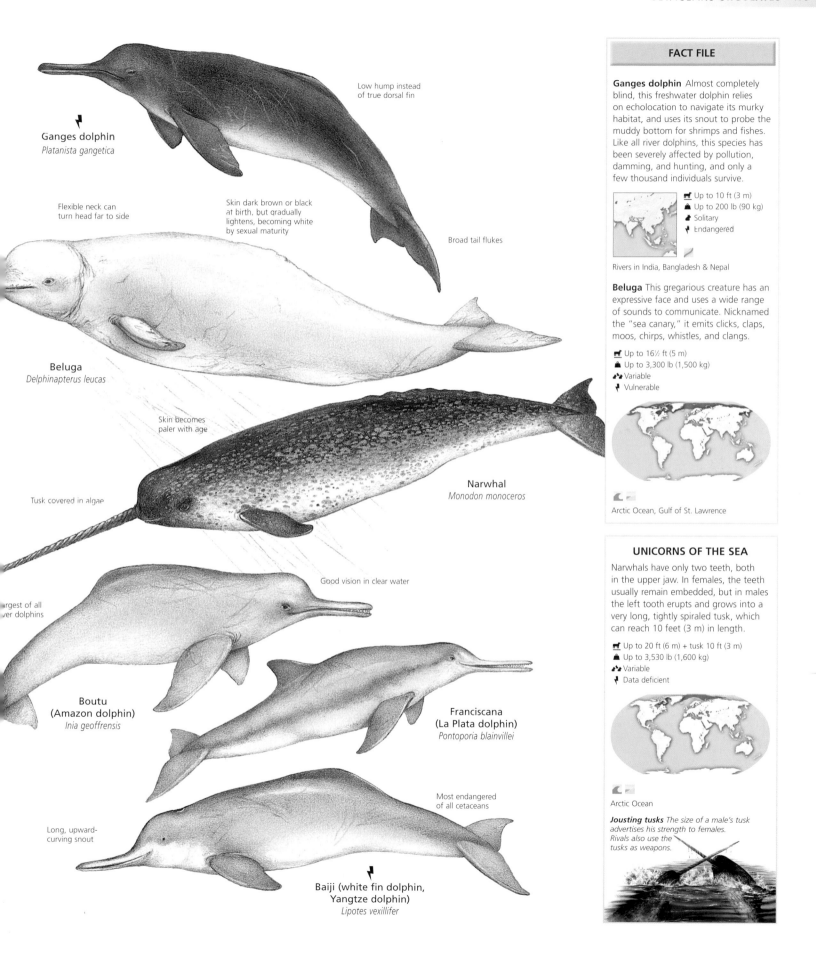

Ganges dolphin
Platanista gangetica

Low hump instead
of true dorsal fin

Flexible neck can
turn head far to side

Skin dark brown or black
at birth, but gradually
lightens, becoming white
by sexual maturity

Broad tail flukes

Beluga
Delphinapterus leucas

Skin becomes
paler with age

Tusk covered in algae

Narwhal
Monodon monoceros

Good vision in clear water

rgest of all
er dolphins

Boutu
(Amazon dolphin)
Inia geoffrensis

Franciscana
(La Plata dolphin)
Pontoporia blainvillei

Most endangered
of all cetaceans

Long, upward-
curving snout

Baiji (white fin dolphin,
Yangtze dolphin)
Lipotes vexillifer

FACT FILE

Ganges dolphin Almost completely blind, this freshwater dolphin relies on echolocation to navigate its murky habitat, and uses its snout to probe the muddy bottom for shrimps and fishes. Like all river dolphins, this species has been severely affected by pollution, damming, and hunting, and only a few thousand individuals survive.

- Up to 10 ft (3 m)
- Up to 200 lb (90 kg)
- Solitary
- Endangered

Rivers in India, Bangladesh & Nepal

Beluga This gregarious creature has an expressive face and uses a wide range of sounds to communicate. Nicknamed the "sea canary," it emits clicks, claps, moos, chirps, whistles, and clangs.

- Up to 16½ ft (5 m)
- Up to 3,300 lb (1,500 kg)
- Variable
- Vulnerable

Arctic Ocean, Gulf of St. Lawrence

UNICORNS OF THE SEA

Narwhals have only two teeth, both in the upper jaw. In females, the teeth usually remain embedded, but in males the left tooth erupts and grows into a very long, tightly spiraled tusk, which can reach 10 feet (3 m) in length.

- Up to 20 ft (6 m) + tusk 10 ft (3 m)
- Up to 3,530 lb (1,600 kg)
- Variable
- Data deficient

Arctic Ocean

Jousting tusks *The size of a male's tusk advertises his strength to females. Rivals also use the tusks as weapons.*

FACT FILE

Bottle-nosed dolphin This is the species made famous by the *Flipper* television series and is most often seen performing in marine parks. In the wild, it is found both inshore and offshore living in groups of about a dozen animals, which sometimes form herds of hundreds. It ranges widely for food, swimming at an average speed of 12 miles per hour (20 km/h).

🐃 Up to 13 ft (4 m)
⚖ Up to 605 lb (275 kg)
🐾 Variable
🏋 Data deficient

Temperate to tropical oceans & seas

Common dolphin The most abundant of all dolphins, this small species lives in herds of several hundred or even a few thousand individuals, which may be joined by white-sided or bottle-nosed dolphins during feeding.

🐃 Up to 8 ft (2.4 m)
⚖ Up to 187 lb (85 kg)
🐾 Herd
🏋 Common

Temperate to tropical oceans & seas

ENTANGLED VICTIMS

The vast nets used in commercial fisheries pose a great risk to dolphins, which follow their prey into the nets and become entangled. Unable to surface to breathe, the dolphins soon drown. Measures to make the nets more conspicuous have helped, but thousands of dolphins are still accidentally captured each year.

Tucuxi (river dolphin)
Sotalia fluviatilis

Found in both marine and freshwater environments

Striped dolphin
Stenella coeruleoalba

Short, stubby beak

Bottle-nosed dolphin
Tursiops truncatus

Largest of the beaked dolphins

Rough-toothed dolphin
Steno bredanensis

Criss-crossing scars from fights with squid prey or other dolphins

Risso's dolphin
Grampus griseus

Common dolphin
Delphinus delphis

Commerson's dolphin
Cephalorhynchus commersonii

Atlantic white-sided dolphin
Lagenorhynchus acutus

Two-tone coloration helps to camouflage animal in its marine environment

Pacific white-sided dolphin
Lagenorhynchus obliquidens

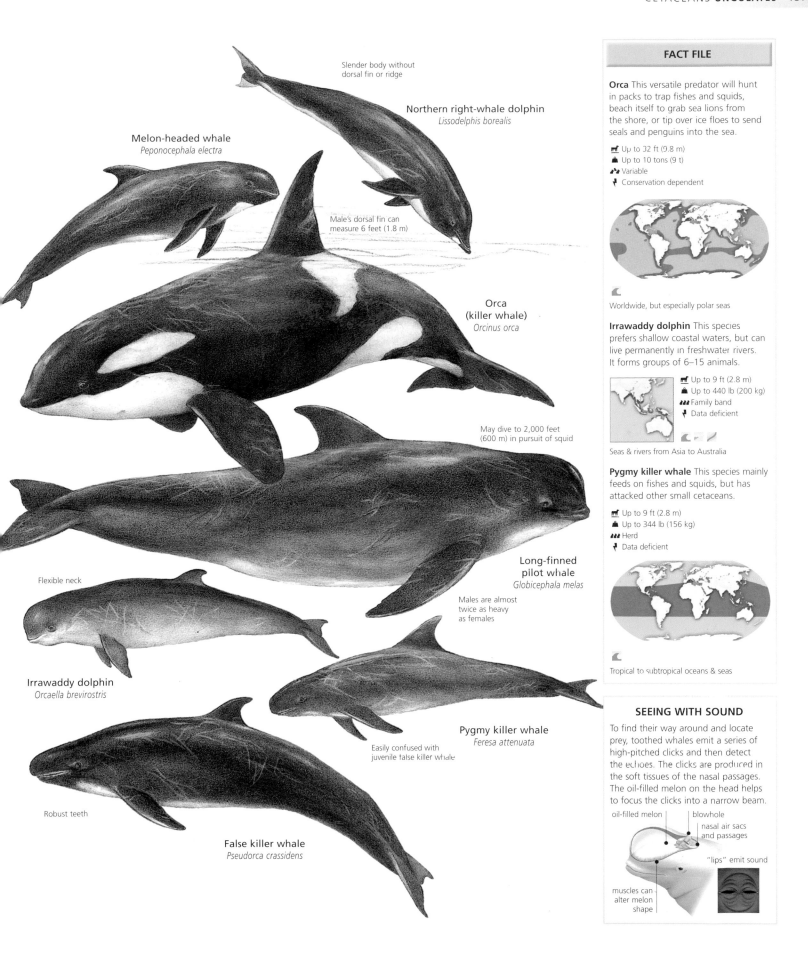

Slender body without
dorsal fin or ridge

Northern right-whale dolphin
Lissodelphis borealis

Melon-headed whale
Peponocephala electra

Male's dorsal fin can
measure 6 feet (1.8 m)

**Orca
(killer whale)**
Orcinus orca

May dive to 2,000 feet
(600 m) in pursuit of squid

Flexible neck

**Long-finned
pilot whale**
Globicephala melas

Males are almost
twice as heavy
as females

Irrawaddy dolphin
Orcaella brevirostris

Pygmy killer whale
Feresa attenuata

Easily confused with
juvenile false killer whale

Robust teeth

False killer whale
Pseudorca crassidens

FACT FILE

Orca This versatile predator will hunt
in packs to trap fishes and squids,
beach itself to grab sea lions from
the shore, or tip over ice floes to send
seals and penguins into the sea.

🐃 Up to 32 ft (9.8 m)
⚖ Up to 10 tons (9 t)
🐾 Variable
🏹 Conservation dependent

Worldwide, but especially polar seas

Irrawaddy dolphin This species
prefers shallow coastal waters, but can
live permanently in freshwater rivers.
It forms groups of 6–15 animals.

🐃 Up to 9 ft (2.8 m)
⚖ Up to 440 lb (200 kg)
🐾 Family band
🏹 Data deficient

Seas & rivers from Asia to Australia

Pygmy killer whale This species mainly
feeds on fishes and squids, but has
attacked other small cetaceans.

🐃 Up to 9 ft (2.8 m)
⚖ Up to 344 lb (156 kg)
🐾 Herd
🏹 Data deficient

Tropical to subtropical oceans & seas

SEEING WITH SOUND

To find their way around and locate
prey, toothed whales emit a series of
high-pitched clicks and then detect
the echoes. The clicks are produced in
the soft tissues of the nasal passages.
The oil-filled melon on the head helps
to focus the clicks into a narrow beam.

oil-filled melon

blowhole

nasal air sacs
and passages

"lips" emit sound

muscles can
alter melon
shape

FACT FILE

Spectacled porpoise Less acrobatic than many other small cetaceans, this porpoise moves slowly through the water. It usually lives alone or in pairs and feeds on fishes and squids.

🐾 Up to 7 ft (2.1 m)
⚖ Up to 255 lb (115 kg)
🐾 Solitary, small group
🏴 Data deficient

Off Argentina, Tasmania & sub-Antarctic islands

Burmeister's porpoise The species name of this animal (*spinipinnis*) means "spiny fin" and was inspired by the small bumps along the leading edge of its dorsal fin, a characteristic shared by most other porpoises.

🐾 Up to 6 ft (1.8 m)
⚖ Up to 154 lb (70 kg)
🐾 Small groups
🏴 Data deficient

Seas & coastal waters from Peru to Brazil

Gulf porpoise Found only in the northern part of the Gulf of California, this species has a more restricted range than any other cetacean. It appears to have evolved from South America's Burmeister's porpoise, but was isolated in the Northern Hemisphere when tropical waters became warmer.

🐾 Up to 5 ft (1.5 m)
⚖ Up to 121 lb (55 kg)
🐾 Not known
🏴 Critically endangered

Estuary of Colorado River; Gulf of California

Common porpoise A rounded shape and small flippers, tail, and fin minimize this cetacean's surface area. Along with a layer of blubber, this helps it survive in cooler waters despite its small size.

🐾 Up to 6¼ ft (1.9 m)
⚖ Up to 143 lb (65 kg)
🐾 Variable
🏴 Vulnerable

Temperate waters of Northern Hemisphere

Spectacled porpoise
Australophocaena dioptrica

Named for circles around the eyes

Dorsal fin set farther back than on any other small cetacean

Burmeister's porpoise
Phocoena spinipinnis

Gulf porpoise (vaquita)
Phocoena sinus

Common porpoise (harbor porpoise)
Phocoena phocoena

Dall's porpoise
Phocoenoides dalli

Less shy and slow than other porpoises

Tail sends up spray in the shape of a rooster's tail

Dorsal ridge rather than fin

Finless porpoise
Neophocaena phocaenoides

CETACEAN STRATEGIES

To reap a rich harvest from the ocean, cetaceans have developed remarkably varied physical characteristics and behavioral strategies. Baleen whales have enormous mouths that can engulf huge quantities of tiny animals, while toothed whales pursue individual prey, relying on echolocation to find it. Many species practise cooperative hunting, using a range of vocalizations to communicate the next move. The success of such efforts rests on a social structure that encourages close relationships.

Clicking pursuit Toothed whales track their food using echolocation. A dolphin may emit up to 600 clicks a second, analyzing the echoes to build up a picture of its surroundings, including the position of prey. Orcas use echolocation when pursuing fish, but rely more on vision to hunt other cetaceans or seals, which would be alerted by the clicks.

transmitted sound

returning echo

Humpback feeding Humpbacks (above) will synchronize their feeding, lunging at prey shoals together or herding scattered prey into clusters. In bubblenet feeding (below), a humpback spirals toward the surface while exhaling, producing a large "net" of bubbles that traps small prey. The whale lunges through the center of the net to capture its meal.

3. Lunge feeding Once the bubblenet has trapped the fishes, the humpback swims through the center, lunging to the surface with its mouth open to engulf the prey.

Bottom feeder A gray whale feeds in shallow waters on bottom-dwelling crustaceans, mollusks, and worms. It dives to the seafloor, turns on its side, and then sucks up a mouthful of sediment. Prey is filtered out by pushing the sediment through its baleen.

1. Slow exhale As a humpback whale spirals to the surface, it slowly lets out its breath, creating columns of bubbles. Small schooling fishes are trapped inside the net of bubbles.

2. Group effort Bubblenetting may be carried out by a single whale, or several whales may cooperate to create the net.

Together and alone Orcas feed mainly on the prey that are most abundant locally, which, in turn, determines their hunting methods. Where fishes such as salmon and herring are common, orcas tend to hunt cooperatively. In Argentina, a single whale will slide up onto the shore to grab a young sea lion (above).

FACT FILE

Sperm whale With a gullet large enough to swallow a human, the deep-diving sperm whale sometimes takes sharks and skates, but mainly feeds on giant squids, octopuses, and deepwater fishes. It is gregarious and lives in groups of 30–100 animals.

🐗 Up to 61 ft (18.5 m)
⚖ Up to 77 tons (70 t)
🐾 Variable
♦ Vulnerable

Deep temperate to tropical oceans & seas

Baird's beaked whale Tightly knit social groups of 6–30 Baird's beaked whales live in deep offshore waters and are led by a dominant male. Rivalry for this position often leads to physical conflict, with most males bearing scars on their beak and back.

🐗 Up to 43 ft (13 m)
⚖ Up to 16½ tons (15 t)
🐾 Variable
♦ Conservation dependent

North Pacific

TUSKED BEAKS

A diet of squids captured through suction has rendered beaked whales virtually toothless. In males, however, one or two pairs of teeth protrude from the mouth to form tusks, which appear to be used as weapons.

Wrap-arounds
In the male strap-toothed whale (Mesoplodon layardii), the tusks are especially long and wrap around the upper jaw. As a result, the mouth can only open an inch (2.5 cm) or so.

Pygmy sperm whale
Kogia breviceps

Sperm whale
Physeter catodon

Hump and ridges on back rather than dorsal fin

Males weigh three times as much as females

Baird's beaked whale
Berardius bairdii

Both males and females have two pairs of protruding teeth

Northern bottle-nosed whale
Hyperoodon ampullatus

Blainville's beaked whale
Mesoplodon densirostris

May spend 30 minutes plunging to depths of 3,300 feet (1,000 m)

Cuvier's beaked whale
Ziphius cavirostris

Female usually a little larger than male

Stubby beak

Sowerby's beaked whale
Mesoplodon bidens

BALEEN WHALES

The giants of the ocean, the baleen whales of the suborder Mysticeti feed on tiny prey, filtering aquatic invertebrates and small fishes through their sieve-like baleen plates. Their remarkable size is a great advantage in cooler waters, since, relative to body mass, they have a small surface area from which to lose heat. A thick layer of blubber provides insulation and can act as a food store for the epic annual migrations that many species undertake. Found in all the world's oceans, baleen whales include the gray whale, the right whales, the bowhead whale, and the rorquals—which comprise the blue whale, fin whale, sei whale, Bryde's whale, humpback whale, and minke whales.

CLASS	Mammalia
ORDER	Cetacea
FAMILIES	4
GENERA	6
SPECIES	13

Legal whaling For nutritional and cultural reasons, the Inuit (above) are permitted to hunt a small number of bowhead whales each year. The eastern bowhead population went into a severe decline as a result of the commercial whaling of the 19th century, but appears to be slowly stabilizing.

BALEEN AND BLUBBER

Baleen whales can be skimmers or gulpers. Right whales move slowly along the surface, skimming little animals from the water that crosses their long baleen plates. Rorquals lunge at shoals of prey with open mouths, gulp in water, and then force the water back out with their tongues, trapping krill and other creatures in their short plates. Gray whales are bottom feeders, filtering crustaceans and mollusks from the sediment with their heavy baleen.

Most of a baleen whale's prey species are minuscule, so it needs to consume vast quantities to stay alive. During summer, a large blue whale may eat 4½ tons (4 tonnes) of krill per day. It feeds very little during the rest of the year and lives off the fat and blubber laid down in summer.

Baleen and blubber, both crucial to the survival of these giants, also attracted commercial whalers. Since 1985, there has been a moratorium on all commercial whaling, but this is not observed by Norway or Japan.

Great gulp Like other rorquals, humpback whales have a pleated throat that expands into a great pouch as they gulp in water and plankton. The throat contracts again as they force the water back out and trap the prey in their bristled baleen plates.

Light bones Rather than supporting the animal's body weight, a cetacean's skeleton simply anchors the muscles. The bones are light, spongy, and filled with oil. The most dramatic feature of a baleen whale's skeleton is the massive head.

Distinguishing marks Right whales are distinguished by the callosities on their head, patches of hardened skin that are often infested with parasites such as lice and barnacles. The callosities are slightly larger on male whales than on females, suggesting that they may be used as weapons by rivals.

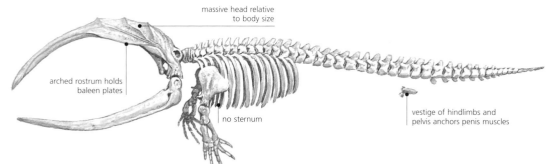

massive head relative to body size

arched rostrum holds baleen plates

no sternum

vestige of hindlimbs and pelvis anchors penis muscles

> **⚡ CONSERVATION WATCH**
>
> All 13 species of baleen whales are listed on the IUCN Red List, as follows:
>
> | | |
> |---|---|
> | 5 | Endangered |
> | 1 | Vulnerable |
> | 4 | Conservation dependent |
> | 1 | Data deficient |

Blue whale
Balaenoptera musculus

50–90 throat pleats

Fin whale
Balaenoptera physalus

80 percent of fin whales were
killed by 20th-century whalers

Differs from other right
whales by having two throat
grooves and a dorsal fin

Small dorsal fin
positioned far
along the back

Pygmy right whale
Caperea marginata

Bowhead whale
Balaena mysticetus

Longest baleen
plates of any whale

24 inch (60 cm) layer of blubber
keeps bowhead warm during
total darkness of Arctic winter

"Necklace"
of black spots

Only whale in
temperate waters
without dorsal fin

Callosities
covered in
whale lice

Northern right whale
Eubalaena glacialis

FACT FILE

Blue whale Consuming about 4½ tons
(4 tonnes) of krill every day during the
main summer feeding season, the blue
whale is the largest animal to have ever
lived. A newborn measures at least
19½ feet (5.9 m) and guzzles 50 gallons
(190 l) of milk per day, adding 8 pounds
(3.6 kg) to its weight every hour. It
may go on to live for 110 years. Blue
whales were relentlessly hunted in
the early to mid 20th century, and the
total population now comprises only
6,000–14,000 individuals.

- Up to 110 ft (33.5 m)
- Up to 209 tons (190 t)
- Variable
- Endangered

All oceans except high Arctic

Fin whale Outsized only by the blue
whale, the fin whale can attain speeds
of 23 miles per hour (37 km/h), making
it one of the fastest cetaceans. While
groups of 300 or more may migrate
together, the species is usually seen in
pairs or small pods of several animals.

- Up to 82 ft (25 m)
- Up to 88 tons (80 t)
- Variable
- Endangered

All oceans except high Arctic

Northern right whale Full of oil and
easy to catch, this species was named
the "right" whale for hunting by early
Basque whalers. There are now only
a few hundred individuals left.

- Up to 59 ft (18 m)
- Up to 99 tons (90 t)
- Variable
- Endangered

North Pacific & W. North Atlantic

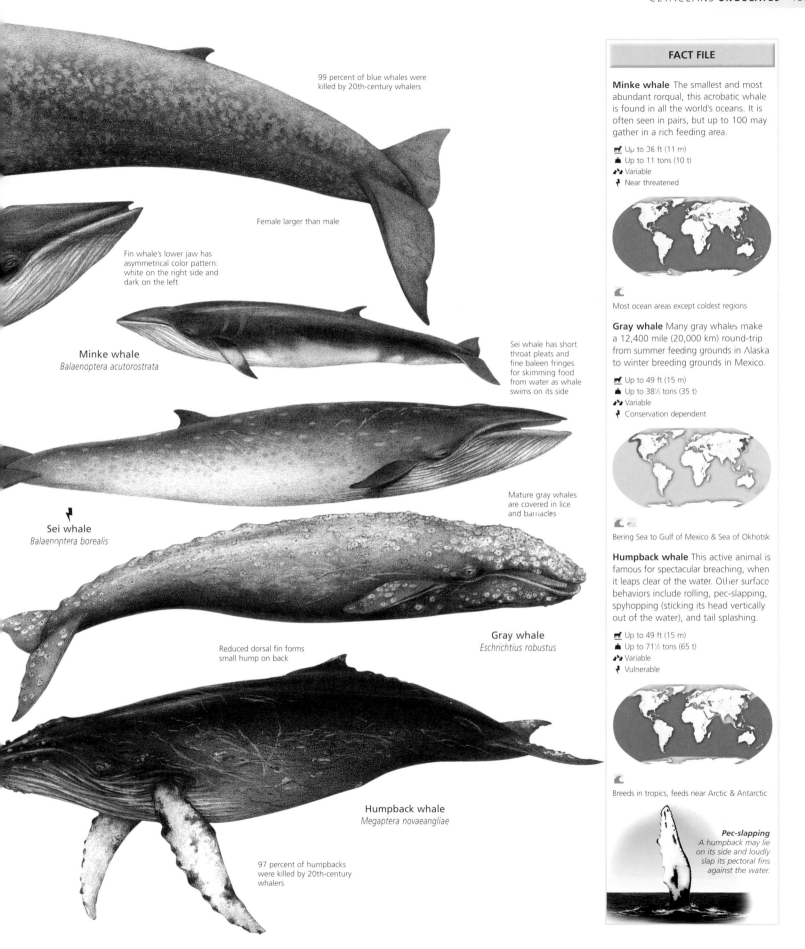

99 percent of blue whales were killed by 20th-century whalers

Female larger than male

Fin whale's lower jaw has asymmetrical color pattern: white on the right side and dark on the left

Sei whale has short throat pleats and fine baleen fringes for skimming food from water as whale swims on its side

Minke whale
Balaenoptera acutorostrata

Sei whale
Balaenoptera borealis

Mature gray whales are covered in lice and barnacles

Reduced dorsal fin forms small hump on back

Gray whale
Eschrichtius robustus

Humpback whale
Megaptera novaeangliae

97 percent of humpbacks were killed by 20th-century whalers

FACT FILE

Minke whale The smallest and most abundant rorqual, this acrobatic whale is found in all the world's oceans. It is often seen in pairs, but up to 100 may gather in a rich feeding area.

- Up to 36 ft (11 m)
- Up to 11 tons (10 t)
- Variable
- Near threatened

Most ocean areas except coldest regions

Gray whale Many gray whales make a 12,400 mile (20,000 km) round-trip from summer feeding grounds in Alaska to winter breeding grounds in Mexico.

- Up to 49 ft (15 m)
- Up to 38½ tons (35 t)
- Variable
- Conservation dependent

Bering Sea to Gulf of Mexico & Sea of Okhotsk

Humpback whale This active animal is famous for spectacular breaching, when it leaps clear of the water. Other surface behaviors include rolling, pec-slapping, spyhopping (sticking its head vertically out of the water), and tail splashing.

- Up to 49 ft (15 m)
- Up to 71½ tons (65 t)
- Variable
- Vulnerable

Breeds in tropics, feeds near Arctic & Antarctic

Pec-slapping
A humpback may lie on its side and loudly slap its pectoral fins against the water.

RODENTS

CLASS Mammalia
ORDER Rodentia
FAMILIES 29
GENERA 442
SPECIES 2,010

With roughly 2,000 species, rodents account for more than 40 percent of all mammal species and have colonized almost every habitat on Earth. A key to their extraordinary success is the ability to reproduce quickly and abundantly, allowing species to survive harsh conditions and take full advantage of favorable ones. In addition, the small size of most rodents has helped them to exploit many microhabitats. Although rodents are among the earliest of placental mammals, with the oldest rodent fossils dating back some 57 million years, the largest family, Muridae (rats and mice), did not appear until 5 million years ago. It now contains almost two-thirds of all species in the order.

Successful spread Members of the order Rodentia are distributed throughout all the world's continents, except for Antarctica. Their association with humans has even helped them to reach isolated islands. They have adapted to a wide range of habitats, including arctic tundra, tropical forests, deserts, high mountains, and urban areas.

Persistent pests Being opportunistic feeders that can reproduce quickly, many rodents have thrived alongside humans. Pests such as black rats (left) not only eat vast quantities of crops and stored food, but also contaminate the remaining food with their droppings and spread disease.

Rapid reproduction Garden dormice usually mate in April or May after waking from their winter hibernation. Following a short gestation period of 22–28 days, the female gives birth to 2–9 young. The newborn are entirely dependent on the mother and will not open their eyes for another 21 days or so. They become independent by 6 weeks and then grow rapidly until their first hibernation. While some rodent species are ready to breed at 6 weeks, it takes about a year for garden dormice to become sexually mature. A captive garden dormouse lived for about 5½ years, a long lifespan for a rodent.

UNIFORM ANATOMY

Rodent size ranges from the tiny pygmy jerboa, less than 2 inches (5 cm) long and weighing just ⅕ ounce (5 g), to the substantial capybara, more than 50 inches (1.3 m) in length with a weight of 140 pounds (64 kg). Typically, however, rodents are small with squat bodies, short legs, and a tail.

The most distinguishing rodent feature is the arrangement of the teeth. All rodents have two pairs of extremely sharp incisors at the front of the mouth that can gnaw through seedpods, nut shells, and other tough matter to get at the nutritious food inside. The incisors grow continuously and are "self-sharpened" against each other. There are no canine teeth behind the incisors. Instead, a gap known as the diastema allows the lips to close during gnawing so inedible material is kept out of the mouth. At the back of the mouth, a series of molars grind up the plant matter that makes up most of a rodent's diet.

While a few rodents are mainly carnivorous, most are opportunistic feeders and eat leaves, fruit, nuts, and seeds, as well as caterpillars, spiders, and other small invertebrates. The indigestible cellulose in plant walls is broken down by bacteria in

Typical rodent The brown rat displays the typical rodent anatomy, with a compact body, short legs, clawed feet, long tail, and sensitive whiskers. A keen sense of smell and sharp hearing help rodents to find food and avoid predators.

Flexible feeder A resident of temperate forests, the red squirrel eats mainly seeds and nuts, but will also consume flowers, shoots, fungi, and small invertebrates. It builds up a cache of buried seeds and nuts that it can raid during the cold winter.

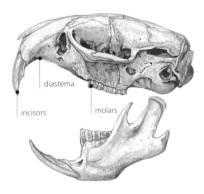

diastema

incisors   molars

Gnawing teeth A gap called the diastema separates a rodent's chewing molars from the sharp, continuously growing incisors. The diastema allows the lips to close behind the incisors and keep out inedible material when the animal is gnawing.

Ecosystem role As key prey species for medium-sized predators such as this barn owl, rodents play an important role in an ecosystem. Their distribution of the spores of fungi that nourish tree roots is also vital in North American and Australian forests.

A rodent's tail The diversity of rodent lifestyles is reflected in the various shapes and purposes of the tail (right). The northern flying squirrel (*Glaucomys sabrinus*) (above) uses its tail for steering and stability as it glides from tree to tree.

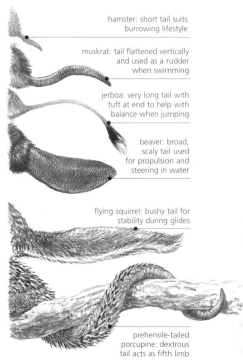

hamster: short tail suits burrowing lifestyle

muskrat: tail flattened vertically and used as a rudder when swimming

jerboa: very long tail with tuft at end to help with balance when jumping

beaver: broad, scaly tail used for propulsion and steering in water

flying squirrel: bushy tail for stability during glides

prehensile-tailed porcupine: dextrous tail acts as fifth limb

the large cecum (appendix) of the rodent digestive system. Some species then take this treated food from the anus and eat it again, gaining maximum nutrition from the meal before passing feces as dry pellets, a process known as refection.

Intelligent and resourceful, rodents have put their relatively uniform anatomy to diverse use. Many species are terrestrial, finding their food in forests, grasslands, deserts, or human settlements. Others spend most of their time in trees, scampering over branches and, in some cases, gliding from one tree to another. Some species make their life underground in extensive networks of burrows. And a few are excellent swimmers,

able to pursue a semiaquatic lifestyle. While a minority of rodents are solitary, most are highly social, a trait culminating in the townships that contain thousands of prairie dogs.

The order Rodentia was once split into three suborders according to the arrangement of jaw muscles: squirrel-like rodents, mouse-like rodents, and cavy-like rodents. These categories are still used informally for ease, but genetic evidence points to a division into just two suborders. The suborder Sciurognathi includes all the squirrel-like and mouse-like rodents, plus the gundis, a family of cavy-like rodents. The other suborder, Hystricognathi, includes all other cavy-like rodents.

> ### ⚡ CONSERVATION WATCH
>
> Some rodent species have thrived alongside humans to the point of becoming serious pests. Many with limited ranges, however, have been threatened or even driven extinct by human activities. Of the 2,010 species of rodents, 33% are listed on the IUCN Red List, as follows:
>
> | | |
> |---|---|
> | 32 | Extinct |
> | 68 | Critically endangered |
> | 95 | Endangered |
> | 165 | Vulnerable |
> | 5 | Conservation dependent |
> | 255 | Near threatened |
> | 49 | Data deficient |

SQUIRREL-LIKE RODENTS

CLASS	Mammalia
ORDER	Rodentia
FAMILIES	8
GENERA	71
SPECIES	383

The squirrels, beavers, and other animals collectively known as squirrel-like rodents share an arrangement of jaw muscles that gives them a strong forward bite. They have simple teeth and have retained one or two premolar teeth in each row, a characteristic not found in other rodents. Aside from the jaw muscles and premolar teeth, the families of squirrel-like rodents share few characteristics and probably diverged from each other early in rodent evolution. They include beavers (family Castoridae), mountain beaver (Aplodontidae), squirrels (Sciuridae), pocket gophers (Geomyidae), pocket mice (Heteromyidae), scaly-tailed squirrels (Anomaluridae), and springhare (Pedetidae).

Winter sleep From October until March or April, the woodchuck (*Marmota monax*) hibernates underground in burrows. During this time, its heartbeat slows, its body temperature falls, and it lives off body fat. It mates soon after emerging in spring.

Arboreal leaper When a tree squirrel such as this American red squirrel leaps from one tree to another, it stretches out its limbs, flattens its body, and slightly curves its tail to maximize its surface area. The long, bushy tail acts as a rudder.

Social species Prairie dogs live in large townships with a complex social structure. A township is made up of many coteries—groups of one male, several related females, and their offspring. Members of a coterie share burrows and food.

BURROWERS AND LEAPERS

The squirrels in the family Sciuridae make up about three-quarters of all squirrel-like rodents. Active by day, tree squirrels have long, lightweight bodies, sharp claws for clinging to bark, and excellent eyesight for judging distances. They move about by scampering along branches, climbing headfirst down trunks, or leaping from tree to tree. The nocturnal flying squirrels glide through the air, aided by a furred membrane along either side of the body. Arboreal squirrels mostly feed on fruit, nuts, seeds, shoots, and leaves, but may supplement this diet with insects. Ground-dwelling squirrels, which include ground squirrels, prairie dogs, marmots, and chipmunks, tend to favor grasses and herbs. Many of these terrestrial species are gregarious with complex social organization.

Scaly-tailed squirrels are only distantly related to true squirrels. Like tree squirrels, almost all species of scaly-tailed squirrels possess a membrane for gliding—an example of convergent evolution.

Beavers are superbly equipped for a life spent largely in water, with a streamlined body, flattened tail, and webbed feet. Their large incisor teeth allow them to cut down trees and build dams and lodges.

Pocket gophers, pocket mice, mountain beavers, and springhares are all burrowing rodents. The pocket gophers and pocket mice both carry food in cheek pouches on either side of the mouth.

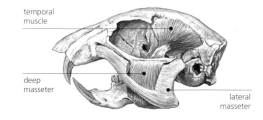

Strong forward bite The chewing muscles are known as masseters. In squirrel-like rodents, the lateral masseter extends to the snout and pulls the jaw forward when biting. The deep masseter is short and direct and simply closes the jaw.

temporal muscle

deep masseter

lateral masseter

🔦 CONSERVATION WATCH

Of the 383 species of squirrel-like rodents, 21% are listed on the IUCN Red List, as follows:

8	Critically endangered
11	Endangered
3	Conservation dependent
58	Near threatened
2	Data deficient

Cheek pouches inside
mouth for carrying food

European souslik
Spermophilus citellus

Spotted souslik
Spermophilus suslicus

Stands on hindlegs to
watch for predators

Bobak marmot
Marmota bobak

Whistles to warn
other marmots
of danger

Alpine marmot
Marmota marmota

Hoary marmot
Marmota caligata

Sturdy, slightly curved
claws for digging

**Thirteen-lined
ground squirrel**
Spermophilus tridecemlineatus

13 stripes
alternating
between light
and dark fur

Poor eyesight but
keen hearing and
sense of touch

Black-tailed prairie dog
Cynomys ludovicianus

Mountain beaver
Aplodontia rufa

MARMOTS

Restricted to the Northern Hemisphere,
marmots are found mainly in mountain
habitats. They are true hibernators,
and spend the harsh winter at rest in
their burrows, living off body fat. All
marmots, except for the woodchuck,
live in family groups. Young female
marmots often stay with their parents
to help raise their younger siblings.

*Face to face Like almost all other marmots,
Olympic marmots (Marmota olympus) are
highly social. Young remain dependent on
the mother for 2 years.*

FACT FILE

Eastern gray squirrel In addition to maintaining a den in a hollow log, this squirrel builds a nest of twigs and leaves lined with grasses and shredded bark in the branches of a tree. The nest is used for resting and feeding, and may also serve as a nursery.

🐀 Up to 11 in (28 cm)
🐁 Up to 9½ in (24 cm)
⚖ Up to 26½ oz (750 g)
♟ Solitary
🐾 Common
🌳🌲

S. Canada to Texas & Florida

Eurasian red squirrel Using its strong incisors, this squirrel can crack a tough nut in a few seconds. It spends much of the day collecting seeds and nuts, as well as fungi, birds' eggs, and tree sap.

🐀 Up to 11 in (28 cm)
🐁 Up to 9½ in (24 cm)
⚖ Up to 10 oz (280 g)
♟ Solitary
🐾 Near threatened

🌳🌲

W. Europe to E. Russia, Korea & N. Japan

SQUIRREL LARDER

Like many tree squirrels in climates with harsh winters, the American red squirrel prepares for the cold months by storing food. It collects thousands of pine and spruce cones and caches them in a larder, known as a midden, which may be hidden under a log or inside a hollow stump. The territory surrounding the midden is vigorously defended.

⚡ CONSERVATION WATCH

Competing squirrels While the Eurasian red squirrel has remained common in much of central Europe, overhunting has led to a fall in numbers in eastern Europe. The species has now vanished from most parts of Great Britain, outcompeted for resources by the eastern gray squirrel, which was introduced from North America in 1902.

Variegated squirrel
Sciurus variegatoides

American red squirrel
Tamiasciurus hudsonicus

White band around eye

Eastern gray squirrel
Sciurus carolinensis

Long tufts on ears in winter

Variegated squirrel
Sciurus variegatoides

Tassel-eared squirrel (Abert's squirrel)
Sciurus aberti

Relies on ponderosa pines for food and shelter

Eurasian red squirrel
Sciurus vulgaris

Eurasian red squirrel coat can be red or black

Coat thickens in winter

Guayaquil squirrel
Sciurus stramineus

Prevost's squirrel
Callosciurus prevostii

Nests high in forest canopy
but feeds at lower levels

Horse-tailed squirrel
Sundasciurus hippurus

Southern flying squirrel
Glaucomys volans

Gliding membrane,
or patagium, is folded
when squirrel is sitting

Siberian
flying squirrel
Pteromys volans

Red bush squirrel
Paraxerus palliatus

Soil often tints coat

Striped ground squirrel
Xerus erythropus

Handles
food with
dextrous
forepaws

Gambian
sun squirrel
Heliosciurus gambianus

Sits up on hindlegs to
eat or look for danger

Smallest squirrel
in the world

Five black
stripes on back

Eastern chipmunk
Tamias striatus

African pygmy squirrel
Myosciurus pumilio

FACT FILE

Southern flying squirrel While this nocturnal glider eats mainly nuts and acorns, it also consumes many insects and young birds. It often lives in pairs, but larger groups may den together during the winter months.

🐾 Up to 5½ in (14 cm)
🐾 Up to 4½ in (12 cm)
⚖ Up to 3 oz (85 g)
🐾 Pair, small group
🌱 Locally common

S. Canada to E. USA

Striped ground squirrel Like prairie dogs, this gregarious animal lives in colonies and is highly vocal, warning of danger with an alarm call.

🐾 Up to 16 in (40 cm)
🐾 Up to 12 in (30 cm)
⚖ Up to 2 lb (1 kg)
🐾 Colonial
🌱 Locally common

W. Africa to Kenya

Eastern chipmunk This usually solitary species shelters in a burrow. When its cheek pouches are stuffed with food, they can be as large as its head.

🐾 Up to 6½ in (17 cm)
🐾 Up to 4½ in (12 cm)
⚖ Up to 5½ oz (150 g)
🐾 Solitary
🌱 Locally common

S.E. North America

African pygmy squirrel About the size of a man's thumb, this species is the smallest of all squirrels. It lives in the hollow trunks of trees.

🐾 Up to 3 in (7.5 cm)
🐾 Up to 2½ in (6 cm)
⚖ Up to ½ oz (17 g)
🐾 Solitary
🌱 Vulnerable

Equatorial Africa

GLIDING

A flying squirrel can glide for more than 330 feet (100 m), using much less energy than climbing would require and allowing it to escape flightless predators. In most species, the gliding membrane that extends from wrist to ankle is tucked away when climbing.

***Putting
on the brakes***
*A flying squirrel
brakes by raising the
tail, and forms a parachute with its
membrane by moving the limbs forward.*

LUMBERJACK RODENTS

The great engineers of the animal world, beavers deliberately alter their environment by building dams, canals, and lodges. While often causing conflict with farmers and other humans, this construction work has an important ecological function, helping to reduce erosion and flooding and creating new habitats for aquatic species. Beavers live in family groups of a monogamous pair and several offspring. They communicate using various calls and postures and will slap their tails against the water to warn of danger. Although similar in appearance and behavior, the two species of beaver—the North American *Castor canadensis* and the Eurasian *C. fiber*—do not interbreed.

Chopping chisels Like all rodents, beavers have self-sharpening incisor teeth that never stop growing. The outer surface is protected by tough enamel, but the inner surface is softer and wears away as the beaver gnaws, creating a sharp, chiseled edge.

Winter quiet Beavers usually feed and build at night. Through snowy winters, however, they rarely emerge from their lodge, which provides a warm environment. For food, they rely on sticks and logs stored underwater, as well as the fat stored in the tail.

Lodges and dams A beaver colony may share a riverbank burrow system or they may build a lodge in the water. A lodge is a dome of sticks and mud with underwater entrances leading to a vegetation-lined living area above the water level. To create a calm pond for their lodge, beavers will construct dam walls that stop the flow of water. They will also dig out canals to link their dam to nearby sources of food and construction material. Several generations of beavers may maintain a dam, but eventually the pond silts up and the resident family must find a new location for their home.

Aquatic adaptations A beaver uses its flat, scaly tail and webbed rear feet to propel its streamlined body through the water. Clear eyelids shield the eyes underwater, while valved nostrils and ears keep out water. Thick, oil-coated fur insulates the animal in cold water.

Beaver babies Beaver litters contain an average of two to four kits, which are nursed for 6–8 weeks. The kits grow quickly, but will stay with their family group for up to 2 years so they can learn the craft of building dams and lodges.

Stopping the flow Beavers use mud, stones, sticks, and branches to construct a dam wall. The pond this creates acts as a moat around their lodge and deters most predators.

Rapid recovery Beavers prefer aspens, poplars, alders, and willows. These are all trees that grow rapidly and may even be reinvigorated after being felled by a beaver.

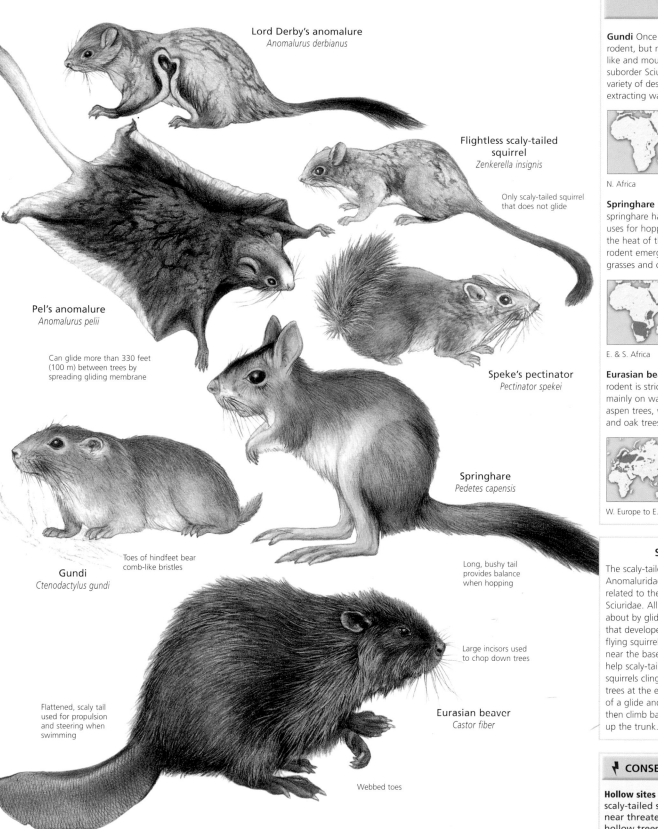

Lord Derby's anomalure
Anomalurus derbianus

Flightless scaly-tailed squirrel
Zenkerella insignis

Only scaly-tailed squirrel that does not glide

Pel's anomalure
Anomalurus pelii

Can glide more than 330 feet (100 m) between trees by spreading gliding membrane

Speke's pectinator
Pectinator spekei

Gundi
Ctenodactylus gundi

Toes of hindfeet bear comb-like bristles

Springhare
Pedetes capensis

Long, bushy tail provides balance when hopping

Large incisors used to chop down trees

Eurasian beaver
Castor fiber

Flattened, scaly tail used for propulsion and steering when swimming

Webbed toes

SCALY TAILS

The scaly-tailed squirrels of the Anomaluridae family are not directly related to the true squirrels of Sciuridae. All but one species moves about by gliding, an adaptation that developed independently in flying squirrels. The scales near the base of the tail help scaly-tailed squirrels cling to trees at the end of a glide and then climb back up the trunk.

FACT FILE

Heteromyidae This family includes pocket mice and kangaroo rats and mice. They are closely related to the pocket gophers of the Geomyidae family, with whom they share cheek pouches and a burrowing lifestyle.

Long-tailed pocket mouse This species is most often found in gravelly desert areas. During drought, females may avoid producing a litter.

🐁 Up to 4 in (10 cm)
🐁 Up to 4½ in (12 cm)
⬛ Up to 1 oz (25 g)
♣ Solitary
🗲 Common

Nevada & Utah to Baja California

Mexican spiny pocket mouse This species can breed at any time of year, allowing it to take advantage of favorable conditions when they arrive.

🐁 Up to 5 in (13 cm)
🐁 Up to 5 in (13 cm)
⬛ Up to 2 oz (60 g)
♣ Solitary
🗲 Uncommon
🏛 ⚎

S. Texas to Mexico

Plains pocket gopher This solitary rodent digs an extensive burrow, with tunnels leading to a central chamber. During the mating season, a male may tunnel through to a female's burrow.

🐁 Up to 8 in (20 cm)
🐁 Up to 4½ in (12 cm)
⬛ Up to 9 oz (250 g)
♣ Solitary
🗲 Common

Tallgrass prairies from S. Canada to Texas

Big-eared kangaroo rat Like other kangaroo rats, this species has long hindlimbs and moves by hopping. The short forelimbs are used for feeding.

🐁 Up to 6 in (15 cm)
🐁 Up to 8 in (20 cm)
⬛ Up to 3 oz (90 g)
♣ Solitary
🗲 Not known

California

Desert kangaroo rat To conserve water in its arid environment, this rodent emerges from its burrow only at night, when humidity is highest, and concentrates its urine. It rarely drinks, obtaining most of its water from food.

🐁 Up to 6 in (15 cm)
🐁 Up to 8½ in (21 cm)
⬛ Up to 5½ oz (150 g)
♣ Solitary
🗲 Common

Nevada to N. Mexico

Long-tailed pocket mouse
Chaetodipus formosus

Tail longer than head and body

Mexican spiny pocket mouse
Liomys irroratus

Trinidad spiny pocket mouse
Heteromys anomalus

Harsh, bristly fur

Loose skin allows pocket gopher to maneuver in tight burrows

Large, projecting teeth used for cutting roots or digging

Thick, ridged skull

Enlarged claws used to dig burrows

Plains pocket gopher
Geomys bursarius

Botta's pocket gopher
Thomomys bottae

Usually moves in hops

Desert kangaroo rat
Dipodomys deserti

Big-eared kangaroo rat
Dipodomys elephantinus

Long tail provides stability when hopping

MOUSE-LIKE RODENTS

CLASS Mammalia

ORDER Rodentia

FAMILIES 3

GENERA 306

SPECIES 1,409

More than a quarter of all mammal species are mouse-like rodents. Once grouped within their own suborder, these rodents share an arrangement of the chewing muscles that provides a versatile gnawing action. They also all have a maximum of three cheekteeth in each row. While their lifespans tend to be short, most are early and prolific breeders. The group is dominated by the Muridae family, which has more than 1,000 species, including Old World and New World rats and mice; voles and lemmings; hamsters; and gerbils. The other families of mouse-like rodents are the dormice of Myoxidae and the jumping mice, birchmice, and jerboas of Dipodidae.

On the scent As many as 50 house mice may live in a family group. They leave deposits of urine as scentmarks throughout their home territory, enabling them to recognize each other and detect intruders.

RAPID RADIATION

The first members of the Muridae family appeared only several million years ago, making it very young in evolutionary terms. Since that time, however, the family has diversified dramatically and now occupies almost every terrestrial habitat in the world, from polar regions to desert. The majority of its members are small, nocturnal, seed-eating ground-dwellers with a pointed face and long whiskers, but some spend much of their time in water or trees and others live underground.

There are more than 500 species of Old World rats and mice. These are highly varied but include the ubiquitous house mouse and brown rat, both of which are well known as urban pests. New World rats and mice range from climbing rats to fish-eating rats, but most live on the ground in forests or grasslands.

While rats and mice account for 80 percent of species in the family Muridae, voles and lemmings, hamsters, and gerbils form distinct subfamilies. Voles and lemmings, found throughout the Northern Hemisphere, have adapted to a diet of tough grasses. Many spend winter living in tunnels beneath the snow. Although popular as children's pets, the hamsters of Eurasia are decidedly solitary in the wild and will react very aggressively to intruders. Gerbils are found mainly in arid parts of Africa and Asia.

The Myoxidae and Dipodidae families are smaller and more specialized than Muridae. Dormice tend to live in trees and hibernate through cold winters. Jumping mice, birchmice, and jerboas all have long back feet and long tails that enable them to move by hopping. Jerboas have evolved to survive in some of the world's harshest deserts.

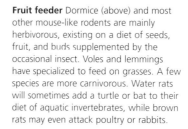

Fruit feeder Dormice (above) and most other mouse-like rodents are mainly herbivorous, existing on a diet of seeds, fruit, and buds supplemented by the occasional insect. Voles and lemmings have specialized to feed on grasses. A few species are more carnivorous. Water rats will sometimes add a turtle or bat to their diet of aquatic invertebrates, while brown rats may even attack poultry or rabbits.

Big families Rats and mice are prolific breeders. Most mature quickly, have short gestation periods, and produce many large litters. In some species, a single pair and their offspring can produce thousands of animals in less than a year.

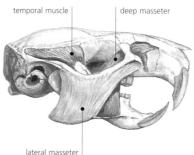

temporal muscle

deep masseter

lateral masseter

Versatile action The arrangement of their jaw muscles provides mouse-like rodents with a versatile gnawing action. The deep masseter extends onto the upper jaw and works together with the lateral masseter to pull the jaw forward for chewing.

FACT FILE

Golden hamster Now a popular pet and the best known of the hamsters, this species is endangered in the wild. It was introduced to the United States and England in the 1930s and has since proliferated in captivity.

- Up to 7 in (18 cm)
- Up to ¾ in (2 cm)
- Up to 5½ oz (150 g)
- Solitary
- Endangered

Middle East, S.E. Europe, S.W. Asia

European hamster This solitary burrower hibernates through winter, waking once a week or so to feed on its massive hoard of seeds and roots. During warmer months, it stocks up this winter food supply, carrying plant matter in its cheek pouches.

- Up to 12½ in (32 cm)
- Up to 2½ in (6 cm)
- Up to 13½ oz (385 g)
- Solitary
- Common

Belgium to Altai Mts of C. Asia

Eastern woodrat Nocturnal and solitary, this species falls prey to owls, weasels, and snakes. It protects its nest by building a shelter of sticks, bones, and leaves in a rock crevice or between tree roots.

- Up to 10½ in (27 cm)
- Up to 7 in (18 cm)
- Up to 9 oz (260 g)
- Solitary
- Common

S.E. USA

Hispid cotton rat After a gestation of just 27 days, females of this species give birth to several fully furred young. The female is ready to mate again almost immediately, while the young are sexually mature within 40 days.

- Up to 8 in (20 cm)
- Up to 6½ in (16 cm)
- Up to 8 oz (225 g)
- Solitary
- Common

S.E. USA to N. Venezuela & N. Peru

Deer mouse This small omnivore has adapted to diverse habitats, from boreal forest to desert. It breeds very quickly, with females producing up to four litters of 4–9 young each year.

- Up to 4 in (10 cm)
- Up to 4½ in (12 cm)
- Up to 1 oz (30 g)
- Solitary
- Common

North America except tundra & far S.E. USA

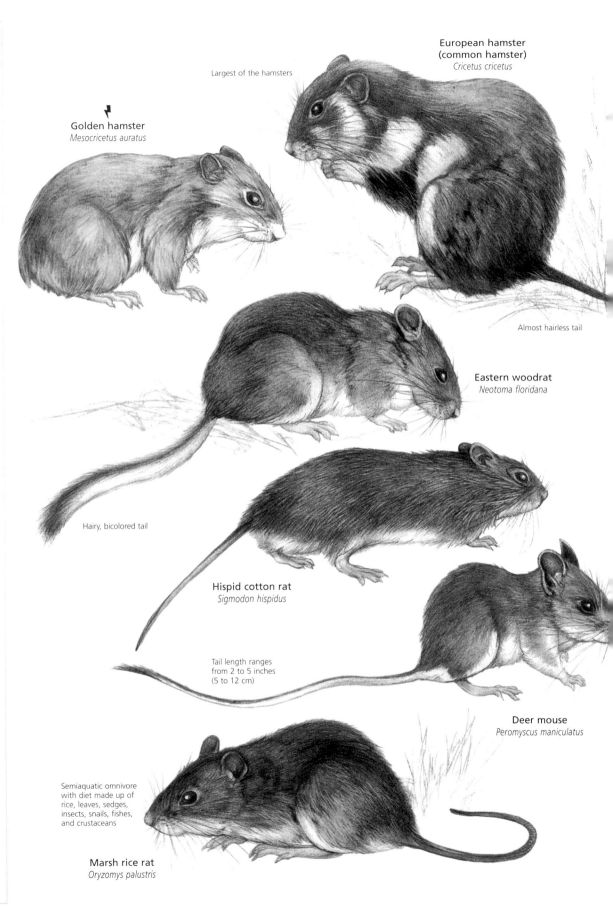

European hamster
(common hamster)
Cricetus cricetus

Largest of the hamsters

Golden hamster
Mesocricetus auratus

Almost hairless tail

Eastern woodrat
Neotoma floridana

Hairy, bicolored tail

Hispid cotton rat
Sigmodon hispidus

Tail length ranges from 2 to 5 inches (5 to 12 cm)

Deer mouse
Peromyscus maniculatus

Semiaquatic omnivore with diet made up of rice, leaves, sedges, insects, snails, fishes, and crustaceans

Marsh rice rat
Oryzomys palustris

Long-clawed mole-vole
Prometheomys schaposchnikowi

Long claws for
digging burrows

European water vole
Arvicola terrestris

Siberian collared lemming
(Arctic lemming)
Dicrostonyx torquatus

White winter coat

Bank vole
Clethrionomys glareolus

Lives farther north
than any other rodent

Brown summer coat

Great gerbil
Rhombomys opimus

Wood lemming
Myopus schisticolor

Norway lemming
Lemmus lemmus

Libyan jird
Meriones lybicus

Tail flattened
vertically for
use as rudder

Largest of
the voles

Small webs
between toes

Muskrat
Ondatra zibethicus

FACT FILE

Siberian collared lemming This tundra species spends summer in shallow burrows in high, rocky areas. In winter, it moves to lower meadows and shelters in tunnels under the snow.

- Up to 6 in (15 cm)
- Up to ½ in (1 cm)
- Up to 3 oz (90 g)
- Solitary
- Common

Arctic Eurasia

Great gerbil To survive cold winters, large groups of these gerbils huddle together in extensive burrows, not only providing each other with warmth but also protecting their stockpile of plants.

- Up to 8 in (20 cm)
- Up to 6½ in (16 cm)
- Not known
- Colonial
- Common

Caspian Sea to Mongolia, China & Pakistan

Muskrat This semiaquatic rodent swims with its large, webbed back feet and uses its naked tail as a rudder. Like the beaver, it lives in a group in a riverbank burrow or a lodge of twigs and mud.

- Up to 13 in (33 cm)
- Up to 12 in (30 cm)
- Up to 4 lb (1.8 kg)
- Small to large group
- Common

USA & Canada except tundra; introd. Eurasia

FLUCTUATING LEMMINGS

Contrary to popular myth, Norway lemmings are not deliberately suicidal, but every 3 or 4 years, their number rises. Intolerant of one another at the best of times, the lemmings become highly aggressive. Such conflicts may trigger mass movements from the crowded alpine tundra to lower forests. When the lemmings meet obstacles such as rivers, panic can cause them to take flight, with some ending up in the sea.

Fighting techniques Norway lemmings may wrestle, box, or adopt dominating postures.

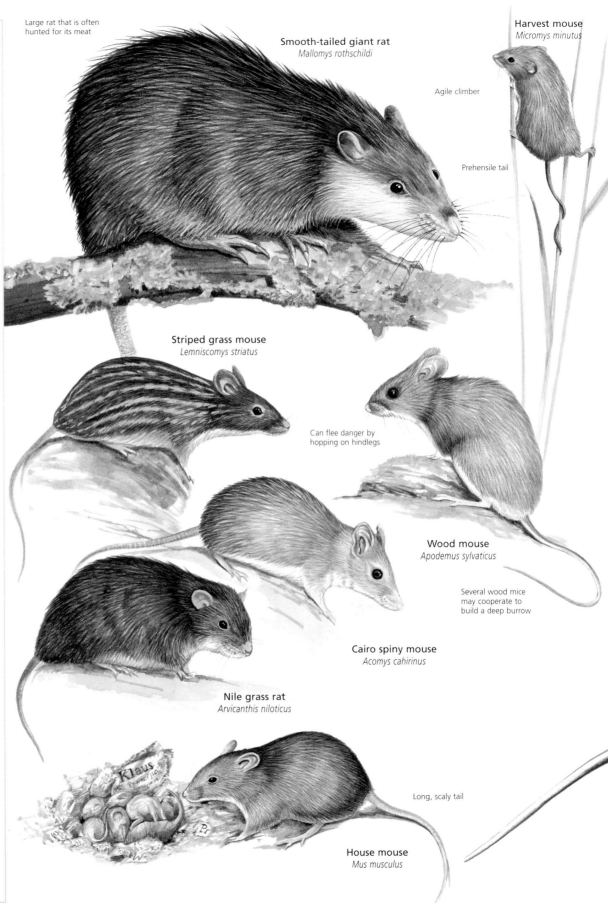

Large rat that is often hunted for its meat

Smooth-tailed giant rat
Mallomys rothschildi

Harvest mouse
Micromys minutus

Agile climber

Prehensile tail

Striped grass mouse
Lemniscomys striatus

Can flee danger by hopping on hindlegs

Wood mouse
Apodemus sylvaticus

Several wood mice may cooperate to build a deep burrow

Cairo spiny mouse
Acomys cahirinus

Nile grass rat
Arvicanthis niloticus

Long, scaly tail

House mouse
Mus musculus

FACT FILE

Smooth-tailed giant rat This arboreal rat makes its nest in a tree hollow and is almost fully herbivorous, feeding mainly on shoots.

- Up to 14½ in (37 cm)
- Up to 16 in (41 cm)
- Up to 3 lb (1.3 kg)
- Solitary
- Common

Central highlands of New Guinea

Harvest mouse One of the smallest mice, this species lives among tall crops, reeds, bamboo, or long grass. For each litter, both parents spend days building a globe-shaped nest that is suspended between stalks above the ground.

- Up to 1 in (2.5 cm)
- Up to 1 in (2.5 cm)
- Up to ¼ oz (7 g)
- Solitary
- Near threatened

England & Spain to China, Korea & Japan

Striped grass mouse This savanna resident shelters in an underground burrow or an abandoned termite nest. It builds a roundish nest for its litters, which are born during the rainy season after a gestation of 28 days.

- Up to 5½ in (14 cm)
- Up to 6 in (15 cm)
- Up to 2½ oz (68 g)
- Solitary
- Common

Sub-Saharan Africa

House mouse Through its association with humans, this species has been able to spread throughout the world. It nests in buildings or nearby fields and will eat almost any human food as well as items such as glue and soap.

- Up to 4 in (10 cm)
- Up to 4 in (10 cm)
- Up to 1 oz (30 g)
- Variable
- Abundant, often regarded as pest

Worldwide except tundra & polar regions

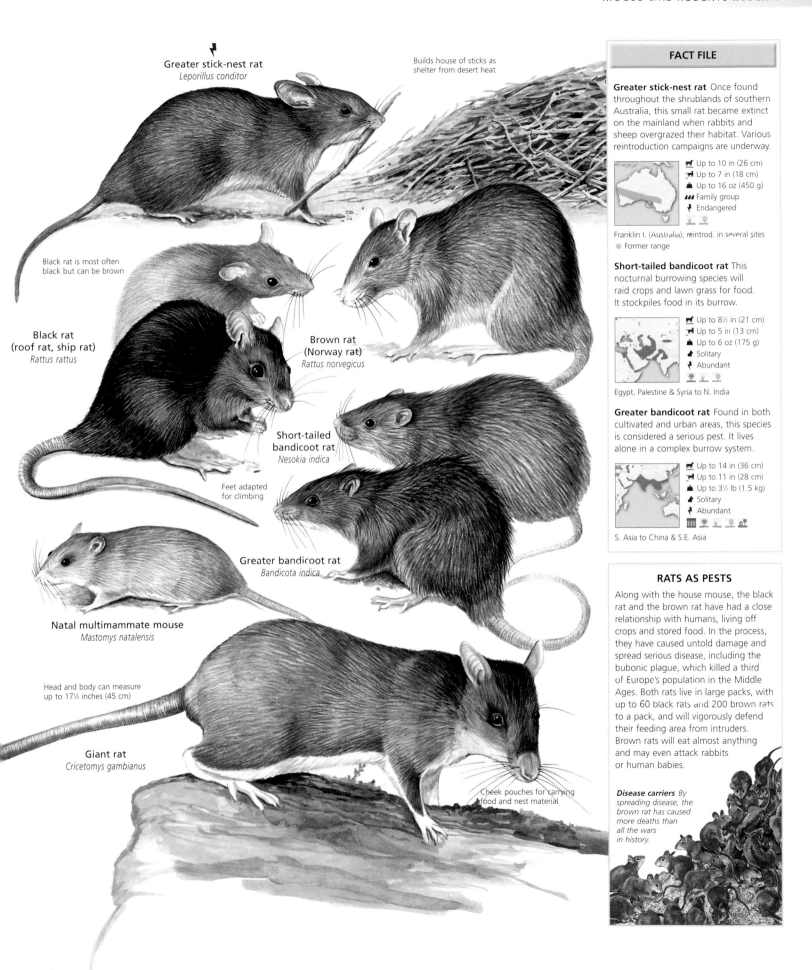

Greater stick-nest rat
Leporillus conditor

Builds house of sticks as shelter from desert heat

Black rat is most often black but can be brown

Black rat
(roof rat, ship rat)
Rattus rattus

Brown rat
(Norway rat)
Rattus norvegicus

Short-tailed
bandicoot rat
Nesokia indica

Feet adapted for climbing

Greater bandicoot rat
Bandicota indica

Natal multimammate mouse
Mastomys natalensis

Head and body can measure up to 17½ inches (45 cm)

Giant rat
Cricetomys gambianus

Cheek pouches for carrying food and nest material

FACT FILE

Greater stick-nest rat Once found throughout the shrublands of southern Australia, this small rat became extinct on the mainland when rabbits and sheep overgrazed their habitat. Various reintroduction campaigns are underway.

- Up to 10 in (26 cm)
- Up to 7 in (18 cm)
- Up to 16 oz (450 g)
- Family group
- Endangered

Franklin I. (Australia); reintrod. in several sites
● Former range

Short-tailed bandicoot rat This nocturnal burrowing species will raid crops and lawn grass for food. It stockpiles food in its burrow.

- Up to 8½ in (21 cm)
- Up to 5 in (13 cm)
- Up to 6 oz (175 g)
- Solitary
- Abundant

Egypt, Palestine & Syria to N. India

Greater bandicoot rat Found in both cultivated and urban areas, this species is considered a serious pest. It lives alone in a complex burrow system.

- Up to 14 in (36 cm)
- Up to 11 in (28 cm)
- Up to 3½ lb (1.5 kg)
- Solitary
- Abundant

S. Asia to China & S.E. Asia

RATS AS PESTS

Along with the house mouse, the black rat and the brown rat have had a close relationship with humans, living off crops and stored food. In the process, they have caused untold damage and spread serious disease, including the bubonic plague, which killed a third of Europe's population in the Middle Ages. Both rats live in large packs, with up to 60 black rats and 200 brown rats to a pack, and will vigorously defend their feeding area from intruders. Brown rats will eat almost anything and may even attack rabbits or human babies.

Disease carriers By spreading disease, the brown rat has caused more deaths than all the wars in history.

FACT FILE

Gray climbing mouse With its long, prehensile tail, this little mouse can easily climb the grasses and shrubs of its savanna home. It may dig a simple burrow to shelter from seasonal fires, but more often occupies a globe-shaped grass nest above the ground.

- Up to 2¼ in (7 cm)
- Up to 3 in (8 cm)
- Up to ¼ oz (8 g)
- Solitary
- Common

Sub-Saharan Africa

Vlei rat Like voles and lemmings, this rat lives in moist grassland, and tunnels through the grass to its feeding areas. It will enter water to escape predators.

- Up to 8½ in (22 cm)
- Up to 4½ in (11 cm)
- Up to 6½ oz (180 g)
- Solitary
- Locally common

S. Africa

Fawn hopping mouse If startled, this nocturnal burrower will bound away on its long hindlegs. Its urine is highly concentrated to help conserve water.

- Up to 4¾ in (12 cm)
- Up to 16½ in (16 cm)
- Up to 1¾ oz (50 g)
- Family group
- Near threatened

Gibber desert of C. Australia

WATER RAT

The Australian water rat lives in burrows that run along the banks of rivers or lakes. Able to withstand pollution, it is often found in urban areas. It depends on fresh water for the bulk of its diet, which includes crustaceans, mollusks, and fish. Broad, webbed feet act as paddles in the water. Its coat is not waterproof, but a pad of fat helps keep the heart warm.

- Up to 15½ in (39 cm)
- Up to 12½ in (32 cm)
- Up to 2½ lb (1.2 kg)
- Solitary
- Locally common

Papua New Guinea, Australia & Tasmania

Aquatic predator *The water rat often takes its catch to a preferred feeding platform.*

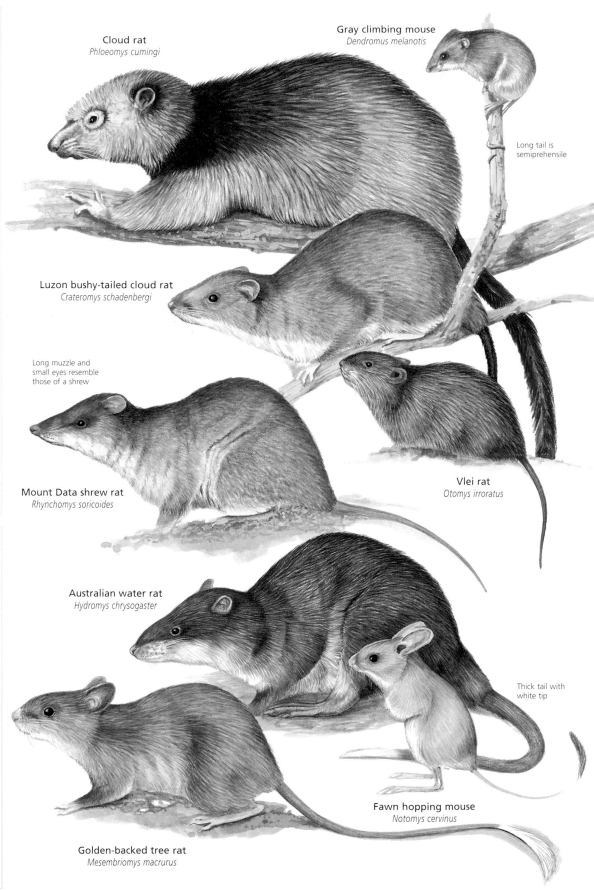

Cloud rat
Phloeomys cumingi

Gray climbing mouse
Dendromus melanotis

Long tail is semiprehensile

Luzon bushy-tailed cloud rat
Crateromys schadenbergi

Long muzzle and small eyes resemble those of a shrew

Mount Data shrew rat
Rhynchomys soricoides

Vlei rat
Otomys irroratus

Australian water rat
Hydromys chrysogaster

Thick tail with white tip

Golden-backed tree rat
Mesembriomys macrurus

Fawn hopping mouse
Notomys cervinus

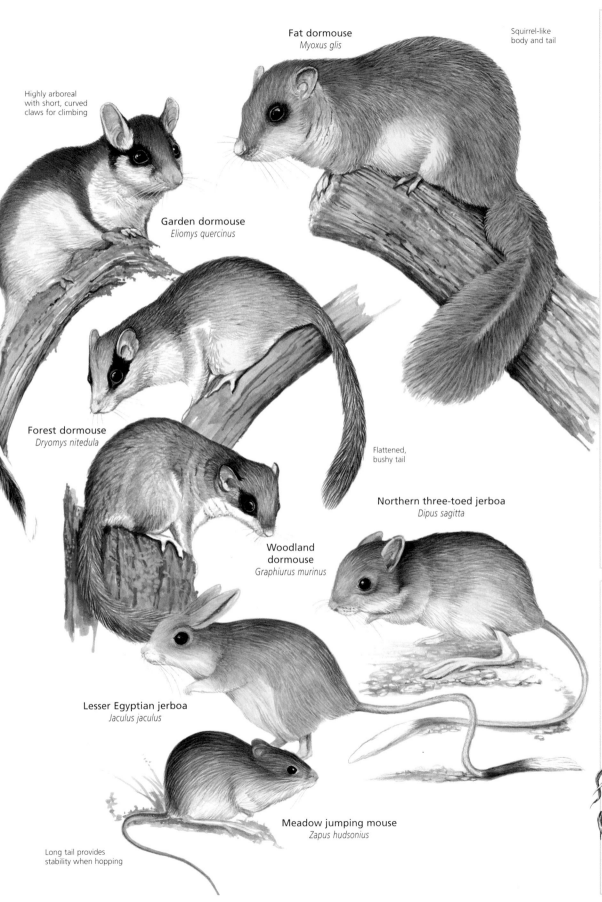

Fat dormouse
Myoxus glis

Squirrel-like body and tail

Highly arboreal with short, curved claws for climbing

Garden dormouse
Eliomys quercinus

Forest dormouse
Dryomys nitedula

Flattened, bushy tail

Northern three-toed jerboa
Dipus sagitta

Woodland dormouse
Graphiurus murinus

Lesser Egyptian jerboa
Jaculus jaculus

Meadow jumping mouse
Zapus hudsonius

Long tail provides stability when hopping

FACT FILE

Garden dormouse This noisy rodent lives in large colonies, making globe-shaped nests of leaves and grass in tree hollows, among shrubs, or in rock crevices. As well as eating acorns, nuts, and fruit, it hunts insects and small rodents and birds.

Up to 6½ in (17 cm)
Up to 5 in (13 cm)
Up to 4 oz (120 g)
Colonial
Vulnerable

Europe

Lesser Egyptian jerboa With back legs four times longer than its front legs, this solitary desert animal will hop its way out of danger. It spends the day in a burrow, plugging the entrance with dirt during summer to create a cooler, humid microclimate.

Up to 4 in (10 cm)
Up to 5 in (13 cm)
Up to 2 oz (55 g)
Solitary
Not known

Morocco & Senegal to S.W. Iran & Somalia

Meadow jumping mouse Although it usually moves in short hops, this mouse can leap up to 3 feet (1 m) in the air when startled. It breeds very soon after emerging from its winter hibernation.

Up to 4 in (10 cm)
Up to 5 in (13 cm)
Up to 1 oz (30 g)
Solitary
Locally common

N. & E. North America

WINTER SLEEP

The dormice of Europe prepare for their long winter hibernation by laying down a layer of fat on their body and stockpiling food in their nest or burrow. Depending on the climate, they can spend up to 9 months of the year asleep. They start mating as soon as they emerge from hibernation.

CAVY-LIKE RODENTS

CLASS	Mammalia
ORDER	Rodentia
FAMILIES	18
GENERA	65
SPECIES	218

With their large heads, plump bodies, small legs, and short tails, the cavies of the Caviidae family—more commonly known as guinea pigs—are typical of cavy-like rodents. There are exceptions to this general body plan: some cavy-like rodents, such as the spiny rats of the Echimyidae family, look more like common mice and rats. All cavy-like rodents share a distinctive arrangement of the jaw muscles that gives them a strong forward bite. Unlike most other rodents, they also tend to have small litters of well-developed young. There are cavy-like rodents in both the Old World and the New World, but their relationship continues to be debated.

Rat-like form The spiny rats of the family Echimyidae look more like the common mice and rats of Muridae than most other cavy-like rodents. If grabbed by a predator, a spiny rat's tail will break off, allowing it to quickly escape.

Living in pairs The mara or Patagonian cavy (*Dolichotus patagonum*) is unusual among mammals in maintaining a lifelong monogamous pair bond. One member of the pair watches for danger while the other feeds. Different pairs of maras rarely interact, but they do share a communal nursery den, where young are visited daily by their parents for nursing.

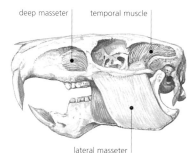

deep masseter   temporal muscle

lateral masseter

Powerful bite Like squirrel-like rodents, cavy-like rodents have a strong forward bite, but it is produced by a different arrangement of the jaw muscles. The lateral masseter closes the jaw, while the deep masseter extends past the eye and pulls the jaw forward for biting.

CONSERVATION WATCH

Of the 218 species of cavy-like rodents, 33% are listed on the IUCN Red List, as follows:

12	Extinct
8	Critically endangered
3	Endangered
15	Vulnerable
24	Near threatened
9	Data deficient

Spiky young New World porcupines, like other cavy-like rodents, give birth to well-developed young and have low infant mortality rates. Newborns have open eyes, can walk almost straight away, and are able to climb trees within a few days.

CAVIES AND THEIR KIN

Although controversy persists as to whether the South American cavy-like rodents came from North America or rafted over from Africa, most of today's cavy-like rodents are found in Central and South America. The cavies of Caviomorpha include not only guinea pigs and similar species, but also the deer-like mara, a long-legged grazer. The semiaquatic capybara is more than 3 feet (1 m) long, making it the largest of all rodents. Chinchillas and viscachas live mainly at high elevations, kept warm by a thick, soft coat. Agoutis have long, slender limbs that allow them to run swiftly from danger. While most of South America's cavy-like rodents are terrestrial, tuco-tucos dig complex burrows. Other South American cavy-like rodents include degus, hutias, pacas, coypu, and pacarana.

New World porcupines, found in both North and South America, are arboreal and climb trees with agility, aided in some species by a prehensile tail. They share many features with the Old World porcupines of Africa, Asia, and Europe, but the latter are mostly ground-dwelling.

As well as porcupines, the Old World's cavy-like rodents include the African mole-rats, cane rats, and dassie rat. The gundis of North Africa (family Ctenodactylidae), have cavy-like jaw muscles, but are now classified in the suborder Sciurognathi. All other cavy-like rodents are now grouped together in the suborder Hystricognathi.

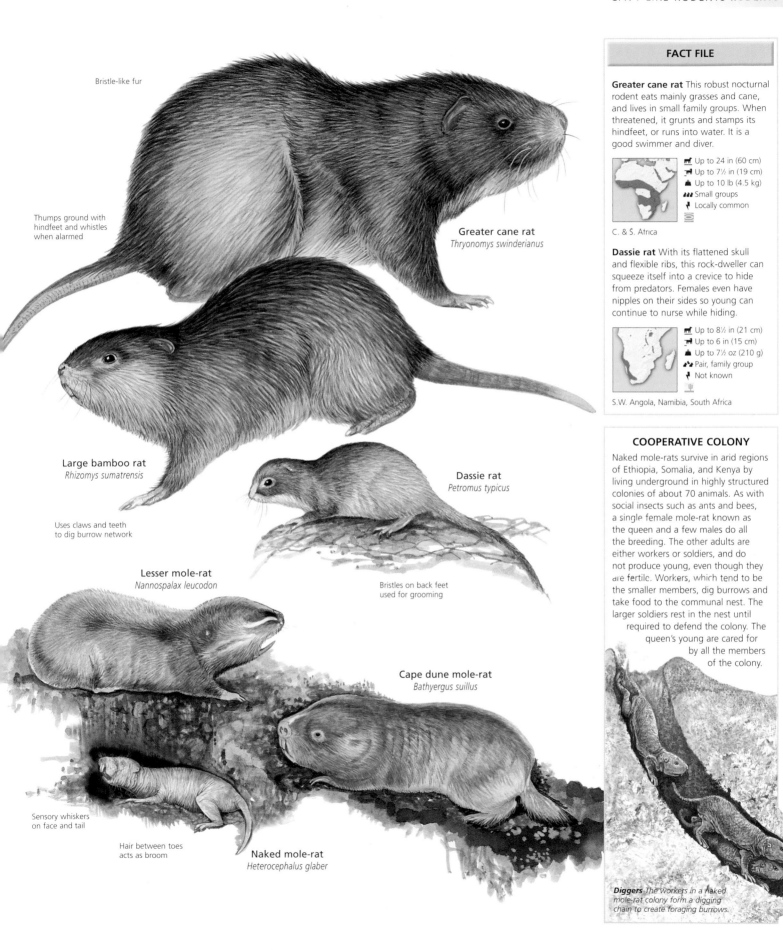

Bristle-like fur

Thumps ground with hindfeet and whistles when alarmed

Greater cane rat
Thryonomys swinderianus

Large bamboo rat
Rhizomys sumatrensis

Uses claws and teeth to dig burrow network

Dassie rat
Petromus typicus

Bristles on back feet used for grooming

Lesser mole-rat
Nannospalax leucodon

Cape dune mole-rat
Bathyergus suillus

Sensory whiskers on face and tail

Hair between toes acts as broom

Naked mole-rat
Heterocephalus glaber

FACT FILE

Greater cane rat This robust nocturnal rodent eats mainly grasses and cane, and lives in small family groups. When threatened, it grunts and stamps its hindfeet, or runs into water. It is a good swimmer and diver.

- Up to 24 in (60 cm)
- Up to 7½ in (19 cm)
- Up to 10 lb (4.5 kg)
- Small groups
- Locally common

C. & S. Africa

Dassie rat With its flattened skull and flexible ribs, this rock-dweller can squeeze itself into a crevice to hide from predators. Females even have nipples on their sides so young can continue to nurse while hiding.

- Up to 8½ in (21 cm)
- Up to 6 in (15 cm)
- Up to 7½ oz (210 g)
- Pair, family group
- Not known

S.W. Angola, Namibia, South Africa

COOPERATIVE COLONY

Naked mole-rats survive in arid regions of Ethiopia, Somalia, and Kenya by living underground in highly structured colonies of about 70 animals. As with social insects such as ants and bees, a single female mole-rat known as the queen and a few males do all the breeding. The other adults are either workers or soldiers, and do not produce young, even though they are fertile. Workers, which tend to be the smaller members, dig burrows and take food to the communal nest. The larger soldiers rest in the nest until required to defend the colony. The queen's young are cared for by all the members of the colony.

Diggers *The workers in a naked mole-rat colony form a digging chain to create foraging burrows.*

FACT FILE

Old World porcupines These porcu-pines are generally terrestrial and their quills are embedded in clusters, while New World species are arboreal with singly embedded quills. The Old World species can be divided into brush-tailed porcupines (with long, slender tails that rustle when shaken), and crested porcupines (with long black and white spines and a short tail that rattles).

Crested porcupine This porcupine has been known to kill lions, hyenas, and humans. When threatened, it raises its quills to make itself seem larger, but if this display fails to deter, it will then back itself into the predator so that the quills become embedded.

🐾 Up to 27½ in (70 cm)
🐾 Up to 4½ in (12 cm)
⚖ Up to 33 lb (15 kg)
♟ Family group
🌱 Near threatened

Italy, Balkans, Africa

African brush-tailed porcupine This species lives in a family group made up of a breeding pair and several offspring. They spend the day together hiding in caves, crevices, or logs, emerging at night to forage alone for roots, leaves, fruit, and bulbs.

🐾 Up to 22½ in (57 cm)
🐾 Up to 9 in (23 cm)
⚖ Up to 9 lb (4 kg)
♟ Family group
🌱 Common

Equatorial Africa

Long-tailed porcupine Unlike other Old World porcupines, this forest-dweller cannot bristle or rattle its quills, but the long tail can break off from the body if snatched by a predator. It climbs trees to reach fruit and other food.

🐾 Up to 19 in (48 cm)
🐾 Up to 9 in (23 cm)
⚖ Up to 5 lb (2.3 kg)
🌱 Not known
🌱 Not known

Malaya, Sumatra, Borneo

⚡ CONSERVATION WATCH

Spiky protection With their spines forming effective armor, porcupines have few natural predators. They are, however, killed by humans for food, sport, and pest control. Most Old World species are common, but the Malayan porcupine is listed as vulnerable, and the crested porcupine and the thick-spined porcupine (*Hystrix crassispinis*) are considered near threatened.

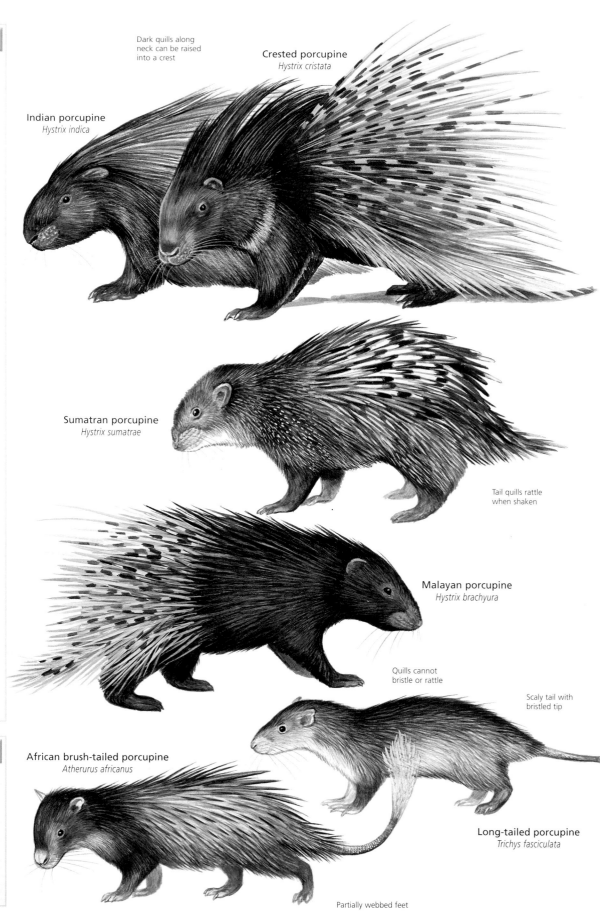

Dark quills along neck can be raised into a crest

Crested porcupine
Hystrix cristata

Indian porcupine
Hystrix indica

Sumatran porcupine
Hystrix sumatrae

Tail quills rattle when shaken

Malayan porcupine
Hystrix brachyura

Quills cannot bristle or rattle

Scaly tail with bristled tip

African brush-tailed porcupine
Atherurus africanus

Long-tailed porcupine
Trichys fasciculata

Partially webbed feet

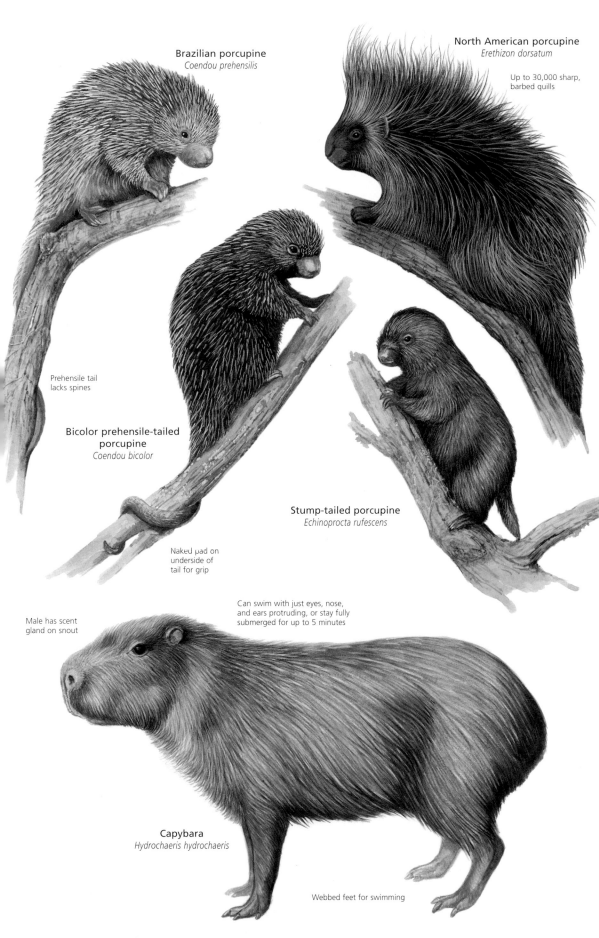

Brazilian porcupine
Coendou prehensilis

North American porcupine
Erethizon dorsatum

Up to 30,000 sharp, barbed quills

Prehensile tail lacks spines

Bicolor prehensile-tailed porcupine
Coendou bicolor

Stump-tailed porcupine
Echinoprocta rufescens

Naked pad on underside of tail for grip

Male has scent gland on snout

Can swim with just eyes, nose, and ears protruding, or stay fully submerged for up to 5 minutes

Capybara
Hydrochaeris hydrochaeris

Webbed feet for swimming

FACT FILE

New World porcupines Aided by large, gripping feet with strong claws and naked soles, these porcupines can climb trees. They have poor eyesight, but good senses of smell and hearing.

North American porcupine This species dens in a cave, rock crevice, or fallen log, emerging at night to browse on the bark of trees and shrubs.

🐾 Up to 3½ ft (1.1 m)
🐾 Up to 10 in (25 cm)
⚖ Up to 39½ lb (18 kg)
♟ Solitary
⚑ Locally common

N. & W. North America

Bicolor prehensile-tailed porcupine A long, gripping tail helps this species clamber through the middle and upper layers of the forest. It climbs down to the ground only occasionally.

🐾 Up to 19½ in (49 cm)
🐾 Up to 21 in (54 cm)
⚖ Up to 10½ lb (4.7 kg)
♟♟ Pair
⚑ Locally common

E. foothills of Andes from Colombia to Bolivia

Stump-tailed porcupine This little-studied species has a short, hairy tail. Its spines become thicker and shorter toward the rear.

🐾 Up to 14½ in (37 cm)
🐾 Up to 6 in (15 cm)
⚖ Not known
♟ Not known
⚑ Not known

Andes in Colombia

THE BIGGEST RODENT

Capybaras are barrel-shaped grazers that feed mainly on grasses growing in or near water. They enter the water to seek refuge from the midday heat, to escape predators, and to mate. These social animals usually live in family groups of one male, several females, and their young, but in dry times may form larger temporary herds of up to a hundred individuals.

🐾 Up to 4½ ft (1.3 m)
🐾 Up to ¾ in (2 cm)
⚖ Up to 143 lb (65 kg)
♟♟♟ Family group
⚑ Locally common

Panama to N.E. Argentina

FACT FILE

Paca This solitary creature spends the day in a shallow burrow. It is hunted for its meat and as an agricultural pest and has lost much of its forest habitat.

🐃 Up to 30½ in (78 cm)
🦡 Up to 1 in (3 cm)
⚖ Up to 28½ lb (13 kg)
👥 Pair
♦ Common
🏛

S.E. Mexico to S. Brazil & N. Paraguay

AGOUTIS AND ACOUCHIS

The young of agoutis and acouchis are born after a relatively long gestation period of approximately 100 days. They emerge fully furred and with their eyes open. Within hours, they are able to run and will nibble on green plants. Even so, they continue to drink their mother's milk for some weeks. Their potential lifespan is long, up to 17 years, but most do not make it through their first year, falling prey to predators such as coatis or starving during the dry season.

Red acouchi Active by day, the red acouchi will bury some food during times of abundance. This ensures the animal a food supply in leaner times, but also helps to disperse seeds throughout the forest.

🐃 Up to 15½ in (39 cm)
🦡 Up to 3 in (8 cm)
⚖ Up to 3½ lb (1.5 kg)
♦ Solitary
♦ Data deficient
🏛

S. Colombia to Guianas, Amazon basin

Gray agouti This species can leap more than 6 feet (2 m) in the air. It walks on its digits and will gallop when in a hurry. Courtship involves the male spraying the female with urine, causing her to make frenzied movements.

🐃 Up to 30 in (76 cm)
🦡 Up to 1½ in (4 cm)
⚖ Up to 13 lb (6 kg)
👥 Solitary, pair
♦ Common
🏛

Upper Amazon basin

Brazilian agouti As in other agoutis, the front part of this animal is slender, while the rear is bulkier, an adaptation to foraging through the undergrowth for its preferred food of fallen fruit.

🐃 Up to 25 in (64 cm)
🦡 Up to 1 in (3 cm)
⚖ Up to 13 lb (6 kg)
👥 Pairs
♦ Common
🏛

E. Venezuela & Guianas to S.E. Brazil

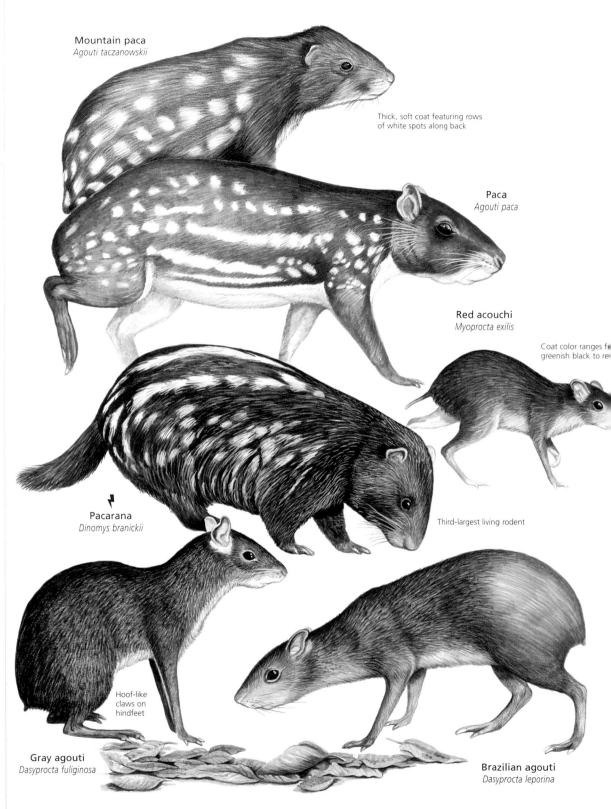

Mountain paca
Agouti taczanowskii

Thick, soft coat featuring rows of white spots along back

Paca
Agouti paca

Red acouchi
Myoprocta exilis

Coat color ranges f[...] greenish black to re[...]

Pacarana
Dinomys branickii

Third-largest living rodent

Gray agouti
Dasyprocta fuliginosa

Hoof-like claws on hindfeet

Brazilian agouti
Dasyprocta leporina

Demarest's hutia
Capromys pilorides

Hispaniolan hutia
Plagiodontia aedium

Scaly tail

Prehensile-tailed hutia
Mysateles prehensilis

Hairy tail

Brown's hutia
Geocapromys brownii

Coypu (nutria)
Myocastor coypus

Fringes of bristles
on hindfeet used
for grooming

White-bellied tuco-tuco
Ctenomys colburni

FACT FILE

Demarest's hutia While this species
has strong claws and easily climbs
trees, it spends more time on the
ground than most other hutias. It
shares with other hutias a stomach
divided into three compartments, the
most complex stomach of any rodent.

  Up to 24 in (60 cm)
  Up to 12 in (30 cm)
  Up to 18½ lb (8.5 kg)
  Pair
  Common, declining

Cuba & adjacent offshore islands

Brown's hutia This terrestrial animal
usually lives alone, but can be found
in family groups of up to 10 animals.
It hides in rock crevices by day, but
waddles out at night to search the
forest for leaves, roots, bark, and fruit.

  Up to 17½ in (45 cm)
  Up to 2½ in (6 cm)
  Up to 4½ lb (2 kg)
  Not known
  Vulnerable

Jamaica

Coypu Equally at home in salt and
fresh water, this semiaquatic species
swims with its webbed hindfeet and
can stay submerged for 5 minutes.
It eats aquatic plants and shellfish.

  Up to 25 in (64 cm)
  Up to 16½ in (42 cm)
  Up to 22 lb (10 kg)
  Pair, family group
  Common

Bolivia & Brazil to Patagonia; introd. elsewhere

White-bellied tuco-tuco This robust
burrower digs tunnels with the strong
claws on its forefeet, cutting through
any roots with its prominent incisors.
Considered a pest, it has been hunted
in great numbers.

  Up to 6½ in (17 cm)
  Up to 3 in (8 cm)
  Not known
  Not known
  Not known

Known from only two localities in Argentina

⚡ CONSERVATION WATCH

Vanishing hutias Living only in
the West Indies, the hutias of the
Capromyidae family are hunted
intensively for food. They also fall
prey to birds, snakes, and introduced
domestic animals. In recent times,
six species of hutia have become
extinct and a further six are critically
endangered, four are vulnerable,
and two are near threatened.

FACT FILE

Coruro Living in complex burrows, this social species communicates through a variety of calls, including a long-distance musical trilling that can last for 2 minutes.

📏 Up to 6½ in (17 cm)
📐 Up to 1½ in (4 cm)
⚖ Up to 4 oz (120 g)
👥 Colonial
⚡ Common, declining

C. Chile

Chinchilla-rat This little rodent has soft fur like that of the chinchilla but a body and head like that of a rat. It is nocturnal, resting by day in a burrow or rock crevice.

📏 Up to 7½ in (19 cm)
📐 Up to 2¾ in (7 cm)
⚖ Not known
👥 Colonial
⚡ Not known

S.W. Peru, N. Chile & N.W. Argentina

Chinchilla Most commonly found in barren, rocky mountain areas, this nocturnal species lives in large colonies of up to 100 animals. Popular as pets, chinchillas are now rare in the wild.

📏 Up to 9 in (23 cm)
📐 Up to 6 in (15 cm)
⚖ Up to 1 lb (500 g)
👥 Colonial
⚡ Vulnerable

Andes of N. Chile

DEGUS AND DOGS

Degus are the ecological equivalent of North America's prairie dogs (left). Both are diurnal rodents that live in large colonies in extensive burrow systems and communicate through a range of vocalizations.

Degus and prairie dogs are only distantly related. Their similarities are the result of convergent evolution, in which both groups adapted in the same way to their semiarid habitats.

⚡ CONSERVATION WATCH

Hunted chinchillids Prized for their soft fur, the chinchillas and viscachas of the Chinchillidae family have been hunted in large numbers. In 1900 alone, 500,000 chinchilla pelts were exported from Chile. The short-tailed chinchilla (*C. brevicaudata*) is now critically endangered, while the chinchilla is considered vulnerable.

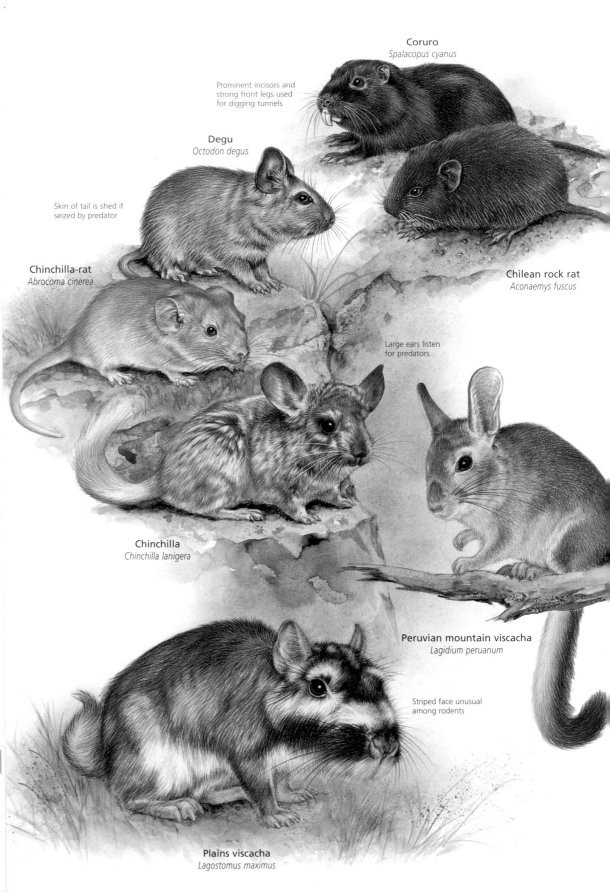

Coruro
Spalacopus cyanus

Prominent incisors and strong front legs used for digging tunnels

Degu
Octodon degus

Skin of tail is shed if seized by predator

Chinchilla-rat
Abrocoma cinerea

Chilean rock rat
Aconaemys fuscus

Large ears listen for predators

Chinchilla
Chinchilla lanigera

Peruvian mountain viscacha
Lagidium peruanum

Striped face unusual among rodents

Plains viscacha
Lagostomus maximus

LAGOMORPHS

CLASS	Mammalia
ORDER	Lagomorpha
FAMILIES	2
GENERA	15
SPECIES	82

The rabbits, hares, and pikas of the order Lagomorpha were once considered a suborder of Rodentia, and they do bear some resemblance to large rodents. They are gnawing herbivores, with large, constantly growing incisors, no canine teeth, and a gap between the incisors and molars. Like rodents, they can close their lips in this gap and gnaw on material without taking it into the mouth. Unlike rodents, they have a second, smaller pair of upper incisors, known as peg teeth, behind the first pair. All lagomorphs are terrestrial. They are found almost worldwide in a diverse range of habitats, from snowy arctic tundra to steamy tropical forest and scorching desert.

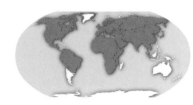

In human company While their close association with humans has allowed lagomorphs to spread almost worldwide, they are absent from southern South America and many islands. Where they have been introduced, as in Australia and New Zealand, lagomorphs have often had a devastating effect, outcompeting both native animals and livestock for food.

Harvesting pika During summer and fall, most pikas prepare for winter, spending up to a third of their time gathering grasses, leaves, and flowers in their mouth and adding them to a haystack sheltered under an overhanging rock.

Fleet of foot With their long, powerful hindlimbs, hares are designed to outrun their predators and have been known to exceed speeds of 45 miles per hour (70 km/h). Even at full speed, these agile animals can abruptly change direction.

Boxing hares Throughout the mating season, male Arctic hares compete for access to females, while each female fends off any males that she is not interested in. Arctic hares most often live in small family groups, but larger bands of more than a hundred individuals can occur, especially on cold, northern islands.

⚡ CONSERVATION WATCH

While a few lagomorph species have become pests, many specialized ones are suffering. Of the 82 species of lagomorphs, 37% are listed on the IUCN Red List, as follows:

1	Extinct
4	Critically endangered
7	Endangered
6	Vulnerable
8	Near threatened
4	Data deficient

RABBITS, HARES, AND PIKAS

Lagomorphs are divided into two families: the rabbits and hares of Leporidae, and the pikas of Ochotonidae. As key prey species for many birds and carnivores, all lagomorphs have eyes on the side of the head that provide a wide field of vision, and relatively large ears that contribute to their sharp hearing. In pikas, the ears are short and round, while rabbits and hares have very long ears.

Many lagomorphs are social species, and all use their scent glands in communication. In pikas, these are supplemented by a variety of vocalizations, which inspired their nickname of "calling hares."

To escape predators, both rabbits and hares have long hindlegs that allow them to run at speed—rabbits tend to flee to cover, while hares try to outrun the danger over open ground. Pikas have shorter legs, but usually live in rocky terrain where they can quickly slip into a crevice.

In spite of their anti-predator tactics, all lagomorph species are an important food source for other animals and suffer a high mortality rate. To cope with this, they tend to be prolific breeders. Gestation periods are short, usually lasting just 30–40 days, and litters are often large. Many species reach sexual maturity quickly—female European rabbits can breed at only 3 months. The female's eggs are released in response to copulation, and she is able to become pregnant almost immediately after giving birth. In some species, the female can conceive a second litter while still pregnant with the first. These reproductive strategies have allowed some species, such as the European rabbit, to become so successful that they are considered pests.

Northern pika Active through long, cold winters, this species stays on the surface until the snow cover is about 12 inches (30 cm) deep, and then retreats into tunnels under the snow.

🐾 Up to 8 in (20 cm)
🐁 None
⚖ Up to 7 oz (200 g)
♟ Solitary
⚡ Not known

Mongolia, Siberia

Royle's pika Although this pika normally nests in natural rock piles, it has been known to live in the rock walls of huts built by humans. Because it forages throughout the year, it does not create a haystack as other pikas do.

🐾 Up to 8 in (20 cm)
🐁 None
⚖ Up to 7 oz (200 g)
♟ Solitary
⚡ Not known

Himalayas of Pakistan, India, Nepal & Tibet

Daurian pika This steppe-dweller is a highly social burrower, living in large colonies made up of family groups. Family members communicate through a repertoire of calls, groom each other, rub noses, and play together.

🐾 Up to 8 in (20 cm)
🐁 None
⚖ Up to 7 oz (200 g)
🐾🐾🐾 Colonial
⚡ Common

Steppes of Mongolia & S. Siberia

American pika Each American pika defends an area of rock, with males and females occupying adjacent but separate territories.

🐾 Up to 8½ in (22 cm)
🐁 None
⚖ Up to 6 oz (175 g)
♟ Solitary
⚡ Locally common

W. North America

Keystone species Considered pests because of their large numbers and burrowing habit, the plateau pikas (*Ochotona curzoniae*) of the Tibetan plateau have been the target of poisoning campaigns. Such measures ignore the key role the pikas play in their ecosystem. Not only do they serve as prey for many predators, but their burrows are used for shelter by many birds and lizards, and their digging increases plant diversity and minimizes erosion.

Large-eared pika
Ochotona macrotis

Nostrils can be completely closed

Northern pika
Ochotona alpina

Turkestan red pika
Ochotona rutila

Calls include a one- or two-note squeak that expresses fear

Royle's pika
Ochotona roylei

Daurian pika
Ochotona daurica

Two main vocalizations are an alarm call and a mating song

American pika
Ochotona princeps

Steppe pika
Ochotona pusilla

Heavily furred feet

Arctic hare
Lepus timidus

Black ear tips

Brown summer coat blends in with tundra vegetation

White winter coat provides camouflage against snow cover

Grows white coat and eats barks and buds in winter

Snowshoe hare
Lepus americanus

Grows brown coat and eats green plants and berries in summer

Antelope jackrabbit
Lepus alleni

Asiatic brown hare
Lepus tolai

Black-tailed jackrabbit
Lepus californicus

Coat lightens in summer

White-tailed jackrabbit
Lepus townsendii

Can flee predators at speeds of 35 miles per hour (56 km/h)

Brown hare
Lepus europaeus

FACT FILE

Arctic hare To survive the harsh Arctic winter, this usually solitary hare may gather in flocks of several hundred individuals, and smaller groups may cooperate to build a protective wall of snow. The Arctic hare also changes color with the season, growing a white winter coat to blend in with the snow, then shedding this for a brown coat to match the summer tundra vegetation.

Up to 24 in (60 cm)
Up to 3 in (8 cm)
Up to 13 lb (6 kg)
Solitary
Common

Iceland, Ireland, Scotland, N. Eurasia

Antelope jackrabbit Like an antelope, this large hare is able to make great leaps. A desert species, it is nocturnal and can survive without drinking water, obtaining all its water from plants.

Up to 24 in (60 cm)
Up to 3 in (8 cm)
Up to 13 lb (6 kg)
Solitary
Common, declining

S. Arizona to N. Mexico

Brown hare Female brown hares can produce four litters a year. For the first month, the young are left in a form, a shallow depression in long grass, and visited once a day for feeding.

Up to 27 in (68 cm)
Up to 4 in (10 cm)
Up to 15½ lb (7 kg)
Solitary
Common, declining

Europe to Middle East; introd. widely

COOL EARS

A resident of North America's deserts, the black-tailed jackrabbit relies on its long ears to keep cool. Hundreds of tiny blood vessels radiate heat to the surface of the ears, allowing the blood to cool before it returns to the heart. A jackrabbit spends the hottest part of the day resting in the shade of a shrub or long grass.

FACT FILE

Eastern cottontail This solitary rabbit spends the daytime resting in a hollow beneath a log or brush. Although blind and naked at birth, young cottontails can leave the nest at 2 weeks of age, disperse at 7 weeks, and are sexually mature at only 3 months.

🐇 Up to 19½ in (50 cm)
🐾 Up to 2½ in (6 cm)
⚖ Up to 3½ lb (1.5 kg)
♟ Solitary
🕯 Common
🌵 🌵

E. & S. North America

Pygmy rabbit The smallest rabbit, this species lives amid dense sagebrush, which forms much of its diet, and digs its own burrow. It emits a distinctive whistle to warn neighbors of danger.

🐇 Up to 11 in (28 cm)
🐾 Up to ¾ in (2 cm)
⚖ Up to 16 oz (460 g)
♟ Solitary
🕯 Near threatened
🌵

W. USA

European rabbit Popular as a game animal, this species was deliberately introduced in many places, often with devastating effects on native fauna.

🐇 Up to 18 in (46 cm)
🐾 Up to 3 in (8 cm)
⚖ Up to 5 lb (2.2 kg)
👪 Family group
🕯 Abundant
🌵 🌵

British Isles; Spain to Balkans; introd. widely

Hispid hare Hunting and domestic dogs have taken their toll, but this animal is most threatened by deliberate burning of its grassland habitat.

🐇 Up to 19½ in (50 cm)
🐾 Up to 1½ in (4 cm)
⚖ Up to 5½ lb (2.5 kg)
♟ Solitary, pair
🕯 Endangered
🌵 🌵

Foothills of Himalayas in Nepal & N. India

RABBIT WARREN

The European rabbit is one of the few rabbit or hare species to dig its own burrow, and is the only one to live in stable, territorial breeding groups. Large numbers of young are raised in the shelter of an underground warren.

Forest rabbit
Sylvilagus brasiliensis

Eastern cottontail
Sylvilagus floridanus

Pygmy rabbit
Brachylagus idahoensis

White tail displayed when running

Brush rabbit
Sylvilagus bachmani

European rabbit
Oryctolagus cuniculus

Volcano rabbit
Romerolagus diazi

No visible tail

Thumps hindleg on ground to warn others of danger

Coarse, bristly outer fur, with softer underfur

Hispid hare
Caprolagus hispidus

Sumatran rabbit
Nesolagus netscheri

The rarest lagomorph, with just one record from 1972 and a photograph taken by remote camera in 1998

Central African hare
Poelagus marjorita

ELEPHANT SHREWS

CLASS Mammalia
ORDER Macroscelidea
FAMILY Macroscelididae
GENERA 4
SPECIES 15

Little studied until recent years and categorized at different times with insectivores, ungulates, tree shrews, and lagomorphs, elephant shrews are so distinctive that they are now placed in their own order, the Macroscelidea. Their long, mobile snout suggested an elephant's trunk to naturalists, inspiring their common name. They are ground-dwellers, relying on keen hearing and vision to detect danger, and on the speed provided by their long, slender legs to escape predators. Some smaller species move in leaps when alarmed, resembling miniature antelopes. Elephant shrews are insect-eaters, but have larger, more developed brains than the insectivores.

African habitats Elephant shrews are found throughout much of Africa, but are missing from West Africa and the Sahara Desert. They occupy diverse habitats, including rocky outcrops, desert, savanna, grasslands, thornbrush plains, and tropical forest. Although terrestrial and often active by day, these secretive, swift mammals are not common and are rarely seen.

INSECT-EATERS

An elephant shrew can spend up to 80 percent of its waking hours foraging. Although elephant shrews have a large cecum similar to that of herbivores and may include some fruit, seeds, and other plant matter in their diet, they are largely insectivorous, feeding mainly on invertebrates such as spiders, beetles, termites, ants, centipedes, and earthworms. Their long, sensitive, mobile snout can root around in leaf litter, detecting the small prey by smell. Some species use their claws and teeth to raid the tunnel systems of ants and termites. Like other elephant shrews, the bushveld elephant shrew (*Elephantulus intufi*) has a long tongue (shown above) that is able to speedily flick insects into its mouth.

Checkered elephant shrew
Rhynchocyon cirnei

Highly sensitive, flexible snout

Together and alone Like other elephant shrews, rufous elephant shrews live in monogamous pairs, usually mating for life. The pairs rarely meet, but share and defend exactly the same territory. They rely on scentmarking to communicate, and maintain a network of trails that allows fast escape from predators. Trespassing male elephant shrews are driven off by the male of the pair, while the female deters female intruders.

Back legs longer than front legs

Large eyes and ears

Rufous elephant shrew (spectacled elephant shrew)
Elephantulus rufescens

Four-toed elephant shrew
Petrodromus tetradactylus

Rat-like, bristled tail

GLOSSARY

adaptation A change in an animal's behavior or body that allows it to survive and breed in new conditions.

algae The simplest forms of plant life.

antlers Bony, often branched growths from the head of deer and moose. In most cases, they are grown and shed each year. They are used as weapons and for display.

arboreal Living all or most of the time in trees.

baleen The comb-like, fibrous plates found in some whales; often referred to as whalebone. The plates hang from the upper jaw and are used to sieve food from sea water.

biodiversity The total number of species of plants and animals in a particular location.

blubber A thick layer of insulating fat in whales, seals, and other large marine mammals.

brachiation A form of movement in which an animal (such as an ape) swings from hold to hold by its arms.

browser A plant-eating mammal that uses its hands or lips to pick leaves from trees and bushes (as in koalas and giraffes) or low-growing plants (as in the black rhino).

camouflage The colors and patterns of an animal that enable it to blend in with the background. Camouflage conceals the animal from predators and helps it to ambush prey.

canine teeth The teeth between the incisors and molars of mammals.

carnassials Special cheek teeth with sharp, scissor-like edges used by carnivores to tear up food.

carnivore An animal that eats mainly meat. Most carnivorous mammals are predators; others are both predators and scavengers. Most carnivores eat some plant material as well as meat.

carrion The rotting flesh and other remains of dead animals.

caudal Relating to an animal's tail.

cephalic Of, relating to, or situated on or near the head.

cloaca An internal chamber in monotremes, into which the contents of the reproductive ducts and the waste ducts empty before being passed from the body.

conspecific Of the same species.

convergent evolution The situation in which totally unrelated groups develop similar structures to cope with similar evolutionary pressures.

deforestation The cutting down of forest trees for timber, or to clear land for farming or building.

dimorphic Having two distinct forms within a species. Sexual dimorphism is the situation in which the male and female of a species differ in size and/or appearance.

display Behavior used by an animal to communicate with its own species, or with other animals. Displays can include postures, actions, or showing brightly colored parts of the body, and may signal threat, defense, or readiness to mate.

divergent evolution The situation in which two or more similar species become more and more dissimilar due to environmental adaptations.

DNA A molecule, found in chromosomes of a cell nucleus, that contains genes. DNA stands for deoxyribonucleic acid.

domestication The process of taming and breeding an animal for human use. Domesticated animals include pets, as well as animals used for sport, food, or work, such as sheep, horses, and dairy cattle.

dorsal fin The large fin on the back of aquatic mammals, which helps the animal to keep its balance as it moves through the water.

echolocation A system of navigation that relies on sound rather than sight or touch. Dolphins, porpoises, and many bats use echolocation to tell them where they are, where their prey is, and if anything is in their way.

ecosystem A community of plants and animals and the environment to which they are adapted.

electroreceptors Specialized organs found in mammals (such as platypuses) that detect electrical activity from the bodies of other animals. They also help the animal to navigate by detecting distortions in the electrical field of its surroundings—for example, those caused by a reef.

embryo An unborn animal in the earliest stages of development. An embryo may grow inside its mother's body, or in an egg outside her body.

endothermic Able to regulate the body temperature internally, as in warm-blooded animals.

evolution Gradual change in plants and animals, over many generations, in response to their environment.

exotic A foreign or non-native species of animal or plant, often introduced into a habitat by humans.

feral A wild animal or plant, or a species that was once domesticated but has returned to its wild state.

flippers The broad front (and often, back) legs of some aquatic animals. Flippers are composed mainly of the bones of the fingers and hand, and act like paddles to row the animal through the water.

food chain A system in which one organism forms food for another, which in turn is eaten by another, and so on. The first organism is usually an alga or other single-celled life form in an aquatic food chain, and a plant in a terrestrial food chain.

fossil A remnant, impression, or trace of a plant or animal from a past geological age, usually found in rock.

fossorial Adapted to digging or burrowing underground.

gestation period The period of time during which a female animal is pregnant with her young.

global warming The increase in the temperature of Earth and its lower atmosphere due to human activity such as deforestation, land degradation, intensive farming, and the burning of fossil fuels. This causes the absorption of heat by water vapor and "greenhouse" gases, including carbon dioxide and methane. The trapped heat, which would otherwise be radiated out to space, may cause the polar ice caps to melt and ocean levels to rise. Global warming is also known as "the greenhouse effect."

Gondwana Ancient southern supercontinent, comprising the present-day continents of Australia, India, Africa, South America, and Antarctica.

grazer An animal that eats grasses and plants that grow on the ground.

greenhouse effect See global warming.

groom Of an animal, to clean, repair, and arrange the fur.

habitat The area in which an animal naturally lives. Many different kinds of animals live in the same environment (for example, a rain forest), but each kind lives in a different habitat within that environment. For example, some animals in a rain forest live in the trees, while others live on the ground.

harem A group of female animals that mate and live with one male.

herbivore An animal that eats only plant material, such as leaves, roots, and seeds.

hibernate To remain completely inactive during the winter months. Some animals eat as much as they can before the winter, then curl up in a sheltered spot and fall into a deep sleep. They live off stored fat, and slow their breathing and heartbeat to help conserve energy until spring.

hoof The toe of a horse, antelope, deer, or related animal that is covered in thick, hard skin with sharp edges.

horns In mammals such as ruminants, pointed, hollow, bony outgrowths on the head. Unlike antlers, horns are not shed.

hybrid The offspring of parents of two different species.

incisors The front teeth of an animal, located between the canines, used for cutting food.

insectivore An animal that eats only or mainly insects or invertebrates. In mammals, a member of the order Insectivora.

introduced An animal or plant species imported from another place by humans and deliberately or accidentally released into a habitat.

ivory The tusks or enlarged teeth of elephants and walrus, or objects manufactured from them.

Jacobson's organ Two small sensory pits on the top part of the mouth of mammals, used to analyze small molecules picked up from the air or ground with their tongue.

keratin A protein found in horns, hair, scales, feathers, and fingernails.

Laurasia Ancient northern supercontinent, comprising the present-day Asia, North America, and Europe.

live-bearing Giving birth to young that are fully formed.

mammal A warm-blooded vertebrate that suckles its young with milk and has a single bone in its lower jaw. Although most mammals have hair and give birth to live young, some, such as whales and dolphins, have very little or no hair; others, the monotremes, lay eggs.

marsupial A mammal that gives birth to young that are not fully developed. These young are usually protected in a pouch (where they feed on milk) before they can move around independently.

migration A usually seasonal journey from one habitat to another. Many animals migrate vast distances to another location to find food, or to mate and give birth.

molars A mammal's side cheek teeth, used for crushing and grinding.

molt To shed an outer layer of the body, such as hair or skin.

monotreme A primitive mammal with many features in common with reptiles. Monotremes lay eggs and have a cloaca. They are the only mammals that lack teats, although they feed their young milk released through ducts on their belly.

morph A color or other physical variation within, or a local population of, a species.

musth In elephants, a time of high testosterone levels when the musth gland between the eye and ear secretes fluid; associated with mating and characterized by increased aggression and searching for females.

mutualism An alliance between two species that is beneficial to both, as in ox-peckers and grazing herbivores.

niche The ecological role played by a species within an animal community.

nocturnal Active at night. Nocturnal animals have special adaptations, such as large, sensitive eyes or ears, to help them find their way in the dark. All nocturnal animals rest during the day.

nomadic Lacking a fixed territory, instead wandering from place to place in search of food and water.

omnivore An animal that eats both plant and animal food. Omnivores have teeth and a digestive system designed to process almost any kind of food.

opposable Describing a thumb that can reach around and touch all of the other fingers on the same hand, or a toe that can similarly touch all of the other toes on the same foot.

order A major group used in taxonomic classification. An order forms part of a class, and is further divided into one or more families.

oviparous Reproducing by laying eggs. Little or no development occurs within the mother's body; instead, the embryos develop inside the egg.

ovoviviparous Reproducing by giving birth to live young that have developed from eggs within the mother's body. The eggs may hatch as they are laid or soon after.

paleontology The scientific study of life in past geological periods.

Pangea Ancient supercontinent in which all the present-day continents were once joined.

parallel evolution The situation in which related groups living in isolation develop similar structures to cope with similar evolutionary pressures.

parasitism The situation in which an animal or plant lives and/or feeds on another living animal or plant, sometimes with harmful effects.

pheromone A chemical released by an animal that sends a signal and affects the behavior of others of the same species. Many animals use pheromones to attract mates, or to signal danger.

placental mammal A mammal that does not lay eggs (as monotremes do), or give birth to underdeveloped young (as marsupials do). Instead, it nourishes its developing young inside its body with a blood-rich organ called a placenta.

pore A minute opening, as in the skin of an animal.

predator An animal that lives mainly by killing and eating other animals.

prehensile Grasping or gripping. Some tree-dwelling mammals and reptiles have prehensile feet or a tail that can be used as an extra limb to help them stay safely in a tree. Elephants have a prehensile "finger" on the end of their trunk so they can pick up small pieces of food. Browsers, such as giraffes, have prehensile lips to help them grip leaves.

proboscis In some mammals, a proboscis is an elongated nose, snout, or trunk. That of an elephant has many functions, such as smelling, touching, and lifting.

quill Long, sharp hair of an echidna, porcupine, anteater, and a few other mammals; used for defense.

rain forest A tropical forest that receives at least 100 inches (250 cm) of rain each year. Rain forests are home to a vast number of plant and animal species.

regurgitate To bring food back up from the stomach to the mouth. Many hoofed mammals use this process to break food down into a more liquid form. This is called chewing the cud.

retractile claws The claws of cats and similar animals that are usually protected in sheaths. Such claws spring out when the animal needs them to capture prey or to fight.

rudimentary Describes a simple, undeveloped, or underdeveloped part of an animal, such as an organ or wing. The rudimentary parts of some modern-day animals are the traces of the functional parts of an early ancestor, but now serve no purpose.

ruminants Hoofed animals—cattle, buffalo, bison, antelopes, gazelles, sheep, goats, and other members of the family Bovidae—with a four-chambered stomach. One of these chambers is the rumen, in which food is fermented by microorganisms before being regurgitated and chewed a second time. This efficient digestive system allows bovids to make the most of low-nutrient foods such as grasses, and to colonize a wide array of habitats.

savanna Open grassland with scattered trees. Most savannas are found in subtropical areas that have a distinct summer wet season.

scavenger An animal that eats carrion—often the remains of animals killed by predators.

sedentary Having a lifestyle that involves little movement; also used to describe animals that do not migrate.

social Living in groups. Social animals can live in breeding pairs, together with their young, or in a colony or herd of up to thousands of animals.

species A group of animals with very similar features that are able to breed together and produce fertile young.

stereoscopic vision Vision in which both eyes face forward, giving an animal two overlapping fields of view and thus allowing it to judge depth.

subantarctic Of the oceans and islands just north of Antarctica.

symbiosis An alliance between two species that is usually (but not always) beneficial to both. Animals form symbiotic relationships with plants, microorganisms, and other animals.

sympatric Of two or more species, occurring in the same area.

syndactyl Having fused toes on the hindfoot, as in bandicoots, kangaroos, and wombats.

taxonomy The system of classifying living things into various groups and subgroups according to similarities in features and adaptations.

temperate Describes an environment or region that has a warm (but not very hot) summer and a cool (but not very cold) winter. Most of the world's temperate regions are located between the tropics and the polar regions.

territory An area of land inhabited by an animal and defended against intruders. The area often contains all the living resources required by the animal, such as food and a nesting site.

torpid In a sleep-like state in which bodily processes are greatly slowed. Torpor helps animals to survive difficult conditions such as cold or lack of food. Estivation and hibernation are types of torpor.

tropical Describes an environment or region near the Equator that is warm to hot all year round.

tropical forests Forests growing in tropical regions, such as central Africa, northern South America, and southeast Asia, that experience little difference in temperature throughout the year. See rain forest.

tundra A cold, barren area where much of the soil is frozen and the vegetation consists mainly of mosses, lichens, and other small plants adapted to withstand intense cold. Tundra is found near the Arctic Circle and on mountain tops.

tusks The very long teeth of such mammals as elephants, pigs, hippos, musk deer, walruses, and narwhals; used in fights and for self-defense.

ungulate A large, plant-eating mammal with hoofs. Ungulates include elephants, rhinoceroses, horses, deer, antelope, and wild cattle.

vertebrate An animal with a backbone. All vertebrates have an internal skeleton of cartilage or bone. Mammals are vertebrates.

vertebral column The series of vertebrae running from head to tail along the back of vertebrates, and which encloses the spinal cord.

vestigial Relating to an organ that is non-functional or atrophied.

vibrissae Specialized hairs, or whiskers, that are extremely sensitive to touch.

viviparous Reproducing by means of young that develop inside the mother's body and are born live; sometimes called placental viviparity. Most mammals are viviparous.

INDEX

monkeys 19, 78–89
    Allen's swamp monkey 89
    blue monkey 88, *88*
    capped leaf monkey *83*
    Chinese snub-nosed monkey *83*
    common marmoset *79*
    common squirrel monkey 81, *81*
    common woolly monkey 82, *82*
    Diana monkey *84*, 88, *88*
    gray woolly monkey *78*
    Mona monkey 88, *88*
    northern night monkey 80, *80*
    patas monkey 89, *89*
    proboscis monkey 83, *83*
    pygmy marmoset 78, 79, *79*
    red-eared monkey *89*
    redtail monkey 88, *89*
    Sykes' monkey 88, *88*
    vervet monkey *84*, 88, *88*, 89, *89*
    see also colobus monkeys; howler monkeys; langurs; macaques; sakis; spider monkeys; tamarins
Monodelphis spp. *42*
Monodon monoceros 178, 179, *179*
monotremes 19, 38–9

ACKNOWLEDGMENTS

t=top; l=left; r=right; tl=top left; tcl=top center left; tc=top center; tcr=top center right; tr=top right; cl=center left; c=center; cr=center right; b=bottom; bl=bottom left; bcl=bottom center left; bc=bottom center; bcr=bottom center right; br=bottom right

APL/CBT = Australian Picture Library/Corbis; APL/MP = Australian Picture Library/Minden Pictures; AUS = Auscape International; COR = Corel Corp.; GI = Getty Images; NHPA = Natural History Photographic Agency; OSF = Oxford Scientific Films; PL = photolibrary.com

PHOTOGRAPHS

Front cover tl, tr, c GI tc PL

1c GI **2**c GI **4**c, cl GI **8**cl GI **12**c GI **14**cr APL/CBT **18**bl, tr GI **19**bl APL/CBT **20**br, tr APL/CBT **21**c APL/CBT **22**b APL/CBT **23**b APL/MP tl GI tr APL/CBT **24**b, tcr APL/CBT **25**bl, tl GI **26**br GI **27**bl APL/CBT tr PL **28**b PL t GI **29**b PL tr GI **30**b APL/CBT **31**b APL/ MP **32**b, bl Jeremy Sutton-Hibbert tr APL/CBT **33**br, tl APL/CBT tr PL **34**b GI tr APL/CBT **35**br GI tr APL/CBT **38**bc PL c APL/CBT tr Kathie Atkinson **40**bl, cl PL **51**tr GI **53**bl, tr APL/CBT c PL **56**bc APL/CBT c PL **60**c GI **61**br PL **62**bl GI cl National Geographic Image Collection **63**cr PL **64**cl APL/CBT tl AUS/D Parker & E Parer-Cook **70**bl AUS/Daniel Cox/OSF c AUS/David Haring/OSF cr AUS/Ferrero-Labat **71**br, c, tl, tr PL **72**br AUS/ Rod Williams cl AUS/T-Shivanandappa r APL/CBT **78**bl, cr PL **90**cl PL tr APL/CBT **93**b, tr APL/MP cl F W Frohawk cr NHPA/Mirko Stelzner **94**bc, c GI tr APL/MP **95**c APL/CBT cr GI t APL/MP **96**cl GI tr PL **102**br PL cl APL/MP **105**c, tl GI tr PL **106**bl, br, c APL/CBT **111**bl AUS/Daniel Cox/ OSF **114**bc PL cl APL/MP **118**tr APL/MP **119**cr APL/CBT **120**bl GI **126**bl GI **132**tr GI **133**bc, cl APL/CBT **134**bl PL tr APL/MP **135**bl APL/MP cr APL/CBT tl GI **136**b APL/CBT c PL tr GI **138**c, cl, tr APL/CBT **140**bc, c APL/CBT bl GI **143**cr APL/CBT **144**bl, c GI tr PL **146**c APL/MP cl PL **147**br PL **148**bc APL/CBT cl APL/MP **161**br APL/CBT tc Kirk Olson tl APL/MP **162**b PL c APL/CBT cl GI **168**bl, tr APL/CBT c PL **169**b GI **170**bl, br, cl APL/CBT **172**c, tr GI **174**c GI cl APL/MP **175**c GI tr APL/MP **176**bl, tr APL/MP cl APL/CBT **177**br Spectrogram Program by Richard Horne (Original from Cornell Laboratory of Orrinthology) cr GI t APL/CBT **178**bl, c APL/CBT tr GI **180**bl COR **183**br AUS cr, tl PL **185**br GI cl PL tr APL/ MP **188**b, cl GI c PL **189**c, tr PL tl GI **190**bl PL cl GI **194**c PL tl APL/CBT tr Bruce Coleman **197**bl APL/CBT cl, tr PL **204**bc APL/MP cl APL/CBT tr GI **211**bc APL/MP c APL/CBT cl GI **215**cl, cr PL

ILLUSTRATIONS

All illustrations © MagicGroup s.r.o. (Czech Republic) - www.magicgroup.cz; except for the following:

Alistair Barnard 16b, 17b t, 39br, 51bl cl tl; **Andre Boos** 122cl, 123br; **Ann Bowman** 177bl; **Peter Bull Art Studio** 14tl, 31tcl tcr tl tr; **Martin Camm** 78tr, 131bl br, 183c; **Simone End** 203br, 214bl; **Christer Eriksson** 52cl, 187br; **Jon Gittoes** 82bl, 90b; **Gino Hasler** 181br; **David Kirshner** 19cr,bl, 27br; **Frank Knight** 18bcr; **Alex Lavroff** 183tr; **James McKinnon** 30tr, 40bc, 74cl, 81br, 104bl, 176c, 97cr, 103br, 125br, 134br, 135br; **John Mac/FOLIO** 69br, 166bl cl tl, 194b, 207br; **Trevor Ruth** 160b; **Kevin Stead** 38bl, 92cl, 176cl; **Guy Troughton** 19tcl, 51bc c cr, 64b, 86b cr, 100bl, 105b, 124t, 132b, 133t, 147t, 154t.

CAPTIONS

Page 1 For at least 20 months, polar bear cubs drink their mother's milk and depend on her for survival.
Page 2 Male and female Japanese macaques have almost equal roles in caring for their young.
Page 4–5 Horses trot freely in the surf of Noordhoek beach, South Africa.
Page 6–7 Zebras and wildebeest cross the Mara River, Kenya, in one of Earth's most impressive animal migrations.
Page 8–9 Hundreds of giant fruit bats circle a tree at dusk in Lampung, Indonesia.
Page 12–13 The Bengal tiger is a skilled swimmer and prefers to hunt alone.
Page 36–37 Giraffe and African elephants graze on grasslands below Mount Kilimanjaro, Kenya.